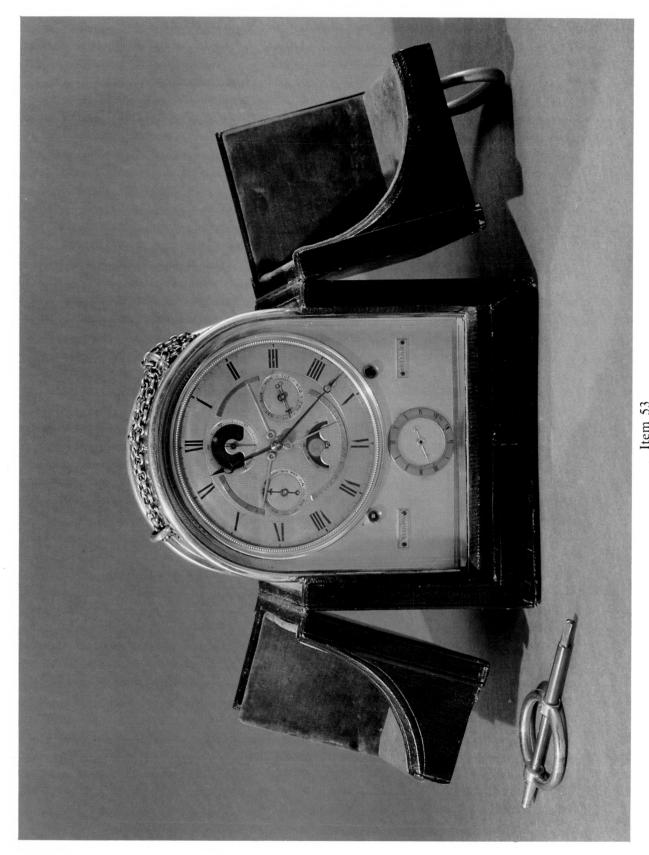

Item 53

A silver gilt portable astronomical clock hallmarked for 1825 and signed J.F. & T. Cole, then in partnership at 3 New Bond Street. *Courtesy British Museum.*

THOMAS COLE
&
VICTORIAN
CLOCKMAKING

Printed privately for the Author

SYDNEY, 1975

National Library of Australia Card Number
ISBN 0-9598503-0-9

Typesetting by G.T. Setters Pty. Ltd., Sydney.

Designed and produced by
Production & Printing Services, Sydney.

Printed by Macarthur Press Pty. Ltd., Sydney.

FOREWORD

It gives me particular pleasure to have been asked to write a short foreword to this specialised horological book dealing with and revealing much concerning the work of Thomas Cole.

John Hawkins has concentrated on a most interesting group of timekeepers often giving supplementary information such as calendar work, thermometers and other innovations. They were all made by a craftsman who demanded high standards of quality, continual change and ingenuity in design of cases, and who gave meticulous attention to engraving and the conceits of ownership. It was Lord Harris and John Hawkins who virtually pioneered the collecting of these clocks of highly individual style and the research that has been conducted has brought to light the fact that Cole was hiding his light under a bushel and was supplier to many firms of repute who put their names to his work.

I consider it a most propitious time to publish horological works on individual makers as we have had many books attempting a world coverage on clocks, all too ambitious and lacking the study of detail which so many collectors now desire.

The number of clocks made by Cole seems to offer an attractive field for the collector-searcher with the possibilities of something more than a fruitless reward for his efforts.

Ronald A. Lee

PREFACE

To the majority of contemporary clock collectors, the name Thomas Cole is completely unknown. By his own contemporaries, he was acknowledged as a maker of repute. The passage of over one hundred years since his death in 1864 has seen that reputation gradually disappear into obscurity, not because it was undeserved but because Cole took great trouble to ensure that the majority of items he made would not readily be traced back to their source.

Of whom in the field of mid 19th century horology could the following be said. He constructed over 1600 clocks each one in some way different to the next; commenced in business on his own aged 40, died at the age of 64; and exhibited at all the major international exhibitions between 1850 and 1864. Completely original in all his designs, he owed the inspiration for his work to no one. Not an easy question to answer and most horologists would say that such a man did not exist or they would have heard of him. However, such a man was Thomas Cole.

The beauty of collecting Cole's work is that one never knows what to expect next. The multiplicity of his designs is enormous. Only two and a half per cent of his output is illustrated in this book, the complete range may only be conjectured. It requires a book such as this to gain people's interest and I hope that those lucky enough to own an example of Cole's work, will contact me for it is by this method that the full range of his activities will be discovered.

This book could not have been produced without the assistance of Mr. Donovan Dawe. I live in Australia and the major sources of Cole material and retailers' working dates are to be found in England. Mr. Dawe undertook on my behalf to research the background and life of Thomas Cole and his retailers' working dates from the London trade directories. His careful and detailed investigations into a very difficult subject have been of the greatest assistance.

Mr. Charles Allix has visited various collections in the United Kingdom and indexed the Thomas Coles therein with his usual expertise and insight and to him I am most grateful. The results of his efforts are acknowledged in the text.

I would also like to thank the following people who have assisted me in the preparation of this book.

Algernon Asprey, 27 Bruton Street, London W1

The Rt. Hon. The Lord Harris

Mr. John Altmann of Melbourne

Dr. N. Johnson of Sydney

Mrs. A.M. Pool

Mr. Terence Cuss of Camerer Cuss

Mr. R.A. Lee and Mr. Charles Lee of R.A. Lee, London

Mr. Rupert de Zoete and the directors of Mallet, London

Mr. P.G. Dawson of Daniel Desbois & Sons, London

Mr. and Mrs. P. Kaufmann of Connoisseur Antiques, Brighton

Mr. Gerald Marsh, Winchester, Hampshire

Mr. L.G.N. Bruford of Wm. Bruford & Son Ltd., Eastbourne

Mr. G.G. Lock for his work in relation to the Payne family of Bath

Mr. John Culme of Sotheby's, Belgravia for his assistance with the biographies of the various Cole retailers

Colonel H. Quill, R.M., for his advice and efforts on my behalf in trying to locate the Cole papers

Mr. Beresford Hutchinson of the British Museum for the photograph and text of the joint venture James Ferguson and Thomas Cole carriage clock in that museum

Messrs. Evans and Evans of Alresford

Mr. George Daniels for his efforts in trying to establish a relationship between the House of Breguet and the Cole brothers

Mr. David Callaghan of Messrs. Hancocks for the history of that firm

Mr. E.A. Battison, Curator of Clocks and Watches of the Smithsonian Institution, Washington, DC

Mr. Chaumet whose firm now controls the House of Breguet in Paris

Mr. J. Carter for allowing me to photograph and index the two miniature Cole carriage clocks

Mr. A. Tyler, Historian, of Nether Stowey, Somerset whose knowledge of the area provided many useful leads as to the Cole brothers' background.

Mrs. P. Currie for typing the manuscript

INTRODUCTION

In 1815, the year of Waterloo, England was still a land of unspoilt beauty. Most English towns were either handsome or picturesque. The factory regions were a small part of the whole but unluckily they were to be the model for the future. The Napoleonic Wars, the onset of the Industrial Revolution, and the large increase in the size and wealth of city populations in the 19th century forced the practising country clockmaker either to seek a living in the cities or country towns or run a general maintenance and repair business selling the products of the London, Liverpool, Prescot, etc. clock manufacturers to a declining rural population.

The course of the Napoleonic War with blockade and counter blockade made business a gamble. England's control of the sea and her new power of machine production, not yet imitated in other lands, gave her a monopoly of many markets in America, Africa and the Far East; but the European markets were alternately open and closed to British goods according to the vagaries of diplomacy and war. The unnecessary war with the United States, 1812-15 was another element of disturbance to trade. The sufferings of the English working class were increased by these violent fluctuations of demand and employment, unemployment being worst of all during the post war slump after Waterloo.

At no period, however, had the landed gentry been wealthier or happier. Wheat rose from 43/- a quarter in 1792, the year before the war broke out, to 126/- in 1812, the year Napoleon went to Moscow. The result of this was increased wealth to the landlords, a prolonged calamity to the wage earner and a gamble for the middle orders of society.

The conclusion of the Napoleonic Wars saw the incomes of the landlords in agricultural England fall by an average of one half. All over the country banks were calling in their money, the Gazette was crowded with bankruptcy notices and tradesmen's books with bad debts. The table of the House of Commons became piled with petitions from farmers and manufacturers. As 1815 gave place to 1816, the situation grew worse with bankers unwilling to advance or discount. No one, not even the rich, seemed to have money to spare, for by the spring, ten thousand livery servants were said to be out of place. Among those who went down in the general ruin being Beau Brummel and Sheridan. Art prices fell to a level unknown in the history of the salerooms; at Phillips a Claude which had fetched 1000 gns. in 1813 went for £70. Even Sir William Beechey was forced to beg for settlement of his account with the Royal Household, "the unexpected alterations to the times making a shocking impression on the arts."[1]

A vast influx of skilled artisans moved to London with their families because it was in that city they could find work. The system of indentured apprenticeships must have been sorely strained, and for many, the teachings of fathers or relations must have been their basic start in the horological trade.

I feel it is in this context of the Napoleonic Wars and the Industrial Revolution that the departure from Nether Stowey in 1813 or 1814 of James Cole and his two sons should be noted. Their ultimate destination was presumably London via Bath which, with its Spa, Crescent and social acceptability may have provided opportunities for apprenticeship or work, second only to the capital.

---

[1]. *The Age of Elegance.* Sir Arthur Bryant

The great firm of English silver retailers, Rundell, Bridge and Rundell found that, despite the problems of the Napoleonic Wars, the increase in wheat prices advanced rents to such high figures that it produced considerable extravagance from the landed gentry and aristocracy. This firm at its height between 1805 and 1816, was the basis of the supremacy, by 1850, of the leading English 19th century silver, jewellery and horological retail outlets. Rundell and Bridge were Dorset men, both being apprenticed to William Rogers of Bath. It is interesting how this connection from Somerset, Wiltshire and Dorset, via Bath, and graduation to London seemed to be a chosen route to success for certain silversmithing and horologically interested families[2]. Bath's importance as a gathering place for potential craftsmen who eventually gravitated to London is, to my mind, hardly given a mention in any of the standard reference books.

Rundell, Bridge and Rundell, although indirectly, play an important part in the Cole saga in that the following silversmiths manufactured goods for sale by them. These silversmiths in their turn founded businesses to which Thomas Cole supplied his work, and three of whom were his major customers.

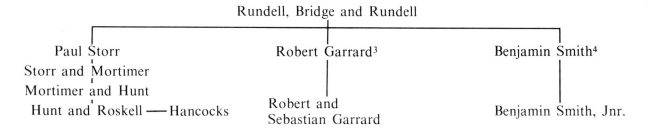

Rundell, Bridge and Rundell

Paul Storr
Storr and Mortimer
Mortimer and Hunt
Hunt and Roskell —— Hancocks

Robert Garrard[3]

Robert and
Sebastian Garrard

Benjamin Smith[4]

Benjamin Smith, Jnr.

THE COLE PAPERS

Major Paul M. Chamberlain in his excellent book "Its About Time" relates how he made the acquaintance of James Ferguson Cole's son in 1924. As a result of visits to the Tower House, Bexley Heath, the J.F. Cole family home, a firm friendship sprang up. James Ferguson Cole, Jnr., handed over to Chamberlain a lot of the documentation, drawings and miscellany relating to his father. These are listed on page 405 in "Its About Time". Extensive enquiries in America and in England to try and trace these papers (through Mr. E.A. Battison at the Smithsonian Institution and Mr. George Daniels who had himself tried to trace them) have proved fruitless. It would appear that Mr. J.L. Roehrich who wrote the appreciation of Chamberlain in the front of "Its About Time" in 1940 knew of their location, but letters to his last known address have proved to no avail. These papers are of great interest and in the light of current knowledge would, I am sure, yield a lot of contemporary information.

A fascinating reference given by Chamberlain is contained on the business card of J.F. Cole at 3 New Bond Street (1823 to circa 1832)[5]. I quote — "James Ferguson Cole engages to repair in a perfect manner the genuine watches of Mons. Breguet however complex or delicate." This, with the surviving J.F. Cole carriage clocks, shows a very close acquaintance with the House of Breguet.

---

[2]. This movement from Bath to London continued into the 20th Century as evidenced by firms such as Mallett whose history through the acquisition of Payne's of Bath, the well-known clockmaking family, gives them a Bath connection back to 1816.

[3]. Paul Storr, N.M. Penzer, Robert Garrard: responsible for a section of the Wellington Ambassadorial Plate.

[4]. Paul Storr, N.M. Penzer: Partner with Digby Scott and worked for Paul Storr.

[5]. *Its About Time*, P.M. Chamberlain.

Enquiries in both Paris, through the kind offices of Mr. Chaumet, who now controls the House of Breguet, and Mr. George Daniels, have failed to find in the work books any reference to an apprenticeship served by either J.F. or T. Cole. With whom they served their apprenticeship remains, to date, a mystery.

The possibility of two brothers from Nether Stowey occupying a shop at 3 New Bond Street and making a silver cased copy of a Breguet carriage clock at the respective ages of 27 and 25, seems remote. Yet, somehow they achieved just that. How, it is impossible to explain. They never became members of the Clockmakers Company. If they served their apprenticeship in London, it would, I am sure, have been with a member of the Clockmakers Company who would have ensured their membership. If apprenticed in Bath, the apprenticeship records in the Inland Revenue Books terminated in 1811 and hence are of no use for the brothers had not left Nether Stowey. If apprenticed in Paris, judging by the type of product made at 3 New Bond Street, it would have been with the House of Breguet but again a blank is drawn.

These problems may well be resolved if and when the Cole papers, formerly in the possession of Major P.M. Chamberlain and believed to now be in America, can be located.

This book is about the work and life of Thomas Cole. The gaps in the story may never be filled in. If any reader can produce information that would be of interest, please do not hesitate to contact me. Similarly, a photograph, the number and dimensions of any further Coles will go a long way to filling in the gaps in this story.

J.B. Hawkins
13 Amherst Street,
Cammeray, 2062
New South Wales,
Australia.

CONTENTS

THOMAS COLE,
HIS LIFE AND BACKGROUND

Thomas Cole, son of James and Catherine Cole of Nether Stowey in Somerset[1] was born in 1800 and baptised there on 17th March.[2] His father can almost certainly be identified as the maker of the clock in the nearby church of Enmore, where the name COLE is found incised, no doubt by its maker, on the winding wheel at the back.[3] An entry in the church-wardens' accounts[4] reveals that his christian name was James but the surname is incorrectly entered as Coles:

1797. Paid Mr. Jas. Coles £26.5.0 for a new Church Clock at Enmore.

The Rev. E.H. Smith, one time rector of Enmore, in a detailed account of the clock accepts this form of the maker's name and (unhappily without giving his authority) asserts that "James Coles" came from Nether Stowey.[5] He goes on:

"This clock had a wooden face and a single hand travelling round the square dial which was over five feet across . . . During the restoration of the church (in 1873) the clock was sent to a Bristol firm for complete reconstruction and a new "face" of ornamental wrought iron . . ."

It seems possible that the same maker was responsible for a single-hand square-dialled clock and bell surmounting an octagonal market shelter which stood in the centre of Nether Stowey until the mid nineteenth century.[6]

The only other positive evidence of James Cole as a clockmaker comes from the village of Spaxton, midway between Nether Stowey and Enmore. The church clock probably dates back to the sixteenth century and bears evidence of having had at one time a foliot escapement. It was in working order until about 1950 and was removed for cleaning and examination by experts in 1967.[7] The Spaxton church records throw some light upon the clock in the seventeenth century and again from 1794 onwards. It is an entry of 1811 in the churchwardens' accounts that refers to James Cole by name and another of 1810 that links him conclusively with Nether Stowey:[8]

1810 Sending the Clock to Stowey, 5/-
Man, horse and cart to Stowey for the Church clock
1811 James Cole for repairing the clock £7.0.0.

James Cole apparently followed — Thristle,[8] a member of a well-known local family of clockmakers,[9] as clock repairer to Spaxton Church. He in turn was succeeded by Andrew Rich in 1814[8], suggesting that by that date James Cole had either died or moved elsewhere. The absence of his name in the Nether Stowey burial register strongly suggests the second alternative.

Thomas Cole's parents, James and Catherine Cole were married at Goathurst church about five miles from Nether Stowey in 1797. The entry in the register[10] reads:

1797 Feb. 27 James Cole of Nether Stowey and Catherine Slocombe (licence).

Although Coles abounded in and around Nether Stowey, James Cole's forebears have not been traced with any certainty. His wife Catherine, daughter of Richard and Mary Slocombe of Goathurst, was baptised there on 8th October 1773.[10]

The church register of Nether Stowey records the baptisms of three of the children of James and Catherine Cole. James Ferguson Cole (whose fame as a clockmaker was to earn him the title of the English Breguet) was baptised on 14th March 1798, almost exactly two years before his brother Thomas, and Elizabeth, born on 30th August 1808, on 6th October of the same year.[2] The birth dates of James Ferguson and Thomas Cole are not recorded.

An interesting interpretation of James Ferguson Cole's christian names is given by Paul Chamberlain[11] apparently on the authority of James Ferguson Cole's son with whom he claimed a personal friendship. (The son, it might be added, inherited both his father's christian names[12] and his profession and died at the age of ninety three in December 1935[13]). It is a well known fact that Samuel Taylor Coleridge was living in Nether Stowey in 1798 and also that William Wordsworth settled at the neighboring mansion of Alfoxden.[14] According to Chamberlain,[11] James Cole was a friend of both poets and told them of the birth of his first son in the local hostelry. In response to

Coleridge's question as to what was to be the child's name, Wordsworth is alleged to have interrupted with "Why James Ferguson Cole to be sure". So James Ferguson Cole it was.

The name is not without significance. James Ferguson, the Scottish-born astronomer and popular scientist, had through his writings a special interest for the clockmaker. "His paradox in gear-work", says Chamberlain, "will preserve his name as long as civilisation continues to use gearing." It could well be that James Cole as a clockmaker had a deep respect for James Ferguson whose death some twenty years earlier had not dimmed his popular appeal. If there is some truth in Chamberlain's story, James Cole might well have revealed an admiration for Ferguson to his illustrious friends.

Any account of Thomas Cole must inevitably involve both his father James Cole and his more eminent brother James Ferguson Cole. The assumption that both brothers learned at least the rudiments of their craft from their father or from local Somerset clockmakers is supported by an intriguing piece of evidence still surviving today in Nether Stowey. In the local primary school, built in 1813 as the village school[14], is a large mantel clock whose eighteen inch diameter dial unmistakably bears the legend:

J.F. COLE
1813

The clock is in a wooden case and the fusee and chain movement is in excellent condition. It has recently been overhauled by Mr. Ray Ingram, jeweller and watchmaker of no. 37 High Street Bridgwater who now has the care of what remains of James Cole's clock in Enmore church.[6]

If the school clock was in fact made by the 15 year old James Ferguson Cole it suggests a remarkably youthful virtuosity. More likely perhaps that the maker was James Cole assisted by his apprentice son. If so the legend on the clock could have been a tribute by his father to his talent.

Thomas Poole, the builder of Nether Stowey school[6], was the son of a Nether Stowey tanner[14] and brought up in his father's business to which he succeeded on his death in 1795.[15] He was also a self-taught scholar, book collector, supporter of Sunday schools and ephemeral writer and his large circle of eminent friends[16] included Wordsworth and Coleridge for whom he found a cottage in Nether Stowey in 1796.[15] James Cole was no doubt closely associated with Thomas Poole who took a lively and active interest in all local matters. Thomas Poole's brother John, it might be added, was appointed rector of Enmore in 1796[17] and opened there a village school[14] which served as a model for Nether Stowey.[6]

It has already been suggested that James Cole and his family left Nether Stowey in 1813 or shortly afterwards. They effectively disappear for the next eight years however and only conjecture can fill a gap not ended until James Ferguson Cole reappears as a clockmaker in London in 1821 and Thomas a year or two later. Is it possible that James Cole in 1813 decided to move to London with his family in order to give his sons James Ferguson, then aged 15, and Thomas, 13, opportunities and experience that only London could supply? Neither served an apprenticeship in the Clockmakers' Company[18] and no apprenticeship outside it has been traced.

However it was achieved, James Ferguson Cole's undisclosed advance to fame was rapid for in January 1821 at the age of 22 he was sufficiently developed in his skill to be granted a patent for a pivoted detent escapement.[19] The evidence for his 1821 address as Hans Place, Chelsea is irrefutable, being none other than the address he supplied when applying for the patent.[20] Nevertheless it is as puzzling as many other facts concerning the brothers' early days in London. He does not appear in lists of residents of Hans Place at that time[21] suggesting that he lodged with one or other of the fifty or so residents. Curiously however they comprise entirely what might be termed upper class private residents of whom a quarter were either officers or clergy, two were titled and a quarter of the remainder women. Individual examination of these names provides no clue as to possible associations of any of them with a young Somerset clockmaker recently arrived in London.

James Ferguson Cole stayed only briefly in Hans Place. By March 1821 he was at no. 10 Park Lane Piccadilly[22] and had moved again by 1823 to no. 3 New Bond Street.[23] It was here that Thomas Cole, two years his junior, shortly afterwards joined his brother in partnership.[24] The exact date is not known but a carriage clock in the British Museum signed by both of them bears the date letter of 1825.[25] From then until about 1829 the brothers worked together in New Bond Street as chronometer, watch and clockmakers before going their separate ways. James Ferguson Cole moved first to no. 1 Maddox Street, Regent Street and then in about 1835 to no. 9 Motcomb Street Belgrave Square where he remained until 1846.[24]

After the brothers' separation, Thomas's movements are untraced until he reappears in 1838 as a watchmaker at no. 11 Upper King Street Bloomsbury.[24] He shared the premises as an undertenant with George Markes who ran a wholesale Italian warehouse. He stayed there at least until October 1841[26] and in the census of that year described himself as a watchmaker.[27]

Of Thomas Cole's first marriage no record has been found. After the death of his first wife he married Charlotte Boulding on 28th October 1841 at St. Pancras.[26] Charlotte, only just 21 years of age and 20 years younger than her husband, was the daughter of Samuel Boulding of Euston Place. The ceremony was witnessed by Newton Wood and Clara Brett.[26]

Shortly after their marriage the Coles moved to no. 47 Lamb's Conduit Street off Theobalds Road[28] of which the main occupant was George Tomlin, a linen draper.[24] Like their subsequent addresses it served Thomas Cole as both home and business premises and it was here that their first child Thomas William was born on 13th August 1842.[28] Within a year or two they had moved again to no. 24 Hart Street Bloomsbury, the premises of William Ostell, stationer and printer,[24] where a second son Arthur Boulding was born on 22nd March 1844.[29] By 1845 they had left Bloomsbury for Clerkenwell, an area of London popular with watch and clock makers. At no. 2 Upper Vernon Street Clerkenwell Thomas Cole now called himself a "designer and maker of ornamental clocks".[24] Charlotte Cole gave birth to her first daughter, Catherine Mary in Upper Vernon Street on 21st May 1847[30] but in April 1851 the absence of the Cole family in the census returns either at Upper Vernon Street[31] or at the address to which Thomas subsequently moved his business[32] suggests that their dwelling house was already at a different place.

James Ferguson Cole's pattern of life bore a remarkable resemblance to that of his brother. He left Motcomb Street for Clerkenwell soon after Thomas and opened his premises at no. 30 Granville Square,[24] not far from Upper Vernon Street. Here he lived with his wife and family[33] and, like Thomas's, his wife was Charlotte (nee Wyatt)[12] who came from the village of Sulhamstead in Berkshire.[33]

Like Thomas, too, he had two sons and two daughters. The sons were both born in Motcomb Street, James Ferguson Cole, junr. on 23rd February 1842[12] and Mortimer George Cole on 18th November 1843.[34] Both were also destined to follow their father's profession.[35] The younger James Ferguson, who never married, later lived in the house Belvedere (afterwards Tower) House Bexley Heath where his father died in 1880[36] and where he himself was to die at the age of 93 in 1935.[13] The daughters were Ada Martha who exhibited portraits and miniatures at the Royal Academy between 1855 and 1872[37] and Jessie who was the subject of one of Ada's portraits.[37]

James Ferguson Cole left Clerkenwell in the early 'fifties for no. 20 Devonshire Street, W.C. and no. 11 Great James Street, W.C. successively[24] while the family made its home at no. 5 Queen Square Bloomsbury.[38]

Meanwhile the Great Exhibition of 1851 presented Thomas Cole with an opportunity for publicising his work, an opportunity which was not taken by his brother.

Thomas Cole, entered in the official catalogue of the exhibition[39] as "inventor, designer and maker of 2 Upper Vernon Street Lloyd Square Clerkenwell" had six items on display which appear in the catalogue as:

Inkstand, containing requisites for writing: and showing the time, the day of month, and the day of week, with thermometer. In metal, engraved and gilt, inlaid with malachite.
Design for a portable eight-day timepiece showing the months and days of the week and the month.
Design for a flat, portable clock, with calendar; metal, engraved and gilt, inlaid with malachite.
Eight-day night and day timepiece or horological lantern.
Small eight-day clock. Improved calendar, in metal frame.
Flat eight-day striking clock, to repeat the hours and quarters, in engraved and gilt case.

The international exhibition held in Paris in 1855 gave Thomas Cole another opportunity for displaying his skill. "Our neighbours at the Paris Exhibition of 1855 accorded him a very distinguished position for true artistic excellence and superior workmanship" wrote his obituary writer nine years later.[40]

By this time Thomas Cole had moved to his final place of business at no. 6 Castle Street Holborn[24] having left Upper Vernon Street late in 1851 or in 1852.[24] Within a year or two of this date Thomas and Charlotte Cole can be identified at their own house no 1 Elizabeth Terrace, Westbourne Park Road.[41] It was their last move. The Castle Street premises served him until his death and no. 1 Elizabeth Terrace around 1860 was renumbered no. 1 Westbourne Park Road.

A second daughter, Florence Eva was born to Charlotte Cole on 17th August 1857 at the house in Elizabeth Terrace.[42]

Thomas Cole was elected to the Royal Society of Arts on 28th June 1861[43] but does not appear to have contributed to its activities. He was also admitted to the British Horological Institute in which his brother James Ferguson Cole played a leading role.

The last contribution to the scene of international exhibitions came in 1862 when both brothers had examples of their work on display in London. James Ferguson Cole was represented by chronometers, watches, tempered springs and what were described in the catalogue as "new horological models",[44] and Thomas by "ornamental and portable clocks of original construction and design".[45] Thomas was awarded a medal for "excellence of taste and design" and the jury, led by Charles Frodsham as its secretary and reporter, had nothing but praise in their official report under the heading "House clocks". "Mr. Thomas Cole's exhibition (U.K.3236) was exclusively devoted to this department and nothing could exceed the beauty of design and good taste of the varied models and general excellence of workmanship. The foreign visitors seem all of them to have accorded him the palm and were anxious buyers of his beautiful works".[46]

Thomas Cole died from typhoid fever[47] at his house no. 1 Westbourne Park Road, Paddington after a short illness[48] on 3rd January 1864. "As a maker of portable clocks", said an obituary writer,[40] "combining excellent mechanical principles with unexceptionable taste in design, and the adaptor of horological and other machinery to articles of drawing-room and other use, he stood without a rival here for design, taste and execution, and this was allowed where, in this branch of the art, few English workers would attempt competition . . . The void made by his decease, in this particular manufacture, will, unless by his sons, with difficulty, if at all, be filled up".[40]

Thomas Cole left no will and total personal estate and effects valued at less than £2000. Letters of administration were granted to his widow Charlotte then at 43 in the prime of her life.[49]

The hopes displayed by the obituary writer regarding Thomas Cole's sons do not appear to have been fulfilled. Both Thomas, jun. and Arthur Cole had described themselves in April 1861 at the ages of 18 and 17 respectively as clockmakers[50] but their future careers remain obscure. Thomas worked as an "art designer" retaining his father's premises in Castle Street for a few years.[24] He last appears there in the London directory of 1869. In the following year, although his name hopefully reappears as a clockmaker at no. 10 Brooke Street, Holborn, it is not repeated in subsequent editions. The assumption must be that both Thomas, jun. and Arthur were employees in firms which remain unidentified.

SOURCES.

G.L.   Guildhall Library, Aldermanbury.

G.R.O. General Register Office, St. Catherine's House, Kingsway.

P.P.R. Principal Probate Registry, Somerset House, Strand.

P.R.O. Public Record Office, Portugal Street.

[1]Evidence that Thomas Cole was born in Nether Stowey comes from Census 1861 RG9/2 fo.21 P.R.O. [2]Nether Stowey parish registers. Nether Stowey church. [3]Information kindly supplied by the Rev. R.S. Jones, Rector of Goathurst (with Enmore). [4]Churchwardens' accounts. Enmore church. [5]Smith, Rev. E.H. Happy memories of West Somerset p.87-8. [6]Information kindly supplied by Mr. Albert F. Tyler, authority on the history of Nether Stowey. [7]Odlum, Rev. M.J. The history of the church and village of Spaxton p.70. [8]Churchwardens' accounts 1794-1872 Spaxton church quoted by Odlum *op.cit.* p.316. [9]Hobbs, J.L. Former clock and watchmakers of Somerset 1968 (typescript). G.L. [10]Goathurst parish register. Goathurst church. [11]Chamberlain, P. Its about time 1941 p.407. [12]Birth certificate of James Ferguson Cole, jun., 23 Feb. 1842. G.R.O. [13]Death certificate of James Ferguson Cole, jun., 3 Dec. 1935. G.R.O. [14]Lawrence, B. Coleridge and Wordsworth in Somerset 1970 p.46. [15]Dictionary of national biography vol. 16, 1960 p.104-5. [16]See also Sandford, Mrs. H. Thomas Poole and his friends, 2 vol. 1888. (Although the Poole and Nether Stowey background is of great interest there appears to be no reference to the Coles). [17]Alumni Oxoniensis 1715-1886 vol. 3, 1888 p.1129. [18]Clockmakers' Company records. G.L. [19]Patent Office. Abridgments of specifications no. 4530, 1821 in vol. 9 pt. 1, 1858 p.33. G.L. [20]Patent Office. Abridgments of specifications index of names. G.L. [21]Boyle's court guides 1820-22. G.L. [22]London journal of arts and sciences vol. 4, 1822 p. 63. G.L. [23]The date and address appear on a clock by J.F. Cole in the British Museum. [24]London directories. G.L. [25]This fine copy of a Breguet carriage clock in a silver gilt case was presented to the British Museum by Mrs. S.E. Prestige in 1969. [26]Marr. cert. of Thomas Cole and Charlotte Boulding 28 Oct. 1841 G.R.O. [27]Census returns 1841 for 11 Upper King Street HO 107/672.6.6 (The entry *very* indistinct). P.R.O. [28]Birth cert. of Thomas William Cole 13 Aug. 1842. G.R.O. [29]Birth cert. of Arthur Boulding Cole 24 Mar. 1844. G.R.O. [30]Birth cert. of Catharine Mary Cole 21 May 1847. G.R.O. [31]Census returns 1851 for 2 Upper Vernon Street Clerkenwell. P.R.O. [32]Census returns 1851 for 6 Castle Street Holborn. HO 107/1527.1.2 fo.99 etc. P.R.O. [33]Census returns 1851 for 30 Granville Sq. HO 107/1517 fo.27 P.R.O. [34]Birth cert. of Mortimer G. Cole 18 Nov. 1843. G.R.O. [35]Census returns 1871 for Bexley, Belvedere House. RG 10/879. P.R.O. [36]Death certificate of James Ferguson Cole 18 Jan. 1880. G.R.O. [37]Graves, A. Royal Academy exhibitors vol. 2, 1905 p.97. [38]Census returns 1861 for 5 Queen Sq. Bloomsbury RG 9/182 fo.1-9. P.R.O. [39]Great exhibition 1851. Official catalogue vol. 1 p.410 (class 10 no. 31). [40]Horological journal vol. 6, 1864 p.71. [41]First evidence in Watkins London directory 1854. G.L. [42]Birth certificate of Florence Eva Cole 17 Aug. 1857. G.R.O. [43]Royal Society of Arts journal vol. 9, 1861 p.588. [44]International exhibition London 1862. Catalogue vol. 2 1862 class XV no. 3235. [45]Op. cit. no. 3236. [46]International exhibition London. Report by the juries 1863 class XV no. 3236. [47]Death certificate of Thomas Cole 3 Jan. 1864. G.R.O. [48]Times 1864 Jan. 8 p.1a. [49]Letters of administration Thomas Cole 22 Jan. 1864. P.P.R. [50]Census 1861 for 1 Elizabeth Terrace. RG9/2 fo.21. P.R.O.

ADDRESSES OF
THOMAS COLE AND JAMES FERGUSON COLE
FROM THE LONDON DIRECTORIES, ETC.

1821   Jan. 27th. Patent taken out by James Ferguson Cole (No. 4530) giving his address as Hans Place, Chelsea

1821   March. James Ferguson Cole, 10 Park Lane, Piccadilly

1823-24 Directory (Pigot) Cole, James Ferguson, Watch, etc. Maker, 10 Park Lane, Piccadilly. (Not in 1822-3 Pigot or any other earlier directory.)

1823   Cole, James Ferguson, 3 New Bond Street, from a signed and dated Breguet style silver carriage clock, hallmarked for that year in the British Museum

1825   Silver cased Breguet style carriage clock, hallmarked for 1825, signed James Ferguson Cole and Thomas Cole, 3 New Bond Street

1826-29 (Pigot) Cole, James Ferguson and Thomas, Chronometer, watch and Clockmakers, 3 New Bond Street

1832   (Robson) Cole, James H. (sic) Watchmaker, 1 Maddox Street, Regent Street

1832-34 (Pigot) Cole, James Ferguson, Watchmaker, etc. 1 Maddox Street

1836-39 (Pigot) Cole, James Ferguson, Watch and Clockmaker, now in Motcomb Street, Pimlico

1838   (Robson) Cole, J.F. Watchmaker, 9 Motcomb Street, Belgrave Square

1839   (Pigot) Cole, Thomas, Watchmaker, 23 Upper King Street, Bloomsbury[1]

1839-40 (Kelly) Cole, James Ferguson, Chronometer, Watch and Clockmaker, 9 Lower Motcomb Street and 1 Grosvenor Street, Bond Street

1839-42 Cole, Thomas, Watchmaker, 11 Upper King Street, Bloomsbury (also 1841 Marriage Certificate)

1842   August 13th, Cole, Thomas, 47 Lambs Conduit Street (Birth Certificate of T.W. Cole)

1840-44 Cole, James Ferguson, Watch and Clockmaker, 9 Motcomb Street

1845   Cole, James Ferguson, Watch and Clockmaker, 9 Motcomb Street and 151B Piccadilly

1846   Cole, James Ferguson, Watch and Clockmaker, 9 Motcomb Street

1846-48 Cole, Thomas, Designer and Maker of Ornamental and Portable Clocks, 2 Upper Vernon Street, Pentonville

1847   Cole, Thomas, 2 Upper Vernon Street, Clerkenwell (Birth Certificate of Catherine Mary)

1849-51 Cole, James Ferguson, Chronometer Maker, 30 Granville Square, Pentonville

1849-52 Cole, Thomas, Clockmaker, 2 Upper Vernon Street, Pentonville

1853-65 Cole, Thomas, Designer and Manufacturer of Ornamental and Portable Clocks, etc. 6 Castle Street, Holborn

1861   Cole, James Ferguson, Watch and Chronometer Maker, 20 Devonshire Street, WC

1862-65 Cole, James Ferguson, Watch and Chronometer Maker, 11 Great James Street, WC

1866   Cole, Thomas, Art Designer, appears at 6 Castle Street, Holborn, but Thomas Cole as in 1853, appears in the commercial section at least up to 1868.[2]

1854-62 (Watkins) 1 Elizabeth Terrace (Residential address)

1862   1 Westbourne Park Road[3]   („   „   )

[1]This is the first reappearance of Thomas Cole in the London Directories since 1829. It is known that Thomas Cole was married twice, the second marriage taking place in 1841. This first marriage may have caused him to cease work or to leave London which would account for his non-entry in the directories

[2]Probably Thomas Cole, Jnr.

[3]1 Elizabeth Terrace was renamed 1 Westbourne Park Road, circa 1862.

CENSUS, 7TH APRIL, 1861

1861 — 1 Elizabeth Terrace — RG9/2/0.21

Thomas Cole, head mar. 61 Clockmaker b. Somerset, Stowey

Charlotte Cole wife mar. 40 b. Middlesex, Paddington

Thomas Cole son unm. 18 Clockmaker b. Middlesex, Paddington

Arthur Cole son unm. 17 Clockmaker b. Middlesex, Paddington

Catherine Cole dau. unm. 13 Scholar b. Middlesex, Paddington

Florence Eve Cole dau. unm. 3 b. Middlesex, Paddington

Elizabeth Day servant unm. 16 Nursemaid b. Middlesex, Paddington

Anne Rimpton servant unm. 31 Cook b. Hants, Sturton

THE RETAILERS OF THOMAS COLE'S WORK

In the interests of giving an overall picture, it has proved necessary to research in some detail the retailers of Thomas Cole's work. It is by changes in designation of the title of the firm over a period of time or by a change of address that it is possible to date Cole clocks via the numbering system employed on his products. For example, a strut clock 1614 inscribed Thomas Cole for H. & E. Tessier, 32 South Audley Street. Henry and Edward Tessier were only in partnership after the death of their father, from 1859-1870. As Cole died in 1864, the number 1614 must comply with a five year date period from 1859-1864.

Cole, in his particular branch of the horological art, was without a peer, as a result, held a monopoly of the trade in his type of product, these being retailed by London's leading jewellery, silver and clock businesses. To date, I have managed to locate items constructed by Cole and retailed by the following firms whose histories are outlined in this chapter. To the best of my knowledge, there is no available source of reference in terms of mid Victorian horology which provides an overall dating system for clocks made in the middle of the 19th century and sold by retailers.

The following business designations and addresses have been extracted from the London Trade Directories. They have been correlated and cross referenced and the earliest and latest entry is as shown. Some firms appear in one directory but not in others at their commencement and similarly at their demise. The earliest date found has been taken as a starting date at this address and the last entry the finishing date. Firms have only been investigated in terms of the addresses from which they sold goods manufactured by Cole, for instance, Robert Garrard, Snr., entered his mark at the Goldsmiths Hall in 1801 but the firm's history in relation to Cole commences at their address at 31 Panton Street, Haymarket in 1819. The three most important retailers of Cole's work in no order of precedence have proved to be Garrards, Hancocks and Hunt and Roskell.

Clocks retailed by these firms and made by Cole are on occasions either crested or monogrammed as an integral part of the dial engraving. It therefore must be assumed that Cole accepted special orders through them at agreed prices and that his clocks were not, as it were, purchased off the shelf. None of the firms listed have any surviving records relating to the wholesale or special order purchase of goods from Cole. It has therefore proved impossible to ascertain the cost structure involved in manufacturing these unique clocks.

Certain retailers, it appears, had no reason not to allow Cole to sign his work on the back cover of the clock; thus we find "Thomas Cole for H. & E Tessier" or "Made by Thomas Cole for R. & S. Garrard." This means that either they did not themselves indulge in making clocks, hence he did not provide them with competition, or that Cole's name was sufficiently well known to be a source of advertising kudos, who knows! In either event, it seems an unlikely practice.

The Great Exhibition of 1851 saw Cole probably at the height of his influence in that in addition to exhibiting himself, his products were on display on the stands of Hunt and Roskell, Hancocks, Phillips Brothers, W. Payne & Co, and possibly Howell and James. Not a bad effort in that they must all have required something different so as to prevent a conflict of interest.

ASPREY, LONDON

The firm of Kennedy and Asprey is first listed in Bond Street in 1846 as Stationers and Dressing Case manufacturers. The Crystal Palace Exhibition Illustrated Catalogue[1] illustrates:
"A jewel casket in the form of a cabinet richly chased and gilt and decorated with a large malachite, also a miniature glass provided with a prop and constructed in the lightest manner so as at once to be elegant and useful. The framework is fanciful in design but it will be seen that its general character is good and useful and convenient for the boudoir table."

Both these items are very much inspired by Thomas Cole and may well have been produced by him. Asprey also retailed strut clocks copied from original Cole designs in the early 20th century by White (see entry). Three such clocks are illustrated, item nos. 58, 59, 60.

1846-47   Kennedy and Asprey (Charles) Stationers and Dressing Case manufacturers, 49 New Bond Street
1848-72   Asprey, Charles, Dressing and Travelling Case, pocket book, etc. etc., manufacturers, 166 New Bond Street (latterly also at 22 Albermarle Street)
1873-79   Asprey & Son, Dressing and Travelling Case, Pocket Book, etc. etc., manufacturers, 166 New Bond Street and 22 Albermarle Street
1880-88   Asprey & Sons (Variations on same theme) 166 New Bond Street and 22 Albermarle Street
1889-1900 Asprey, C. & G.E. (Variations on same theme) 166 New Bond Street and 22 Albermarle Street
1901-1906 Asprey, Travelling Bag, etc., 165-6 New Bond Street and 22 Albermarle Street
1907-1909 Asprey & Co., Goldsmiths, Silversmiths, Jewellers, Watch and Clockmakers (first description of this kind), 165, 166, 167 New Bond Street and 22 Albermarle Street
1910-   Asprey & Co. Ltd., Goldsmiths, Silversmiths, Jewellers, Watch and Clockmakers, 165, 166, 167 New Bond Street and 22 Albermarle Street.

[1]Crystal Palace Exhibition Illustrated Catalogue London, 1851, Unabridged Republication of the Art Journal Special Issue printed by Dover Press, page 126.

THOMAS BOXELL, BRIGHTON

Boxell obviously catered for a wealthy and retired London Clientel, purchasing the majority of his stock from manufacturers in London and selling jewellery, silver and clocks. Only one very fine tripod clock, item No. 39 has so far come to light made by Cole and sold by this retailer.

(Brighton and Sussex directories not available each year)
1845   (first entry — no entry in 1843) Boxell, Thomas, Watch and Clockmaker, 55 Albion Street, Brighton
1846   Boxell, Thomas, Watch & Clockmaker & Manufacturing Goldsmith, 56 (sic) Albion Street
1848-50 Boxell, Thomas, Watch & Clockmaker & Manufacturing Goldsmith, 5 North Quadrant
1854   Boxell, Thomas, Watch & Clockmaker & Manufacturing Goldsmith, 145 North Street
1858   Boxell, Thomas, Watch & Clockmaker, The Brighton Observatory, 40 King's Road
1862-89 Boxell, Thomas, Watch & Clockmaker & Manufacturing Goldsmith, 43 King's Road
The next Brighton directory of 1892 does not mention him. He does not appear in the Sussex directories after 1878, i.e. he does not appear in 1882.

DENT, LONDON

Cockspur Street in circa 1860 was quite a horological centre with Dent at No. 33, Phillips Brothers at No. 23 and E. White, formerly employed by Dents, at No. 20.

Two strut clocks — one signed Dent, 34 Cockspur Street, the other, a standard form strut clock with cast border decoration signed M.F. Dent 33, 34 Cockspur Street Charing Cross, have been noted.

1841-43	Dent, E.J., 82 The Strand
1844-46	Dent, E.J., 82 The Strand and 33 Cockspur Street
1846-52	Dent, E.J., 82 The Strand, 33 Cockspur Street and 34 and 35 Royal Exchange
1852-53	Dent, E.J., 61 The Strand, 33 Cockspur Street and 34 and 35 Royal Exchange
1853-60	Dent, F.W., 61 The Strand, 34 and 35 Royal Exchange
1860-97	E. Dent & Co., 61 The Strand, 34 and 35 Royal Exchange
1897-1921	E. Dent & Co. Ltd., 61 The Strand and 4 Royal Exchange

1853-58	Dent, R.E., 33 Cockspur Street
1858-62	Dent, M.F., 33 and 34 Cockspur Street
1862-72	Dent, M.F., 33 and 34 Cockspur Street
1872-1916	Dent, M.F., 34 Cockspur Street
1916-21	Dent, M.F., 28 Cockspur Street
1921	Business merges with E. Dent & Co. Ltd. — E. Dent & Co. Ltd., 28 Cockspur Street and 4 Royal Exchange

The above references to Dent have been extracted from *Carriage Clocks* by C.R.P. Allix and P. Bonnert.

EMANUEL, LONDON

The firm of M. Emanuel is another example of a large firm of manufacturing silversmiths that have slipped into twentieth century obscurity. They exhibited at the 1851 exhibition a large variety of objects such as gilt candelabra, gilt plateaux with china racks and medallions. Illustrated in the Art Journal Illustrated Catalogue is a large silver clock designed by "Mr. Woodington, the well known sculptor". In the 1862 London Exhibition as Harry Emanuel, they were again large exhibitors. Essentially manufacturing silversmiths and retailers, as with Garrards and Tessiers, they had no objection to Thomas Cole signing his work, as per item No. 5.

1826-39	Emanuel Bros. Silversmiths and Jewellers, 1-2 Bevis Marks
1842-43	Emanuel Bros. Wholesale jewellers to the Queen & Roy. Fam., 1 Bevis Marks & 5 Hanover Sq.
1844-46	Emanuel Bros. Wholesale jewellers to the Queen & Roy. Fam., 5 Hanover Square
1847-54	Emanuel, Michael, gold and silversmiths, 5 Hanover Square
1856	Emanuel, Harry, gold & silversmiths, 5 Hanover Sq.
1860	Emanuel, Harry, managing goldsmiths, silversmiths, jeweller & diamond & pearl mercht., 5 Hanover Sq.
1861	Emanuel, Harry, diamond & pearl mercht. & gold & silversmith, 70-71 Brook St. W
1862-64	Emanuel, Harry (as above) to the Queen (etc.) 70-71 Brook St. & 21 B Hanover Sq.
1865-73	As above but address 18 New Bond St. & 12 Clifford St. W
(last)	

J.M. FRENCH, LONDON

James Moore French became a Freeman of the Clockmakers Company by redemption in 1810. In other words, he did not serve an apprenticeship to a member of that Company.

It should be noted that the various addresses given, 15 Sweetings Alley, 80 Cornhill and 9 Royal Exchange, all relate to the Royal Exchange buildings.

The clock item No. 43 is another example of Cole's ability from the start of his return to the horological trade to act as a wholesaler and supplier leaving the retailing of the clock to this firm.

1811-28 J.M. French, 15 Sweetings Alley, Watch and Clockmaker
1828-38 J.M. French, 15 Sweetings Alley, Clock, Watch and Chronometer Maker
1839-41 J.M. French, 86 Cornhill, Watch, Clock and Chronometer Maker
1842-45 J.M. French, 80 Cornhill, Watch, Clock and Chronometer Maker
1846   John French Chronometer Maker, 9 Royal Exchange (last entry)
In Robson's Directory of 1843, J.M. French, Chronometer Watch and Clockmaker, successor to T.W. Morrice.

R. & S. GARRARD, LONDON

The history of Garrards revolves around the Panton Street address and goes back many years prior to 1800. From the point of view of Thomas Cole, it would seem appropriate to take the addresses and designations from the death of Robert Garrard, Snr. (1758-1818) who died on 26th March, 1818, and was succeeded in the business by his sons, Robert James and Sebastian. On the accession of William IV in 1830, Garrards succeeded Rundell and Bridge as Crown Goldsmiths and on 13th February, 1843, Garrards were appointed Crown Jewellers, a post which the firm still holds today.

Garrards, primarily silversmiths manufacturing large and ornate centrepieces, race trophies and candelabra, exhibited at the Crystal Palace 1851 exhibition and the International Exhibition of 1862. On the death of Robert Garrard in 1881, he was succeeded in the family firm by his nephew, James Mortimer Garrard, the name Mortimer, in this case, deriving from his mother's maiden name. The firm finally moved from Panton Street in 1911 to 24 Albermarle Street and 17 Grafton Street. Sebastian died in 1946. Since he and his brother, James Robert Lindsay, reared between them eight daughters and no sons, 154 years of control of the firm by the Garrard family sadly came to an end.[1]

Cole seems to have supplied this firm with predominantly miniature timepieces of one form or another. As with the firm of Tessiers, Garrards were not manufacturers of this type of article and seemed to have no objection to Cole, on occasions, signing his work — see illustration.

1819-36   Garrard, R.J. & S., Goldsmiths, 31 Panton Street and 25 Haymarket
1837-42   Garrard, Robert & Sebastian, Goldsmiths, 31 Panton Street & 25 Haymarket. (Note some directories give the change from R.J. & S. to R. & S. as early as 1833)
1843-48   Garrard, Robert & Sebastian & Co., Goldsmiths, 31 Panton Street & 25 Haymarket
1849-56   Garrard, Robert & Sebastian, Goldsmiths and Silversmiths, 25 Haymarket
1857-59   Garrard, Robert & Sebastian, Goldsmiths and Silversmiths to the Crown, 25 Haymarket
1860-63   Garrard, Robert & Sebastian & Co., Goldsmiths and Silversmiths to the Crown, 25 Haymarket
1864-1909   Garrard, Robert & Sebastian & Co., Goldsmiths and Silversmiths to the Crown, 25 Haymarket and 25-32 Panton Street
1910-   Garrard & Co. Ltd.
[1]The Connoisseur, June 1974, Garrard & Co. by Christopher Lever.
For additional information, see Heal's London Goldsmiths under Garrards.

Signature from small diamond-shaped desk clock unnumbered made between 1843-1848

THE GOLDSMITHS ALLIANCE LTD., LONDON

The Goldsmiths Alliance Ltd. was formed into a limited company in 1866, the original shareholders being Joseph Savory, Snr., Albert Savory, Snr., Joseph Savory, Jnr., Albert Savory, Jnr. and other members of the Savory family. The firm, latterly a manufacturing retail concern, traced its roots back to one Jonas Cockerton in 1751. By the middle of the 19th century their silver manufactory was at Finsbury Place South, Finsbury, and later at 18 Red Lion Street, Clerkenwell (where the silversmiths Samuel and William Smily were in charge of operations — which explains why so many pieces of silver stamped 'GOLDSMITHS ALLIANCE LIMITED' also bear the makers' marks WS or SS). The senior partner at the end of the 19th century was Sir Joseph Savory 1st Bt., who became Lord Mayor London (1890/1). The firm went into voluntary liquidation in about 1893 and was wound up; the stock and goodwill being purchased by The Goldsmiths & Silversmiths Co. Ltd. (now controlling Garrard & Co. 1975).

A fine mantel clock Item No. 34 is signed the Goldsmiths Alliance Ltd., Corn Hill, London and is unnumbered. From the list below, the earliest date that the clock could have been sold is 1866. As Cole died in 1864, the clock must have been finished in his workshop by his sons and sold to this firm. This is interesting in that stylistically, with its marine chronometer movement, the clock could be dated circa 1825. However, the other mantel clock of nearly identical form is numbered 1550, putting it at the latter end of Cole's production so the late date ties in neatly.

1843-53 A.B. Savory & Sons, Manufacturing Silversmiths and dealers in foreign coin and bullion at 14 Corn Hill
1853-66 11-12 Corn Hill " " " "
1867-93 Goldsmiths Alliance Ltd., 11-12 Corn Hill
1893   Taken over by the Goldsmiths and Silversmiths Co.

C.F. HANCOCK, LONDON

The partnership between John Samuel Hunt, John Hunt, Robert Roskell and Charles Frederick Hancock, Goldsmiths, Silversmiths and Jewellers of 156 New Bond Street and Harrison Street, Grays Inn Road, and at Manchester under the style of Hunt and Roskell, was dissolved 29th January, 1849 so far as regards Charles Frederick Hancock (dated 1st March, 1849, and extracted from the London Gazette, 1849, Pt. 1, p. 768).

Hancock entered the partnership with Hunt and Roskell between 26th December, 1843 (see Hunt and Roskell) and 29th January, 1849. He uses the form of address "a successor of Storr and Mortimer" and it must be assumed that at some stage, he was associated with Storr and Mortimer, becoming a partner in Hunt and Roskell after 1843. This connection with the firm of Storr and Mortimer is interesting in terms of family Christian names. Charles Frederick Hancock christened his eldest son, born in 1844, Mortimer Hancock, possibly as a tribute to John Mortimer who retired in 1843. James Ferguson Cole christened his second son, born in 1844, Mortimer Cole. Such an unusual Christian name may mean a close relationship between J.F. Cole, C.F. Hancock and John Mortimer. This may have provided Thomas Cole, through his brother, with the introduction to Hancock, and Hunt and Roskell.

The numbering and sale of Cole's work through Hancock's business is somewhat complex. The earliest Cole known to me sold by Hancocks is series number 528 and all Cole's work sold by Hancock appears to be numbered.

Series numbers 528, 544 and 706 are all engraved "C.F. Hancock, a Succefsor of Storr and Mortimers by appointment to HM Queen Adelaide and HIM the Emperor of Rufsia, 39 Bruton Street, London." Hancock received the Royal Warrant from Queen Victoria in 1849/50 and clock series number 789 is engraved "C.F. Hancock, Jeweller and Silversmith to the Queen."

The conclusion to be drawn from the above is that Hancock, on establishing his business in January 1849, purchased a large quantity of Cole's stock in hand. Cole must have commenced numbering his clocks circa 1846-47 to allow for the unnumbered Hunt and Roskell strut clocks. Series numbers 528, 554 were old Cole stock of circa 1845 numbered in 1846/47 and sold to Hancock in 1849. Series number 706 was stock in hand circa 1848 and purchased by Hancock in 1849. Series number 789, as it bears the change in Royal Appointment with no mention of Queen Adelaide, must have been a current model just completed and purchased by Hancock in 1850.

The preponderance of early clocks bearing Hancock's name and the sudden drop in those bearing Hunt and Roskells in the numbered series, may indicate that Hancock agreed to take Cole's output in exchange for an exclusive agency. Some form of arrangement must have been entered into for a short number of years to allow for the large number of Hancock retailed pre-1850 strut clocks.

Hancocks exhibited at the 1851 exhibition and from the Official Descriptive and Illustrated Catalogue, Vol. II, page 692:
"Gilt eight day carriage clock, the movement by Cole, strikes the hours, half hours and quarters and repeating also the minutes."

Although the name Cole only is mentioned, I have no record of James Ferguson Cole working for C.F. Hancock but it is interesting that the movement only of the clock is designated by Cole.

Charles Frederick Hancock must be considered a human dynamo in terms of the rapidity with which he established his business after leaving Hunt and Roskell. He may well have taken a certain amount of their stock with him as a condition of the partnership dissolution for by 1851 in the Great Exhibition, he had a large variety of goods on view. The 1855 Exhibition in Paris saw Hancock spending no less than five months supervising his exhibits in France.[1] One of the most important commissions to which the firm is still entitled is that of the manufacture of the Victoria Cross entrusted to Mr. C.F. Hancock by Lord Panmure on 1st March, 1857.

For a lot of the information contained in this entry, I am indebted to Mr. David Callaghan of Messrs. Hancocks & Co., and I illustrate by courtesy of that firm their current billhead which has been merely extended as the "honours" have been gathered. For example, Queen Adelaide who died in 1849 had given her Royal Appointment to Hancock within a few months of his leaving Hunt and Roskell, most of the Royal Appointments being collected by 1873.

1848-53   Hancock, Chas. F. Jeweller and Goldsmith, 39 Bruton Street, Bond Street, manufactory 4 Little Bruton Street

1854-58   Hancock, Chas. Fredk., Jeweller, Gold and Silversmith to the principal sovereigns and courts of Europe, 39 Bruton Street and 152 New Bond Street

1859-60   Hancock, Chas. Fredk., Jeweller, Gold and Silversmith (much the same description) 39 Bruton Street and 152 New Bond Street

1861   Hancock, Chas. Fredk. (same description) 38-9 Bruton Street and 152 New Bond Street

1862-66   Hancock, Chas. Fredk., Jeweller, Gold and Silversmith to the Queen and Prince and Princess of Wales, 38-9 Bruton Street and 152 New Bond Street

1867-70   Hancock, C.F. Son & Co. (as above)

1871-1916 Hancocks & Co. (various descriptions, e.g. jewellers, goldsmiths, silversmiths, pearl and diamond merchants to the Queen, etc.) 38-9 Bruton Street and 152 New Bond Street

1917-30   Hancocks & Co. (as above) 25 Sackville Street

1930-   See letterhead illustrated

[1]C.F. Hancocks business diary in the possession of the firm

ESTABLISHED IN BRUTON St. BOND St. IN 1848.

BY APPOINTMENT TO
H.M. QUEEN ELIZABETH
THE QUEEN MOTHER
GOLDSMITHS & SILVERSMITHS.

HANCOCKS & CO.
(JEWELLERS) LTD.
G.L. HANCOCK DORE   JOHN A. BOURNE   D.J. CALLAGHAN   C.I.H. MORTON   G.R.A. WIXLEY

JEWELLERS, SILVERSMITHS,
AND MERCHANTS IN
PEARLS, DIAMONDS & PRECIOUS STONES.
ANTIQUE SILVER & OLD SHEFFIELD PLATE.

1 BURLINGTON GARDENS,
LONDON, W1X 2HP

JEWELS AND PLATE VALUED, PURCHASED OR TAKEN IN EXCHANGE.
BANKERS: NATIONAL WESTMINSTER BANK LTD.
TELEPHONE: 01-493 8904
CABLES: HANDORE, LONDON

THE LATE
QUEEN VICTORIA
THE EMPRESS OF AUSTRIA
THE QUEEN OF PORTUGAL
THE EMPRESS OF RUSSIA
QUEEN ADELAIDE
EMPRESS EUGENIE
THE QUEEN OF THE BELGIANS
THE QUEEN OF HOLLAND
QUEEN AMELIE
THE QUEEN OF BAVARIA

THE LATE
THE EMPEROR OF AUSTRIA
THE KING OF PORTUGAL
EMPEROR NAPOLEON III
KING LOUIS PHILLIPE
THE EMPEROR OF RUSSIA
THE KING OF HANOVER
THE SHAH OF PERSIA
THE SULTAN OF TURKEY
THE KING OF PRUSSIA
THE KING OF ITALY

Incorporating J. PARKES (Founded 1777) and In Association With JOHN MORTON LTD. 48 Nassau Street, Dublin 2

HOWELL AND JAMES, LONDON

This was an unusual firm, the origins of which are difficult to trace. The firm first appears in the London Directories of 1820 and was still there in 1880, the address throughout remaining constant at 5, 7, and 9 Regent Street. In the directories up until the 1860's at least, they called themselves Warehousemen and only Robson's directory of 1843 defines them as silk mercers, perfumers, bronzists, jewellers, milliners etc.

Although originally Howell and James, they were styled Howell & Co. from 1836-40 and thereafter, Howell, James & Co. They exhibited at the 1851 exhibition as Howell, James & Co.

The clock item No. 42 in my opinion dates circa 1840-42 and may be the result of Cole's return to the horological trade. The description Howell, James & Co. dates the clock after 1840. It is sufficiently experimental to be an early example of case design, construction and engraving.

In the Art Journal Illustrated Catalogue is shown a large ornate mantel timepiece, page 51, "It is designed by Mr. Adams, an artist of talent who has in this produced an elegant work of art with emblems most appropriate to the subject." How appropriate is left to the reader and I quote: "Below the dial are four bas relief children representing the seasons and on each side are family groups symbolising childhood, youth, womanhood and old age." One might say, an ornate pastiche depicting the passage of time.

In the 1862 exhibition, see Appendix D, they illustrate a number of clocks which owe their inspiration to the design work of Cole.

HUNT AND ROSKELL, LONDON

This firm was intimately connected by descent with Rundell, Bridge and Rundell as were Garrards and Hancocks. By 1855 these three firms were the biggest manufacturing and retailing silversmiths in London. The firm was founded by Paul Storr and graduated by 1822 to a partnership between Storr and Mortimer. It is known that the firm was selling watches, clocks and jewellery as well as silver from this time. The partnership between Paul Storr, John Mortimer and John Samuel Hunt of New Bond Street, Parish of St. George, Hanover Square, Goldsmiths, Silversmiths and Jewellers, carrying on business as Storr and Mortimer, was dissolved 31st December, 1838 and carried on by Messrs. Mortimer and Hunt. (Extracted from the London Gazette, 1839, Pt. 1, p. 11).

The partnership between John Mortimer, John Samuel Hunt and John Hunt, Goldsmiths, Silversmiths and Jewellers of 156 New Bond Street and at Harrison Street, Grays Inn Lane, known as Mortimer and Hunt, terminated when John Mortimer retired from the business 26th December, 1843 (Extracted from the London Gazette 1843, Pt. 2, P. 4579.) Presumably at this stage, Robert Roskell enters the partnership and the firm becomes Hunt and Roskell.

It is interesting that Hancock describes himself as a Successor to the Firm of Storr and Mortimer. It must be assumed that having severed the contact with Hunt and Roskell in 1848, he did not wish to advertise the strength of the competition and hence used the words "a Successor to Storr and Mortimer."

Hunt and Roskell exhibited Cole's work at the Great Exhibition in 1851 and the following items some of which may be definitely attributed to the workshop of Cole, have been extracted from the Official Descriptive and Illustrated Catalogue of the Great Exhibition 1851, Vol. II printed by William Clowes. The entry is taken verbatim as follows from page 688. Nos. 2, 3, 4, 5, 6 and 7 may be ascribed potentially to Cole, either in the design or manufacture.

1. Highly finished eight day marine chronometer in rosewood case.
2. Eight day striking clock engraved gilt case, chronometer escapement and day of the month calendar.
3. Eight day striking clock engraved gilt case with aneroid barometer, and thermometer, detached lever escapement.
4. Large oval eight day timepiece engraved gilt case with aneroid barometer, day of the month calendar and thermometer, detached lever escapement, compensation balance.
5. Small oval eight day carriage timepiece engraved gilt case with thermometer and detached lever escapement.
6. Square shaped eight day carriage timepiece engraved gilt case with day of the month calendar, detached lever escapement. The flatness of this clock renders it peculiarly adapted to the carriage. (Possibly similar to item Nos. 1 and 2.)
7. Oval eight day carriage timepiece engraved gilt case with perpetual day of the month calendar, detached lever escapement.

The firm of Hunt and Roskell commenced in 1844 but the earliest directory listing is for 1847. Item Nos. 1 and 2 are examples of pre-numbered Cole clocks made circa 1844-46 sold by this firm. Early strut clocks with Hunt and Roskell's address on them appear to have no Cole series number. They can be no earlier than the dissolution of the partnership between Mortimer and Hunt in December 1843 and no later than the death of Queen Adelaide in 1849 for by this time, Hancock had sold clocks up to series No. 706. This helps to establish the date at which Cole introduced his numbering system 1846/47.

1822-38	Storr and Mortimer
1839-44	Mortimer and Hunt (late Storr and Mortimer) Jewellers to Her Majesty, 156 New Bond Street
1844-97	Hunt and Roskell (late Storr, Mortimer and Hunt) Jewellers, Goldsmiths and Silversmiths to Her Majesty, 156 New Bond Street
1898-1911	Hunt and Roskell Ltd., Jewellers, etc. 156 New Bond Street
1912-65 (last)	Hunt and Roskell Ltd., Jewellers, etc. 25 Old Bond Street
1966-	J.W. Benson at this address

JENNER AND NEWSTUB, LONDON

The very late cake basket clock, item no. 51 retailed by this firm is, as far as can be ascertained, unnumbered. At no stage prior to 1880 did the firm advertise as watch and clockmakers, their principal line of business being the making of dressing cases, travelling bags, etc. The late production of this Clock by Cole or his sons is further confirmed by this retailer's working dates.

1858-59 (first)	Jenner & Knewstub (sic) dressing case mkrs., stationers, cutlers, etc., 33 St. James's St.
1860-61	Jenner & Knewstub, dressing case and travelling bag mkrs., stationers, die sinkers, cutlers, engravers, gold, silver, ormolu and buhl makers, 33 St. James's St.
1862-70	Jenner & Knewstub, dressing case mkrs. 33 St. James's St. & 66 Jermyn St.
	(Between 1870 and 1880 the form of entry changes to the form below)
1880-90	Jenner & Knewstub, dressing case mkrs, watchmakers, jewellers, stationers and engravers, 33 St. James's St. & 66 Jermyn St.
1891	As above but address 60 Piccadilly
1892-93 (last)	Jenner & Knewstub, stationers and bag makers, 60 Piccadilly

N.B. The clock is definitely signed NEWSTUB. However, the directory entries consistently give the spelling as KNEWSTUB.

LONDON AND RYDER, LONDON

This firm occupied the same premises at 17 New Bond Street from 1859-1940 and appear to have been retailers rather than makers of any one object. They were preceded at this address from 1842-58 by Thomas Hancock, a jeweller. No relationship between Charles Hancock and Thomas Hancock is apparent.

The large Cole tripod, item No. 36 was, I am sure bought from the defunct Cole business, circa 1864/6. Cole may well have kept it as a form of advertising for, by its number 968 2, it would date circa 1852.

1859-1940 London & Ryder (successors to Hancock), Goldsmiths, Silversmiths and Jewellers, 17 New Bond Street.

(The description, but not the name or the address, varies, e.g. in 1869 described as jewellers, goldsmiths, silversmiths, diamond merchants, inventors of monogram jewellery, makers of the Doncaster, Goodwood and other racing cups, yachting prizes, military testimonials, etc., patent keyless watches, chronographs . . .)

1941 Finnigans Ltd. appears at 17 New Bond Street. This firm as Finnigans Ltd., Department Store is (1975) at 198 Sloane Street.

ORTNER AND HOULE, LONDON

Item No. 9 bears the inscription "Ortner and Houle, Jewellers, Engravers and Draftsmen, 3 St. James's Street, S.W." in gilt to the interior of the original red leather travelling case. This firm were the second retailers, the original retailers being C.F. Hancock. It is possible that there may have been some form of connection between Cole and this firm as the working dates, to a certain extent, correlate.

1852
(first)-56   Ortner, Evan, seal engraver, die sinker and medallist, 55 Rupert Street, Haymarket
1857   Ortner, Evan, seal engraver, die sinker, and medallist, 55 Rupert Street, Haymarket and 3 St. James's St.
1858-61   Ortner, Evan, pract. seal and gem engr. die sinker, medallist & gen. engraver, 3 St. James's St.
1862-76   Ortner & Houle (description as above) 3 St. James's St. & 4 Pickering Place
1877-1918   Ortner & Houle, jewellers, 3 St. James's St. and 4 Pickering Place
(last)

W. PAYNE & CO., LONDON

This firm by the middle of the 19th century occupied three floors of a large and imposing business at 163 New Bond Street, see illustration. From their entries in the various directories, apart from advertising as pedometer makers 1839-40 and as clock and pedometer makers from 1852-1905, their sole business would have appeared to have been that of watch and clock making.

The following items are known to have been retailed by this firm, a tripod No. 1835 69 of standard form similar to item No. 40; the miniature strut clock, item No. 12; the carriage clock, item No. 57 and the strut clock item No. 29. The design of the case of the carriage clock may be attributed to Cole in his capacity as an ornamental clock case designer (he exhibited clock designs in the 1851 Exhibition). The method of construction with the finials unscrewing and the whole top rising up so that the side panels slide out to expose the movement is a feature of his work. The engraving of the case is stylistically very much Cole in design, however, the execution is similar to the quarter striking musical strut clock, item No. 29. This very unusual strut clock again owes its inspiration in design to Cole both in the format of layered construction, the design of the carrying brace to the handle and the strut. Unlike the zodiacal carriage clock, the movement is not signed and cannot be attributed to S.B. Gaze.

To recap on this firm, we have a direct connection between Cole whose products they retailed, between S.B. Gaze whose movements were included in Payne clocks, and clocks in cases which show from their design a lot of the ideas originating from Cole.

1816 (first entry) - 24.   Payne, Wm. Clock and Watchmaker, 62 South Molton Street

1825-38   Payne, Wm. Watchmaker, 163 New Bond Street

1839-40   Payne, Wm. Watch & Pedometer Maker, 163 New Bond Street

1841-46   Payne, Wm. Watchmaker, 163 New Bond Street

1847-50   Payne, Wm. Watchmaker, 163 New Bond Street & 62 New Bond Street

1851   Payne, Wm. Watchmaker, 163 New Bond Street

1852-1905 Payne, Wm. & Co. Watch, Clock & Pedometer Maker, 163 New Bond Street

1906-1908 Payne, Wm. & Co. Watch & Clockmakers & Jewellers, Diamond Merchants & Pedometer Makers, 163 New Bond Street

1909-10   As 1906-8 with addition of "antique silver, etc."

1911   Payne, Wm. & Co. Clockmakers, (sic) 163 New Bond Street

1912-15
(last)   Payne, Wm. & Co. Clockmakers, 165 (sic) New Bond Street (same address as Aspreys)

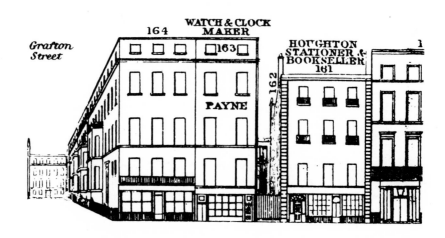

PHILLIPS BROTHERS, LONDON

This firm exhibited in the 1851 exhibition as per the Official Descriptive Illustrated Catalogue of the Great Exhibition 1851, Vol. II, printed by William Clowes Page 684, the following items that could be attributed to the workshop of Cole.

1.   Camp time piece, patent detached lever escapement, enamelled second dial plate in circular bronze case with engraved and gilt handle and *spring adaptation to support an inclined position,* with travelling case.

2.   Carriage timepiece in a *gilt engraved case,* patent detached lever escapement, jewelled, etc., *portable from its flatness and rendered secure, on standing, by a new application for feet.*

The firm became well known in the 1860's and 70's. They supplied a certain amount of silver on a retail basis but their main interest by that date, seems to have been in jewellery especially of the archeological type. In the International Exhibition, London 1862, they showed works in gold, silver, coral and were awarded a medal for excellence in design and manufacture.

(The italic sections are the basis of my attribution to the workshop of Cole.)

1839	First appearance in addenda to Pigot's 1839 directory as: Phillips Brothers, Watchmakers & Jewellers, 31 Cockspur Street (also 1840 P.O. Directory)
1841-55	Phillips Brothers, Watchmakers & Goldsmiths, 31 Cockspur Street
1856-69	Phillips Brothers, Watchmakers, Gold and Silversmiths, 23 Cockspur Street (sic) (1869 directory describes as watchmakers, gold & silversmiths, jewellers, coral merchants, Sole gold medal for goldsmiths work for England, Paris exhibition 1867)
1870-1902	(last) Phillips Brothers & Son, Art Goldsmiths, Coral Merchants, Watchmakers, 23 Cockspur Street

E.W. ROBINS, LONDON

It would appear from the directory entries that Robins was a manufacturer and not a retailer. It has been impossible to date to establish any connection on a manufacturing basis between Cole and Robins. The connection, however, between two manufacturing wholesalers as distinct from a manufacturing wholesaler and a retailer may well, in the future, prove to be important.

The strut clock, Item no. 63, is very much in the manner of Cole, both in the support for the handle and the strut for the base.

For further notes see Imitators of Cole's Work, p168.

1857	Robins, Edward Winter, Watchmaker, 28 Queen's Road, Bayswater; Manufactory 4 Red Lion Street, Clerkenwell
1858	Robins, Edward Winter, Wholesale Watch & Chronometer Manufacturer, 28 Queen's Road, Bayswater; Manufactory, 14 Myddleton Street, Clerkenwell
1859	Robins, Edward Winter, Wholesale Watch & Chronometer Manufacturer, 28 Queen's Road, Bayswater and Maldon, Essex

He does not appear in Essex directory of 1855. In 1862 and 1866 he is entered under Maldon as "Watchmaker, High Street." He does not appear in next issue of 1870.

BENJAMIN SMITH, JNR., LONDON

Son of Benjamin Smith who, with Digby Scott and James Smith, produced large quantities of silver for Rundell, Bridge and Rundell, the firm established in Lime Kiln Lane, Greenwich in 1802, moved to Camberwell in 1814.

Benjamin Smith, Snr. died in 1823 and the firm was carried on by his son who eventually married into the Elkington family of Birmingham, the electroplate patentees. Smith moved to 12 Duke Street, Lincolns Inn Fields in 1822 from Token House Yard and died soon after becoming bankrupt in 1850. A carriage clock illustrated in the March, 1974 edition of the Antique Collectors Guide, page 39, attributed to Cole and sold by this firm is the only connection proved to date.

The business was carried on by his son Stephen Smith and his partner William Nicholson as Smith, Nicholson & Co. Latterly, the business transferred to King Street, Convent Garden as Stephen Smith & Son and was wound up or taken over in the mid 1880's, the main interest going to Martin Goldstein, an early partner in the firm now called C.J. Vander Ltd.

The firm of Smith, Nicholson & Co. exhibited at the Great Exhibition in 1851 presentation silver, etc. There is no reference to their being connected to Cole or exhibiting clocks.

1822   Smith, Benjamin, Jnr. & Co., Silver and Bronze Manufacturer, Token House Yard
1823-24 Smith, Benjamin, Jnr., Silversmith, 12 Duke Street, Lincoln's Inn
1825-50 (last) Smith, Benjamin, Silversmith, 12 Duke Street, Lincoln's Inn Fields (Jnr. dropped after 1824)

STREETER, LONDON

Mr. Streeter was an amazing character, being the Harry Winston of the 19th century. In addition to being a writer of authoratative books on fine gem stones, he conducted a leading London business specialising in very large single stones.

Item No. 5 initially retailed by M. Emanuel was subsequently sold again by this firm. As the working dates of Cole do not correlate with this retailer, there can be no direct connection. However, he is such an interesting man, that having researched him, I feel honour bound to commit him to paper.

1868 (first) Streeter, Edwin W. jeweller, see Hancock, Burbrook & Co. Ltd.
1866 (first) Hancock & Burbrook, jewellers & silversmiths, 37 Conduit St.
1868   Hancock, Burbrook & Co. Ltd. (now Edwin W. Streeter) introducer of 18 carat gold machine-made jewellery by appointment, 37 Conduit Street
1869   Streeter, Edwin W. (late Hancock & Co. Ltd.) introducer of 18 carat gold machine made jewellery, watches and clocks by appointment, 37 Conduit St.
1870-74   As 1869, adding "factory Burlington Steam Works, Saville Row W"
1875-80   Streeter, Edwin W., F.R.G.S. (gold medallist of the Royal Order of Frederic), author of "Precious Stones" (etc.) (late Hancock & Co. Ltd.) pearl and diamond merchant . . . by appointment . . . 18 New Bond St. & 12 Clifford St. W, also Colombo, Ceylon.
            (During the period 1875-80, the description of the firm evolves to reach the above form by 1880)

1881-90   Streeter, Mr. F.R.G.S. pearl fisher, diamond miner, importer of diamonds and all other precious stones direct from the principal mines of the world . . . 18 New Bond St.

1886-95   Each year has a separate entry for Streeter & Co. (estab. 1670) 18 New Bond Street

1896-1904
(last)   Streeter & Co. Ltd., diamond and gem merchts., goldsmiths, jewellers and lapidarists, 18 New Bond St.

1910   Directory has "Streeter & Co. Ltd., transferred to Kirkby & Bunn, 17 Cork St. W"

H. & E. TESSIER, LONDON

This firm commenced in business at 32 South Audley Street in 1844 being run by a goldsmith, Louis Tessier, the business eventually being taken over by his sons, Henry and Edward. It is interesting to note that at no stage in their directory entries did the firm advertise as watch or clockmakers. However, the Cole, item No. 23 is interesting in that it is signed "Tho. Cole for H. & E. Tessier". Obviously, in terms of their own business, as with Garrards, there was no conflict of interest and it in no way embarrassed Messrs. Tessiers to allow goods being sold through their shop to bear the original manufacturers name.

1844-45   Tessier, Louis, Goldsmith, 32 South Audley Street

1846-50   Tessier, Louis & Sons, Goldsmiths and Jewellers, 32 South Audley Street,

1851-58   Tessier, Louis & Sons, Artists in Hair, 26 New Bond Street and Goldsmiths & Jewellers, 32 South Audley Street

1859   Tessier, Henry & Edward, Goldsmiths, 32 South Audley Street (Louis & Sons at 26 New Bond Street)

1860-70   Tessier, Henry & Edward, Goldsmiths, 32 South Audley Street and 26 New Bond Street

1871-87   Tessier, Henry, Goldsmith, 32 South Audley Street

1888-1904   (Last) Tessier, Henry, Goldsmith, 104 Mount Street, Berkeley Square (106 Mount Street from 1900)

1871-1920   Tessier, Edward, Manufacturing Jeweller, Gold and Silversmith, 26 New Bond Street

1921-   (Present day) Tessier Ltd., 26 New Bond Street

THOMAS COLE AND HIS WORK

This investigation has been extremely problematic in that Thomas Cole was, in the main, a wholesaler and not a retailer. The only accurate contemporary note in Horological literature is in the first edition of Britten's Former Clock and Watch Makers and Their Work published in 1894. "Thomas Cole, 11, Upper King Street, Bloomsbury, an excellent maker of spring clocks, brother of J.F. Cole, 1840-64". This information may well have been given to Britten by J.F. Cole before his death.

The dates are correct in that Cole's working life has to be divided into two distinct sections, circa 1825-1829 in partnership with his brother at 3 New Bond Street and from 1839-64 when the work by which he is best known was produced. The ten years in between include a first marriage and a complete absence from the horological trade.

I am certain that in the period 1839-64 the two brothers were independent of each other, J.F. Cole having no interest or influence over his brother's business. This is to a certain extent, confirmed by the fact that they exhibited separately at the Paris Exhibition of 1855 and the London Exhibition of 1862.

The movements of Cole's clocks are unusual, at least two bear the legend "Thos. Cole designer and maker", confirming that his workshop was responsible for the overall construction.

This section is divided into:
> Cases
> The numbering system and known numbered clocks and their dates
> Keys and Hands
> Case and Dial Engraving
> Strut clocks
> Mantel clocks
> Tripod clocks
> Clocks of an unusual format or design
> Carriage clocks

The 62 clocks illustrated and described cover a fairly large proportion of the Cole clock styles and show the originality of this maker both in his designs and methods of construction. Movements have not been dealt with under a separate heading, but have been closely investigated in certain clocks during the course of the text by Mr. Charles Allix, to whom I am most grateful.

CASES

Cole's clock cases have one major feature in common; they are all based on a central casting. To this casting are applied various layers of decoration. Cole realised that he could not get precise, clean cast edges except by using this layered system of construction. Each case is different from the next and although the overall design may be similar, it would appear that Cole at no stage used the same central casting twice. These castings are nearly always flawless. To achieve this, they may well have been cast on the lost wax process. This gives a perfectly clean finish but does not allow for repetition of the casting and explains why no two cases are identical. It would have been typical of Cole's attention to detail to use this process so as to ensure perfection in body casting. Each layer subsequently applied to the central casting is cut from sheet brass to the required pattern and then drilled and fitted, thereby building up the design and body of the clock.

The first illustration depicts the breakdown of a pre-numbered strut clock, item No. 2 circa 1845. The central casting (6) is shown with the movement not dissembled inside it. The photograph indicates the ten layers of construction including the central casting and dial that are required to give the sharp edges and perfect finish to these cases.

Photographic Index: 1. Engraved front bezel   2. Engraved decorative dial cover   3. Depthing piece to take the dial glass   4. Dial, below the dial the calendar mechanism   12. Depthing piece between dial and movement   5. Movement   6. Cast central body with feet and handle removed   7. First layer of back cover   8. Second layer of back cover   9. Third layer of back cover   These three layers are necessary to allow the movement which projects slightly outside the central casting (6) to fit into the case.   10. Back strut allowing the clock to sit at an angle. This bears Cole's secret signature.   11. The final layer holding the spring operated shutter that exposes the escapement. Between 10 and 11 are shown the springs which operate both these mechanisms.

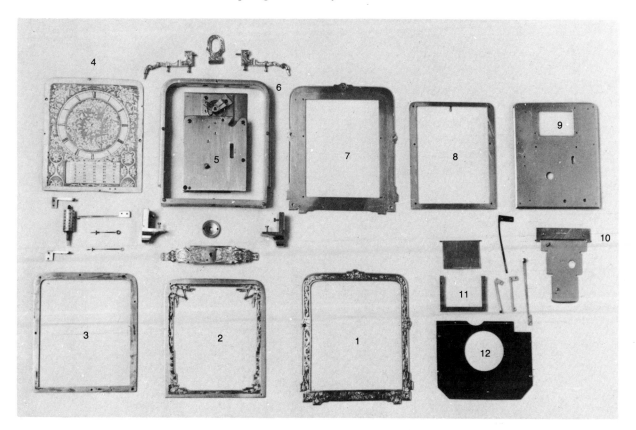

A large mantel clock with a chronometer escapement is shown with one pillar removed and the top and sides dissembled. The top construction is removed by undoing the finials and lifting it off complete. This section to emphasise the clean finish breaks down into eleven layers of 18 separate pieces if the finials are taken into account. The clock is numbered 1550 and it is at this period circa 1858 that Thomas Cole cases, to my mind, are at their finest. The doors are braced on either side by screwed in surrounds, one to each side. The same applies to the door panels giving nine separate parts to the door, or each panel. It is interesting to note that the layer above the clock which is held down by the finials has a riveted border, the rivets to the underneath having been filed off leaving a perfect dotted finish exposed to view on the top edge. Item No. 34 is placed alongside for comparison.

These two clocks may look identical from the photograph, however, the cases are proportionally quite different. The pillars are of the same design but of different thicknesses, the plinths on the pillars of each clock are of different heights, the finials that hold down the roof structure are of a noticeably different diameter. In fact, the whole clock, proportionally, is marginally different. This further emphasises, to my mind, the problems which Cole set himself. I cannot understand why he did not run off a series of castings so as to manufacture identical clocks unless he could only get the finish required via lost wax castings.

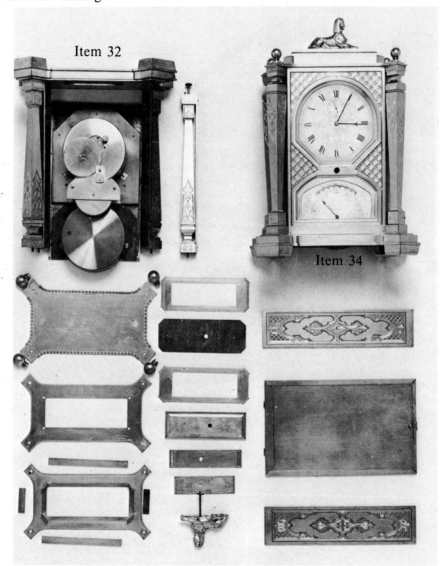

Item 32

Item 34

Item 32 only is dismantled and Item 34 is shown complete for comparison.

Case photograph No. 3 shows the breakdown of the "compendium for the writing table", item No. 52. The complexity of this case is obvious from the photograph even though it is not fully dissembled. If completely dismantled, exclusive of the screws and movement, it comprises 51 separate pieces. The clock case is constructed around a centre which on this occasion is not cast but a strip of flat brass of double the normal thickness. To the back there are three layers, to the front, two layers plus the glass. The actual compendium is built around a central body cast in two parts, clamped together (16 and 17) and hollowed so as to accept the drawers. The top layer is covered with a decorative engraved plate so as to give an effective finish. The breakdown is as follows:

1. The knurled square ended screws that hold down the top plate of the inkwell. 2. The feet of the inkwell. 3. The base holder for the inkwell on the same level as the feet 4. The cover to that base 5. The bottom layer of the support for the clock 6. The top layer for the support of the clock. 7. The main body of the clock above two connecting brackets. This bears Cole's secret signature. 8. The engraved decorative dial cover. 9. Engraved bezel. 10. The cast body of the inkwell in two parts 11. The back cover of the movement. 12. & 13. The two intervening layers between the back cover and the central body to allow for the depth of the movement. 14. The movement. 15. The key. 16. The bottom plate of the inkwell showing drawer slides with tensioned copper sides so as to prevent the drawer sliding out and the sides of the inkwell holder. This plate also bears Cole's secret signature 17. The top showing the drawer springs that stop the up and down rattle of the drawers. 18. The decorative top plate to the inkwell, a superb piece of engraving. 19. One drawer completely dissembled. 20. The gold engraved pen shown in the extended position. This concertinas for putting in the drawer. 21. The inkwell with top alongside.

THE NUMBERING SYSTEM

Thomas Cole numbered his clocks in sequence. This sequence seems to have started at 500, circa 1846/47 and terminated on his death at a figure no higher than 1900 in 1864. This gives a total output of approximately 1400 numbered clocks and I estimate 200 pre-numbered clocks made prior to 1846. Clocks were numbered consecutively throughout the sequence; these I shall call the series numbers. Certain styles were allotted a separate numbering system to run concurrently with the series numbers. These I have called style numbers.

A most popular style was the small oval thirty hour strut clock. The highest numbered example known to me, see item No. 21, is 1602 212 so the series number is 1602 and style number is 212 i.e. by clock number 1602, Cole had made 212 in this style. On an average basis, therefore, one in five of his clocks were in this style if the numbering system starts at 500. With approximately 300 more clocks made before the end of his life, this would, on the same averaging basis, add a further sixty, giving a total of small oval design strut clocks of approximately 275.

The second best selling Cole design, the rectangular strut clock, was never allocated a style number but was produced on a straightforward series number basis. The lowest number so far noted, see item No. 3 is 528 and the highest number 1614 and I would estimate that these clocks were produced in slightly larger quantities than the oval strut clocks previously noted, approximately 300 examples.

Another popular design must have been the tripod clocks. The highest style number noted to date is 69 from tripod No. 1835 69. The series number 1835 would leave approximately another 65 numbered clocks to be produced to reach a total of 1900. On this basis, I would estimate a total of 75 tripod clocks were manufactured by Cole.

If we add these three styles together, we have a total output of approximately 650 clocks. These three styles therefore, are the backbone of Cole's business.

The diamond shaped desk clock, item No. 46 must have been completed on or after Cole's death and introduces a further number into the numbering system, i.e. the movement number. This clock is numbered 1876 856 6. The case is numbered throughout 856, stylistically the correct series number. Six is the style number indicating a total of six made up to series number 856. Number 1876 is the movement number and this is stamped only on the movement. This can mean two things — either on Cole's death, his sons introduced a further extension of the numbering system or, which is more probable, that this movement was destined for another clock but so as to finalise his affairs, was put into this clock to make it saleable. It is interesting to note that the 6 in 1876 is completely different to the 6 in 856 and the 6 showing that the punch used was not the same and that this number was added later. As this difference occurs on all three sides of the diamond, it is not just a badly struck punch.

It is very difficult to correlate the numbering system and the date of manufacture as various factors influence the final sale of the clock from Cole's workshop.

In Charles Allix's excellent book on carriage clocks, two examples are given under English carriage clocks of the length of time they took to construct. A carriage clock No. 1052 made by Vulliamy for Mr. Shafto was commenced on June 30th 1830 and delivered on May 28th 1834, a total of four years being taken in its construction. Victor Kullberg's clock No. 6079 for Mr. John Ogilvy was commenced July 27th, 1894 and delivered May 18th, 1897, a total of nearly three years. Most of the work entailed in the production of clocks at this period was farmed out to various craft trades in the Clerkenwell district of London. To correlate the work of dial makers, case makers, hand makers, movement makers, escapement makers, into a clock took many years. It was not a streamlined process and Cole's designs with their inherent complexity must have caused considerable delays. The question to be answered, therefore, is whether he numbered his designs and applied this number on completion to the clock or numbered the central casting as and when it was made or numbered the clock on completion, irrespective of the design. My feeling is that all three courses were adopted.

C.F. Hancock left the partnership with Hunt and Roskell in January 1849. We have a large number of strut clocks with low numbers bearing Hancocks address. A rectangular strut clock, No. 528, bears the inscription — "By appointment to HM Queen Adelaide". This is important in that Hancock must have purchased it between January 1849 and 2nd December, 1849 when HM Queen Adelaide died. The fact that it is crested would indicate that the clock had remained in Cole's workshop for some time awaiting a buyer who wished to have a crested or monogrammed clock. For this service, Cole presumably charged extra through the retailer. It is very noticeable that clocks with either blank dials inside the chapter rings or crested and monogrammed dials are stylistically, in many cases, out of sequence with the numbering system.

It is my opinion that Cole decided to number his clocks circa 1846/47. It is reasonable to assume that he would number all clocks in their various stages of production in his workshop. This would allow for the large numbers of clocks bearing closely related numbers that were sold to Hancock on the commencement of his business.

Illustrated are Cole's punches for two strut clocks with series and style numbers, item No. 6,633 18 and item No. 13, 999 22.

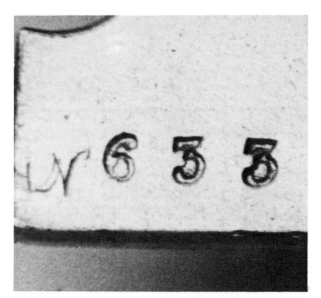

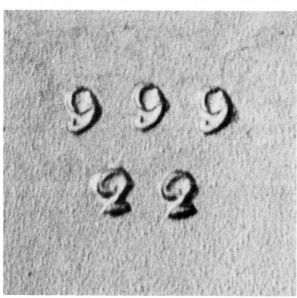

LIST OF NUMBERED CLOCKS

Item No. in text	Series No.	Style No.	Description	Retailer	Approximate Date
3	528		Rectangular strut clock	Hancock	1845
4	554		Rectangular strut clock	Hancock	1845
5	628		Striking rectangular strut clock	Emanuel	1846
6	633	18	Oval 30 hour strut clock	Hancock	1846
7	706	3	Oval eight day strut clock with calendar	Hancock	1849
8	789		Rectangular strut clock	Hancock	1850
9	811	76	Oval strut clock	Hancock	1851
10	833		Rectangular strut clock	Hancock	1851
	839	22	Miniature clock in the form of a cake basket	Hancock	1851
	842		Strut clock with calendar	Hunt and Roskell	1851
11	863	78	Oval strut clock	Hancock	1851
	886	9	Tripod clock	—	1851
35	939	12	Tripod clock	Hunt and Roskell	1852
36	968	2	Tripod clock with glazed stand and long pendulum	London and Ryder	1852
13	999	22	Milestone strut clock		1852
14	1049		Rectangular strut clock	London and Ryder	1852
41	1107		Cheval clock	—	1853
15	1309		Oval strut clock	Hancock	1855
16	1316		Large strut clock	T. Cole	1855
	1323	14	Oval strut clock with pierced monogrammed border	Hancock	1856
17	1367		Very large oval strut clock	Hancock	1856
18	1373		Rectangular strut clock	Hancock	1856
19	1374		Rectangular strut clock	—	1856
37	1437	49	Tripod	Hunt and Roskell	1857
	1523		Rectangular strut clock	Thos. Cole	1858
20	1535		Oval strut clock	Hancock	1858
32	1550		Mantel clock	Thos. Cole	1858
21	1602	212	Oval strut clock	London and Ryder	1860
22	1613		Large oval strut clock	Hancock	1860
23	1614		Rectangular strut clock	Tessiers	1860
38	1642		Tripod with cauldron pendulum	T. Cole	1861
24	1700		Porcelain dial strut clock	Payne	1862
39	1797		Tripod clock	Boxell	1863
40	1831	67	Tripod clock	Thos. Cole	1864
	1835	69	Tripod clock	Payne	1864
46	856				
	1876	6	Diamond shaped desk clock (For explanation of numbering system, see under that heading.)	—	1865

KEYS

Presumably because of the problems involved in access to the movements of his clocks, Cole was forced to design specially made keys, a selection of these being shown. Like all his work, they show meticulous attention to detail.

Top Left. From the Urn clock item No. 48, the key has to be this long to enable it to be turned. Note the typical Cole engraved handle. *Top Right.* From the compendium item No. 52 again an engraved key specially made to fit in the left hand drawer. *Bottom left.* The coromandel wood mantel clock, item No. 33. These keys are built up in layers like the clocks they wind and riveted together. *Bottom right.* Standard tripod key with spanner end for adjusting the nuts to put the clock in beat from item No. 37.

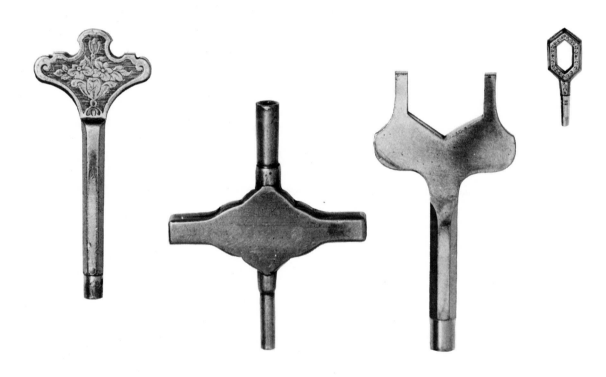

HANDS

Cole used two types of hand design — the Fleur de Lis and the Spade. These may be allocated to clocks as follows:

Strut Clocks — Fleur de Lis hour and Fleur de Lis minute hands *Very large strut clocks* — Fleur de Lis or Spade hour hands, plain minute hands *Mantel clocks* — Fleur de Lis hour hands, plain minute hands *Tripod clocks* — Spade hour hands and plain minute hands

These hands, in all probability, were made by Peter Pendleton, Manufacturer of Watch and Chronometer Hands, Yewtree Place, Prescot, Lancashire. He received a medal for his clock hands in the International Exhibition of 1862.

CASE AND DIAL ENGRAVING

The two keys to dating Cole clocks are the numbers, and in their absence, the style of the engraving. Cole's engraving varied considerably over his manufacturing period. This period discounts the time spent working with his brother at 3 New Bond Street between 1825-29 and commences after his reappearance circa 1840 at Upper King Street, Bloomsbury.

The two clocks, item Nos. 1 and 43 are examples of his work conducted during the period 1840-45 as an ornamental case maker and designer. This rather free flowing pierced style on a matted ground precedes that on the lined background and although to describe it in words is difficult, close observation of the photographs should make it self-explanatory. These very early clocks have no serial number, therefore cannot be correlated in an exact date sequence.

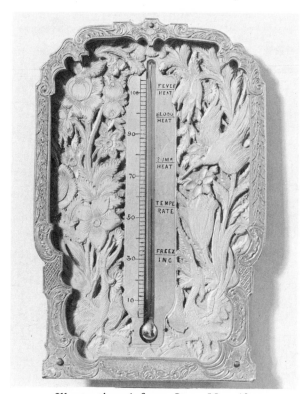

Illustration 1 from Item No. 43

Illustration 2 from Item No. 1

The dial of the pre-numbered clock, illustration No. 3, shows the introduction of the lined background to the floral engraving. The dial of this clock was not left blank for cresting or monogramming and gives a good indication of the standard of the engraving, circa 1845, carried out in Cole's workshop.

Illustration No. 4 is from the diamond shaped desk clock circa 1846-47, item No. 45 all three dials are shown. In comparison with illustration No. 3, the bezel is the standard bezel found on pre-numbered and pre-1850 Cole clocks in that it is Arabesque and florally engraved on a lined background. The dial centres have started to be divided up into small ovals and circles containing bunches of flowers but the main underlying theme of the decoration is still floral.

Illustration 3 from Item No. 2

Illustration 4 from Item No. 45

The engraving of the dial centres steadily becomes less floral and more segmented and arabesque. The introduction of a new border to the bezels in the form of engraved arches, see illustration No. 5 of item No. 13, occurs circa 1852. This bezel design changes from the engraved arches to a line and ball border or to no design on the bezel at all circa 1856-57. The dial becomes truly divided into four quarters circa 1857-58, see illustration No. 6, item No. 32 series No. 1550, circa 1858. This decoration is further changed in that the segments instead of containing Arabesque decoration contain plain floral decoration with no lined background, see item No. 22 series No. 1613, circa 1860. The final phase is indicated in the engraving on the cases of the cake basket clock and the strut clock item No. 30 which were probably completed after Cole's death circa 1865-70.

The changing bezel and dial designs are noted in the clock descriptions and this should make a difficult subject more easily understood.

Illustration 5 from Item No. 13

Illustration 6 from Item No. 32

Illustration 7 from Item No. 22

THOMAS COLE'S SECRET SIGNATURE

Possibly at the request of his customers who did not wish the name of the supplier to be known, Cole adopted a system of signing his clocks with the punch illustrated, generally in the most inaccessible place. This punch seems to have been common throughout his working life and is always in the form "Thos." rather than the name in full and the "Co" of Cole is set slightly higher than the "le". Three separate punches are used — "Thos.", "Cole" and "London". Cole was allowed by certain retailers to sign his work, particularly Tessiers and Garrards. An example of the Garrards form of signature is illustrated under Garrards in the section on Retailers.

Clocks signed "Thos. Cole", are always late in period and would date after 1855. It is possible that Cole who exhibited in the Paris Exhibition of that year found his name was sufficiently well established to run a half wholesale, half retail business.

Late period Coles with no number and no signature on the dial or movement may be examples of his signed work where resilvering of the dial has caused his signature to be obliterated, thus leaving the clock with no number and no hidden punched signature. This is purely conjecture, of course.

Likely position of punches is as follows:
Oval strut clocks — on the front of the central casting.
Early Rectangular Strut clocks with spring loaded shutter opening backs and struts — on the inside edge of the bar holding the spring loaded back strut. To find it, the whole of the back of the clock has to be taken apart.
Late Strut clocks — on the dial plate.
Tripod clocks — under one of the pillars.
Carriage or Mantel clocks — on the top plate of the superstructure.

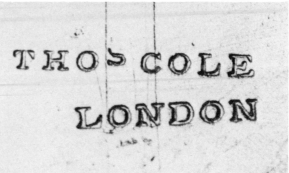

STRUT CLOCKS

Strut clocks were designed by Cole around two basic shapes, Oval and rectangular, the rectangular strut clocks being in three sizes based on the same format. These clocks were the mainstay of his business, and derive their name from the method of support.

He first conceived the idea of the strut clock circa 1845 and continued to manufacture them until his death in 1864. The idea is unique to him and words such as "the flatness of this clock renders it peculiarly adapted to the carriage" and "portable from its flatness and rendered secure on standing by a new application for feet" in the Great Exhibition Catalogue of 1851, indicate the reception the design received.

In their own time, they were considered to be carriage clocks, i.e. carriage in terms of portable, and as such were fitted with handles and travelling cases. It should be remembered that these clocks gained their popularity from their flatness or thinness as distinct from the square bulk of the carriage clock we know today.

This striving for flatness means that the escapement has to be in the vertical position to fit in the case. No one considers that a pocket watch designed to fit in the pocket should have its escapement planted in any other way than to allow the balance wheel to run parallel to the case, thinness or flatness again being the prime consideration.

Pre-1850 back with extra layers to accommodate strut   *Simplified construction with fold out foot, after 1850*

The criticism that the escapement should be horizontal as this gives a better standard of timekeeping may be countered by the evidence that these strut clocks with their vertical escapements keep good time.

As noted under numbering, Cole produced about 275 oval strut clocks and 300 rectangular examples. Initially they obviously sold well as a large proportion bear low serial numbers. The profits from these clocks must have been the foundation on which Cole's business success was based.

The oval strut clocks are designed to be as thin as possible and are generally fitted with bought in Swiss watch movements of thirty hour duration. With late numbered examples the strut angles out from the base of the case, thereby simplifying the construction of the back of the clock, see illust. p.44. Towards the end of his life, Cole designed some very large oval desk clocks, two of which are illustrated in this section. These must be considered rare.

The rectangular strut clocks have specially made Cole movements and are of eight day duration. The simplification of the design of the back of the case by doing away with the angled strut in later clocks is illustrated below.

Strut clocks are to be found with manual weekly or monthly calendars, visual phase of the moon and age in days of the phase of the moon as additional features. Cole also make striking rectangular strut clocks, an unusual departure in that most of his products are timepieces.

Pre-1850 complicated back occurs on rectangular-shaped strut clocks with both square and rounded tops.

Simplified back with no inclined support, 1850-64

ITEM 1

A strut clock, the gilt dial with the inscription:
HUNT & ROSKELL
162 NEW BOND ST.
and also bearing the insignia of a raised hand[1] and elsewhere engraved with curious and unusual stylised representations of fruit and foliage.

Hands: Cole-type fleur de lis.

Dial: Unusual and uncharacteristic foliate engraving see photograph. All chapters and lettering are painted. In this clock all dial writings are original and have never been restored. Note that the beautiful engraved design is not symmetrical.

Additional Features: Calendar work changed manually once a month (except non-Leap Year Februaries). Fine original key.

Duration: Eight days. The clock is wound with a detachable key.

Signature: Clock inscribed with vendor's name as noted above.

Number: No number found on case or movement.

Dimensions: 5¾" tall approx. with pendant up.

Casework: Gilt brass, the front, top and sides decorated with engraved flowers and foliage and also with hatching. The strut is held in its stowed-away position by means of a detent. When a release button is pressed then a secret spring brings the strut out ready to prop up the clock. This clock also has an alternative support in the form of a turnbuckle foot with a two-position detent. At the top of the back of the case is a hinged rectangular door opening downwards and secured when closed against an opening-spring by a catch or detent. The detent is released by pressing the steel release-pin seen in the photograph. When the back door is opened the escapement is visible and so is the top of the back movement plate bearing the engraved inscription
HUNT & ROSKELL LONDON

Movement: The movement has rectangular plates with radiused corners. The back plate measures about 2½" vertically and 2¼" horizontally. The front plate measures about 3½" vertically. The platform escapement is secured by screws and steady-pins to the inside of the front movement plate, the escapement arbors lying in the same plane as the train arbors. The typically English right-angled single roller lever escapement has pointed-tooth wheel. The plain steel balance has a flat spring.

Collection: Private collection England.

Illustrations: 1. Front. 2. Rear showing the movement of the clock when back of case removed. 3. Rear showing the back of the case (removed from the clock). Note the strut support with its release button (bottom right) and the door giving access to the movement (release pin above door). 4. View showing other side of the back panel of the case, showing detents and release arrangements.

Compiled by C.R.P. Allix

Notes by J.B. Hawkins

A prenumbered strut clock of standard construction. The back shows the early method of inclined support requiring the extra layers of construction. This model with the square tops has the bezel secured by knurled nuts. Circa 1845.

---

[1]Possibly the crest of the Myddleton family of Chirk Castle.

1

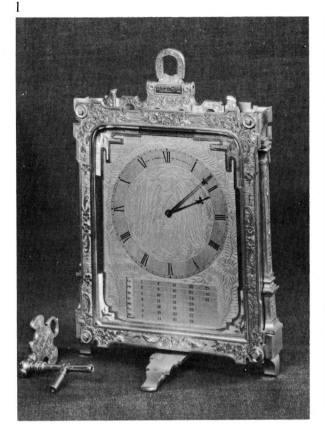

2

3

4

Item 1

ITEM 2

A very early strut clock, pre numbered, and of exactly the same format as the next item. It has the normal revolving strut attachment to the base for support, and to the rear for inclined support, a spring loaded catch operated bracket, see illustration. The supports to the suspension hook at the top should be noted in that early strut clocks of this shape appear to have the brackets running to the edge and over the side of the case, they being made in two separate halves, clamping the suspension handle between them. In later models, the suspension handle and the brackets are one piece and the overall length across the top of the clock is much reduced. The backs of these early strut clocks are beautifully constructed. The shutter that exposes the escapement is again spring loaded and operated from a small button at the top of the case.

Movement: Vertical lever escapement with uncompensated balance.
Hands: Fleur de Lis
Dial: Silvered, with Arabesque engraving. Painted numbers.
Additional Fitments: Manual monthly calendar
Duration: Eight days.
Signed: Hunt and Roskell, London.
Number: No number. This, in my opinion, is a pre-numbered clock but possibly only 30 to 40 clocks prior to the next item.
Dimensions: 16.5 cm high × 10.5 cm wide.
Date: Circa 1845.
Collection: Private collection, Australia.

Group of early or pre-numbered Cole clocks all made prior to 1850.

Item 2

ITEM 3

A very early strut clock with the same strut attachments for support as the previous item, see illustration. The dial engraved with the crest of a hand clasping a dagger is an example of a special order clock as the decoration is integral with the crest and the crest has not been applied later. The construction of the backs of these early strut clocks show a lot more attention to detail and complexity than do those produced circa 1855-60.

Movement: Vertical lever escapement, uncompensated balance.
Hands: Fleur de Lis
Dial: Silvered with Arabesque decoration incorporating a crest, painted numbers.
Additional Features: Nil
Duration: Eight days
Signed: "C.F. Hancock, a Succefsor of Storr and Mortimers, by appointment to HM Queen Adelaide and HIM The Emperor of Rufsia, 39 Bruton Street, London."
Number: 528. The dial centre has been left blank at the time of manufacture so that it could be engraved when sold with the new owner's crest. This earliest known numbered Cole would date circa 1845 and was sold circa 1849 as from the retailers inscription, Queen Adelaide was still alive (she died 2nd December, 1849) and Hancock was only just in business in Bruton Street 1848/9.
Dimensions: 16 cm high × 10.5 cm wide.
Date: Circa 1845.
Collection: Private collection, Australia.

Item 3

ITEM 4

A striking strut clock, the back of the case bearing the inscription:

C.F. HANCOCK
a Successor of
STORR & MORTIMER'S
by appointment to
H.M. Queen Adelaide
&
H.I.M. the Emperor of Russia,
39 Bruton Street,
London

Hands: Cole-type fleur de lis.

Dial: Silvered and engraved with a beautiful pattern which appears to be symmetrical and which in fact is not.

Additional Features: Hour striking on a wire gong disposed round the outside of the movement.

Duration: Eight days.

Signature: As above.

Number: No. 554 is stamped on the bottom of the case, which was not completely dismantled. See postscript.

Dimensions: 6¼" approx. with pendant up.

Casework: Gilt brass engraved with much use of hatching of various forms on the sides and top. Winding holes without shutters. The strut and back door have secret springs to open them and latches to hold them closed.

Movement: The going and striking trains are planted each with their separate back plates but sharing a common front plate. Both trains employ going barrels, and in the trains are found repeated changes in pitch.

The single roller English right-angled lever escapement has a plain steel balance furnished with a steel balance spring with overcoil. Compare this clock with Cole's Item No. 5 in the report of which will be found further notes concerning the movement. Note that while the two clocks are exceedingly similar, yet they contain so many detail mechanical differences as to prove beyond all question that they were made piece-meal one at a time and were not the product of any sort of mass production system. The clock is wound and the hands set by means of a double-ended detached key. Access to the hand-setting square is through the top back door. The winding holes are not protected by shutters.

Collection: Private collection England.

Illustrations: (1) Front showing the clock supported by means of the turnbuckle foot. (2) Side showing the laminated case construction, the turnbuckle foot and also the pendant which is cranked towards the back of the clock for convenience in hanging it upon a nail anywhere. (3) Back showing Hancock's inscription. (4) Rear view with back of clock case removed.

In May 1975 this clock was further stripped, particular attention being given to the front laminations. Inside the bezel at 12 o'clock is stamped once again the serial number '544'. This number is also repeated at 12 o'clock at the top of the front of the dial where it is hidden both by the mask and by a plate behind the mask. In my opinion this clock was produced by Thomas Cole beyond all question; but there appears to be no secret signature anywhere.

Compiled by C.R.P. Allix

Notes by J.B. Hawkins

The urn shaped striking clock item No. 48 has a similar system of plate division for the striking and going trains. On the rare occasions that Cole constructed striking clocks he seems to have employed

1

Item 4

this technique wherever possible. This becomes obvious when the movement of this clock is seen in the photograph. The clock must have taken some time to complete, the number 528 is an early number, circa 1845, and from the dial engraving the clock would have been completed circa 1848-9.

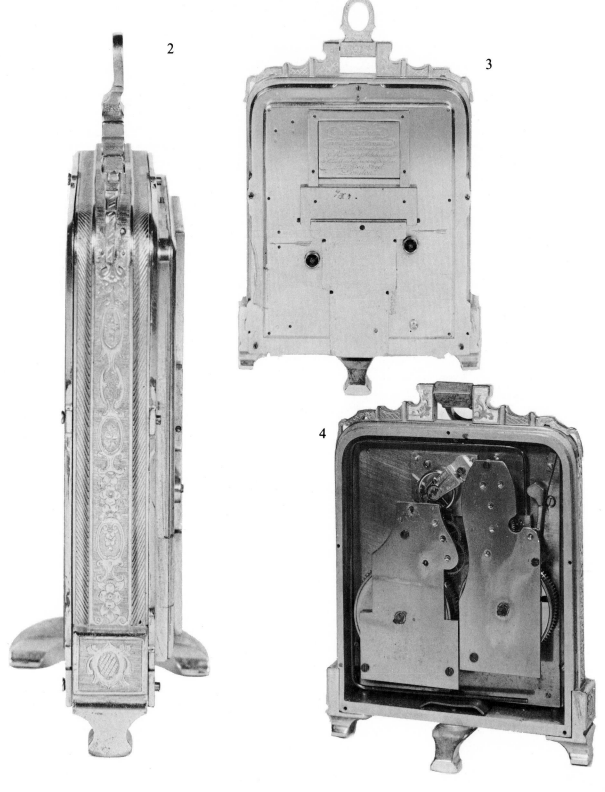

2

3

4

Item 4

ITEM 5

Hour striking strut clock similar to item No. 4 with original travelling case. This travelling case now bears printed in gilt on green silk to the interior the legend "Mr. Streeter (late) Hancock & Compy Lmtd Goldsmiths and Jewellers. To the Royal Family. 37, Conduit St. Bond St." This firm being the second retailer, see under Retailers. On the back of the clock is engraved the following legend "Made by Thos. Cole, for M. Emanuel. 5, Hanover Square, London.", M. Emanuel being the initial retailer.

Movement: The clock is completely portable, and the striking work springs are all so arranged that the under-dial work cannot flop about. For instance, the rack hook is kept nicely in place by a spring above it, while the rack tail is also firmly under the control of a nice long straight spring. The motion work embodies an idle minute wheel in order to achieve the desired geometry between the lifting pin and the long tail of the rack hook. The reason behind these peculiar arrangements is that Thomas Cole striking clocks do not warn and hence the clock has quite a lot of work to do in releasing the striking train accurately on the hour at each hour. The minute wheel arbor passes through a clearance hole in the front movement plate and is run in the portion of the divided back movement plate which covers the going train. A hand-setting square projects through the plate at the top close to the balance. The double-ended key is used for both winding and setting. The key is numbered on its shank "628".

Returning to the striking work it will be noted that Thomas Cole, instead of using a pin wheel to raise the hammer, employs an eight-pointed star wheel. See illustration 4. The striking train is locked by means of a "paddle" carried on the pinion immediately above the star wheel pinion. This paddle is almost the same diameter as that wheel with which it shares a pinion.

Hands: Fleur de Lis.

Dial: Silvered and engraved with flowers all over as befits this early number.

Additional Fitments: The two methods of support, the operation of which is illustrated, photograph 1. Plus original key.

Duration: Eight days.

Signed: As noted above.

Number: The number 628 is punched on the bottom of the main case casting under the turnbuckle strut, on the front bezel, on top of the front of the dial and on the movement under the dial.

Dimensions: 6¼" high with pendant up.

Date: Circa 1846.

Collection: Private collection, Australia.

1

2

Item 5

The under dial rack striking system showing the various springs that prevent the clock accidentally striking while being moved.

ITEM 6

Small oval strut clock with the early number 633 18. This particular flat form of desk or bedroom clock must have been one of Cole's best selling lines. With minor variations, he continued it for most of his working career.

Features to be observed in early strut clocks are the overall engraving to the dial with no reserve panels. In this case, the dial centre has been left blank which means that the clock was designed to be crested when the new owner was known. The early number puts it circa 1845/6, but when sold by Hancock not before 1848/9, the purchaser decided against having the dial centre engraved with monogram or crest, hence remains blank to this day. The bezel containing the glass is engraved with scroll decoration with the traditional line background which must have been remarkably difficult to do on an oval surface. The backs were designed around the movement, generally thirty hour watch movements which were purchased from an outside source and inserted in the cases.

Movement: 30 hour watch movement, vertical lever escapement.
Hands: Hour hand Fleur de Lis, minute hand plain which seems to have been common with the small oval strut clocks as distinct from the square ones.
Dial: Silvered with painted numbers, the engraving badly rubbed at some stage in the preparation for resilvering.
Additional Features: Nil
Signed: C.F. Hancock, 39 Bruton Street, London.
Number: 633 18
Dimension: 12½ cm high × 8¼ cm wide.
Date: 1846.
Collection: Private collection, Australia.

ITEM 7

Oval strut clock, the back of the clock bearing the inscription:

C.F. HANCOCK
a Successor of
STORR & MORTIMER
by Appointment to
H.M. Queen Adelaide
&
H.I.M. the Emperor of Russia
39 Bruton St. LONDON

Hidden inside the case appears the secret punched signature of Thomas Cole.

The dial of this clock is engraved with a cypher and with a coronet. It belonged to Lady Canning when her husband, the second Lord Canning, was the first Viceroy of India. (A document establishing this provenance survives with the clock).

Hands: Cole-type fleur de lis.

Dial: Silvered with engraving and coronet. Chapters and lettering all painted.

Additional Features: The calendar of this clock is a variation of Thomas Cole's arrangement described in connection with Item No. 8, but with the day-of-the-month tabulation re-arranged and with the days-of-the-week on a movable ring instead of a roller.

This clock has a strut support with no detent.

There is no turnbuckle foot.

The winding key is detachable.

Duration: Eight days.

Signature: The signature "THOˢ COLE LONDON" is punched inside the main case casting where it cannot be seen unless the clock is dismantled.

Number: The number 706 is punched on the back of the right hand foot of the clock as seen from the front, and the number 3 on the back of the left hand foot as seen from the front.

Dimensions: 6⅜" pendant up.

Casework: Gilt brass engraved. Notice the "apple" type of engraving and also a top pendant which does not fold flat.

Movement: The movement has an oval back plate with a shaped top and a completely oval front plate. The escapement is steady-pinned and screwed to the inside of the front plate. The escapement is an English right-angled single roller lever with plain steel balance and steel spring with overcoil. The train is similar to those already described incorporating many changes of pitch. The movement was not completely dismantled but apparently it was neither numbered nor signed.

Collection: Private Collection England.

Illustrations: (1) Front. (2) Clock case dismantled showing movement, lever for operating calendar, and above all the main case casting bearing the Cole signature and numbers.

compiled by C.R.P. Allix

Notes by J.B. Hawkins

This clock unlike most oval strut clocks has a cast body with a Cole movement. It was the third of this model made series number 706 style number 3. The clock would date circa 1847 and it is patently obvious from the photograph that the centre of the dial was left blank and monogrammed at a later date on its final sale by Hancock, the styles of engraving being completely different.

Item 7

Item 7

ITEM 8

A strut clock, the silvered dial centred with an engraved capital H. Below the dial a manually-operated calendar showing the days of the week on a roller visible through an aperture, and the date of the month by means of a 31-day tabulation.

The clock is complete in its fitted travelling box covered in red morocco leather with decorative rules and lined inside in blue velvet and silk. Printed in gilt upon the silk lining of the door is the name of the vendor:

C.F. HANCOCK

Jeweller & Silversmith

TO THE QUEEN

38 & 39 BRUTON ST.

BOND STREET

A loop is provided in the bottom of the box to house the key used for setting hands and calendar. The travelling case is not provided with a strut.

Hands: Typical Cole-type fleur de lis.

Dial: Silvered and florally engraved with designs suggesting apple blossom and apples. Note a design which looks perfectly balanced without being strictly symmetrical. The engraved letter "H" at first glance looks like a monogram. All chapters and figures on the dial are painted.

Additional Features: This clock is provided with both a strut (easel support like a picture frame) and also with a turnbuckle foot. The strut supports the clock so that it leans backwards at an angle of about 30° from the vertical. When the foot is used, then the clock is kept upright. The strut is arranged to latch in its stowed position. The turnbuckle has no such detent arrangements and turns freely. The winding key is a fixture. It folds flat into a sink in the back of the case.

The unusual calendar was probably intended to help with the planning of appointments in advance, but it was also to avoid the necessity of daily alteration by hand or by the clock. The system, like all compromises, is not entirely without its disadvantages. The main difficulty is that in order to be able to find out the date it is necessary to know not only the day of the week but also the week of the month. The fixed date of the month table is set out like a sheet calendar but arranged vertically instead of horizontally. The roller "table" displays the days of the week set our vertically from top to bottom. Each of the seven "columns" starts a day later than the one to the left of it. The calendar is thus arranged as follows:

MO	TU	WE	TH	FR	SA	SU		1	8	15	22	29
TU	WE	TH	FR	SA	SU	MO		2	9	16	23	30
WE	TH	FR	SA	SU	MO	TU		3	10	17	24	31
TH	FR	SA	SU	MO	TU	WE		4	11	18	25	
FR	SA	SU	MO	TU	WE	TH		5	12	19	26	
SA	SU	MO	TU	WE	TH	FR		6	13	20	27	
SU	MO	TU	WE	TH	FR	SA		7	14	21	28	

The day-of-the-week roller does not require to be reset at the end of February, except in Leap years when it must be advanced one column. In ordinary years the roller is advanced by hand two columns at the end of April, June, September and November, and three columns at the end of January, March, May, July, August and October. This may all sound rather complicated, but in fact it is only mentioned here as a matter of interest. The great beauty of this calendar is that there is absolutely no need to understand it in order to be able to use it! All that is necessary is to twiddle the day of the week roller (by means of one end of the key which has to be inserted through a hole in the base of the clock) until the appropriate day for the first of the month appears in the top column.

Item 8

Duration: Eight days.

Signature: None visible when back removed. The clock was not stripped completely. The clock was sold by Hancock as evidenced by its original surviving travelling box.

Number: "789" on underside of case which, however, was not completely dismantled. No number was apparent on movement.

Dimensions: 5¾" tall approximately with pendant up.

Casework: Gilt brass constructed upon Cole's laminated principle and engraved with flowers and foliage against a background of horizontal hatching. The engraving is symmetrical on the front of the clock but on the sides the engraver varies his patterns considerably.

Movement: Single roller lever escapement with plain steel balance and flat steel balance spring. The escapement is visible through a circular aperture protected by a shutter slide in the back of the clock case. The movement has rectangular plates, the back one with radiused corners. The back plate measures 2½" vertically and 2⅜" horizontally (approx.). The front plate measures 3½" vertically and 2⅜" horizontally (approx.). The platform escapement is secured by screws and steady pins to the inside of the front movement plate, the escapement arbors lying in the same plane as the train arbors. The whole construction of the movement is most interesting, being a very curious amalgam of clock-work and watch-work. The going barrel is provided with teeth of a very coarse pitch and drives an intermediate pinion with 12 leaves of the same module. The intermediate wheel has teeth of a much finer pitch and drives a correspondingly finer centre pinion with 10 leaves. The third pinion of 8 leaves is naturally of the same pitch as the centre wheel, but in the third wheel the pitch is changed yet once again. The third wheel drives a fourth pinion of 8 leaves. A final change of pitch occurs with the fourth wheel which drives a 'scape pinion of 8 leaves. This type of practice and movement layout is typical of Thomas Cole clocks.

Collection: Private Collection England.

Illustrations: (1) Front showing dial and calendar (turnbuckle support is in its stowed position). (2) Rear with back removed to show the movement, the escapement and also the turnbuckle foot supporting the clock.

In May 1975 the casework was stripped almost completely. It was found that the number '789' is repeated being punched on the inside of the engraved bezel on the top rail, and also on the front of the dial in the top left hand corner and where it is hidden by the applied mask which is situated immediately under the glass. The primary reason for the further stripping of the clock was the hope of discovering a hidden Cole signature. Unfortunately none seems to exist, although in my opinion the clock is an undoubted Thomas Cole.

Compiled by C.R.P. Allix

Notes by J.B. Hawkins

This is the style of strut clock copied by White of Jermyn Street. See item Nos. 58, 59, 60. The pillars to the side of the clock are used on the campanile clock item No. 49. This model was never given a style number and is unusual in that it is the only style in which the bezel is screwed on from the front with knurled nuts. Normally, the bezel is secured from behind with hidden screws. The dial has again been monogrammed at a later date. The clock dates from circa 1850.

Item 8

ITEM 9

Small oval strut clock going for 30 hours bearing the engraved legend on the back of the case:

C.F. HANCOCK
39 Bruton St.
LONDON
No 811

The clock retains its original red leather travelling box lined with velvet and silk, the silk bearing the printed inscription

ORTNER & HOULE
JEWELLERS
ENGRAVERS & DRAUGHTSMEN
3, ST. JAMES'S STREET
S.W.

Hands: Hour hand — Cole-type fleur de lis. Minute hand — plain.
Dial: Silvered and engraved with representations of flowers and foliage. There is a mask below chapter XII.
Additional Features: Strut only with stowage detent.
Duration: 30 hours.
Signature: Inscriptions as above.
Number: As already stated the series number 811 appears on the back of the case. This number is repeated at the bottom of the case where there also appears the punched style number 76.
Dimensions: 4" tall.
Casework: Gilt brass engraved. No pendant.
Movement: Typical Swiss Geneva bar cylinder movement mid to late 19th century bearing engraved inscription

E Raffin à Geneve

and the *ébauche* maker's mark E3J

This is a mass-produced Geneva bar movement with hanging barrel and plain brass balance. It is of exactly the type produced by the million by Vacheron & Constantine to be sold under very many different names. This type of movement had its heyday from perhaps about 1830 to about 1860; and so it comes perfectly into the required period. There is every indication that this is the first and only movement that the clock ever had. The only possible alternative theory, which seems very unlikely in view of the thinness of the clock, is that it originally had a Cole-type movement. If the Geneva movement is not original to the clock, then neither is the plate in which the movement is mounted. Also, how do you account for the fact that the winding, setting and regulating holes in the original back of the clock line up perfectly with this Geneva movement? In my opinion, any non-original-movement hypothesis absolutely does not hold together.
Collection: Private Collection, England.
Illustrations: (1) Front. (2) Rear of clock dismantled to show Swiss Geneva bar movement.

Compiled by C.R.P. Allix

Notes by J.B. Hawkins
The engraving of the dial is earlier in style than the number allows. The engraved face below the figure twelve on the chapter ring occurs on the Compendium Item No. 52. A large number of oval strut clocks were produced and if the dials were engraved in bulk, it would account for the prenumbered style of dial engraving. Made circa 1851.

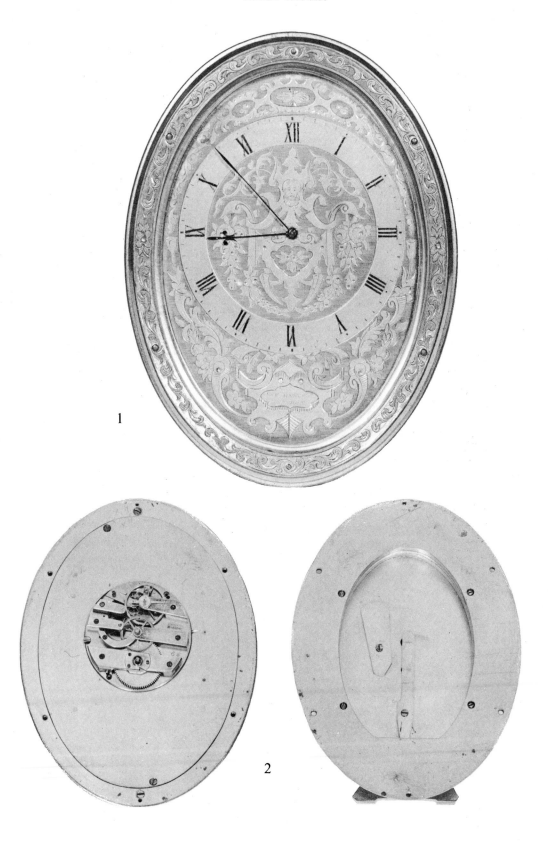

1

2

Item 9

ITEM 10

This is an early period clock and this is indicated by the pierced dial cover, floral border to the bezel and dial. The centre of the dial has been left blank and monogrammed later. The overhanging handle in three parts is another early feature.

Numbered 833, this clock confirms the above and may be dated circa 1850/51, it was retailed by C.F. Hancock.

Item 10

Item 11

ITEM 11

This early period strut clock with its floral engraving to the dial and bezel was never designed to be crested, the style of engraving to the dial centre being identical to that on the rest of the dial.

The number is 863,78 which ties in well with the previous item 811 76 in terms of series and style numbers. From the number and the engraving, the clock would date circa 1851.

General descriptions taken from photographs, the clocks not being seen by the author.

ITEM 12

A rare miniature strut clock by Cole in its original travelling case, florally engraved all over to the back, front and sides. Typical Cole layered construction. Miniature clocks by this maker are amongst his most appealing and from the style of the engraving and the lack of a number, this clock may be considered to be from his early period.

Movement: 24 hour watch movement obviously bought in and adapted for this case. Lever escapement.

Hands: Fleur de Lis.

Dial: Silvered, florally engraved, painted numbers.

Additional Features: Original travelling case.

Duration: 24 hours.

Signed: The clock is unsigned, the travelling case, however, retains the original label, W. Payne, 163 New Bond Street.

Number: Nil.

Dimensions: 7.5 cm high × 5 cm wide.

Date: Circa 1850.

Collection: Private collection, Australia.

Illustrations: (1) Rear view (2) Front view

Item 12

ITEM 13

A fine early strut clock with two methods of support, the standard swivelling strut to the base and an inclined strut operated by a sliding catch to the rear which supports the clock in an inclined position. This clock is particularly well made having a total of ten layers of construction, including the glass, in a depth of 3.2 cm from back to front.

Movement: Specially constructed for this particular case and stamped Thomas Cole, London, with manual monthly calendar, the age in days and the visual phase of the moon being operated by the clock. Vertical lever escapement with compensated balance.

Hands: Fleur de Lis.

Dial: Silvered dial divided into quarters and florally engraved with painted numbers. The clock was finished circa 1855-60 and we know that at least 22 were made. They may well have not been good sellers, the last few being engraved well after their cases, etc. were completed for 999 is a circa 1852 case number.

Additional Features: Manual monthly calendar, age in days of the phase of the moon and visual phase of the moon.

Duration: Eight days.

Signed: No retailers signature.

Number: 999 22 signifying that at least 22 of this model were made.

Dimensions: 18 cm high × 12 cm wide.

Date: Circa 1852 made, from dial circa 1855-60 completed.

Collection: Private collection, Australia.

Item 13

ITEM 14

General description taken from a photograph, the clock not being seen by the author.

This clock is not such a mystery as it would first appear. Cole constructed the case casting circa 1852 from the series number 1049. This is confirmed in the dial engraving outside the chapter ring which is of the early period, being floral in nature. The dial was left blank for monogramming which was done at the earliest circa 1859 nearly ten years later when the clock was sold to London & Ryder who opened their business in that year. At some intervening date, circa 1855, the lined arch bezel was applied to the clock.

   The clock shows the complexity of Cole's business but it is still impossible to judge its size. A tremendous number of clocks must have been in the course of production and certain common models at the latter end of his business career must have been completed as and when they were required.

Photograph by Courtesy
of Mallett, 40 New Bond Street,
the clock the property of R.E. de Zoete, Esq.

ITEM 15

As with the next item, the engraving to the case and dial epitomises that to be found in the middle period of Cole's work. The clock has no strut and despite its thinness, is free standing.
Movement: Uncompensated lever escapement in the vertical position, stamped Thos. Cole London.
Hands: Fleur de Lis.
Dial: Silvered with painted numerals and arabesque engraving.
Duration: Eight days.
Signed: C.F. Hancock, 39 Bruton Street, London.
Number: 1309.
Dimensions: 20 cm high, handle up, × 13 cm wide × 5 cm deep.
Date: 1855.
Collection: P. Hamilton, Esq. Christchurch, England.

ITEM 16

A large strut clock in the style of item No. 24 but without the porcelain dial. The case with its arabesque engraving helps to date the clock to Cole's middle period. The dial was left blank for cresting and engraved on sale with a bunch of flowers in a vase, circa 1860.

Movement: Oval in shape with going barrel, vertical lever escapement, uncompensated balance.
Hands: Fleur de Lis.
Dial: The numerals and signature are engraved as distinct from painted, a most unusual departure by Cole.
Additional Fitments: Nil.
Duration: Eight days.
Signed: Thos. Cole London on the movement and T. Cole on the dial.
Number: 1316.
Dimensions: 30 cm high × 23 cm wide.
Date: 1855.
Collection: P. Hamilton, Esq. Christchurch, England.

ITEM 17

The largest known example of a Thomas Cole strut clock with an unusual pierced surround, topped by a basket of fruit. The dial is engraved to the centre with a pierced urn full of flowers on a pedestal, to the base of which are scattered various fruits. The standard of engraving in this particular clock is extremely high. It is difficult to know how this clock would have been placed — it would have to be either on a desk or on a mantelpiece but its sheer size seems to obviate the reason for its flatness as it is not particularly transportable.

Movement: Special order fitted Cole movement with a compensated bi-metallic balance and vertical lever escapement.

Hands: Spade hour hand plain minute hand.

Dial: Silvered, florally engraved with painted numbers.

Additional Features: Nil.

Duration: Eight days.

Signed: Hancock & Co., Bond Street, W. This form of designation for Hancocks was used between 1870 and 1917. As the dial has obviously been repainted, I would suggest that the repairs, cleaning and overhaul were done by Hancocks, the firm from which it was originally purchased and their current title repainted on the dial. Circa 1900.

Number: 1367.

Dimension: 49 cm high × 38 cm wide.

Date: 1856.

Collection: Private collection, Australia.

N.B. A small strut clock of similar shape but with 30 hour movement, includes a monogram in the pierced border. Numbered 1323 14 and retailed by Hancock. It is an example of a special order clock.

Item 17

ITEM 18

General description taken from a photograph, the clock not being seen by the author.

The case shows this to be a middle period clock for it has the shorter carrying handle, the simpler unpierced dial cover and the more formal division of the engraving on the dial centre. This engraving is not all over floral (early period) but arabesque (middle period) and not yet divided into true quarters (late period). The number 1373 confirms this attribution, dating the clock circa 1856.

The retailer was C.F. Hancock and the clock is fitted with a manual monthly calendar.

Photograph by Courtesy of Hancocks and Co.,
1 Burlington Gardens.

ITEM 19

Small strut clock with the standard swivelling strut for support. Cole has modified the design with the passage of time doing away with the inclined back support thereby simplifying the case construction to the rear and reducing it to only one layer. The handle bracket is shorter and has been constructed in one unit. The design of the dial cover layer changes from that of item No. 23 and is standard to the middle period strut clocks.

Movement: Standard Cole movement, stamped Thomas Cole, London. By this date, because of the popularity of this type of clock, the movement was standard. Fitted with a vertical uncompensated balance lever escapement.

Hands: Fleur de Lis.

Dial: Silvered dial, Arabesque engraving, possibly considerably earlier than the clock.

Additional Features: Nil.

Duration: Eight days.

Number: 1374.

Signed: There is no retailers signature on the dial, however the movement is stamped THOˢ COLE.

Dimensions: 16 cm high, handle up, × 11 cm wide.

Date: Circa 1856.

Collection: Private collection, Australia.

Item 19

Item 24
A porcelain dial strut clock Number 1700, retailed by Payne, 163 New Bond Street and constructed by Cole, circa 1862.

ITEM 20

Small oval strut clock, the back of the case bearing the engraved name and address:

C.F. HANCOCK
39, Bruton St
London

and on the dial the painted legend

C.F. HANCOCK LONDON

Hidden inside the clock and punched at the bottom of the back movement plate appears the secret punched signature of Thomas Cole, thus:—

THO^s COLE   LONDON

Hands: Cole-type-fleur-de-lis.

Dial: Silvered, engraved and inscribed as noted above. Below chapter VI is a coronet above a monogram.

Additional Features: The clock has a strut support only. The winding key is a fixture.

Duration: Eight days.

Signed: Inscription and also a "secret signature" as noted above.

Number: The clock case was completely dismantled, both casework and movement. On the top of the front of the dial hidden by the bezel is the number "1535" and close beside it the number "12". The front of the front movement plate is punched "1535". The number "35" is repeated on various of the main case components, which incidentally are "popped" to assist in the difficult jig-saw like re-assembly.

Dimensions: Approx. 6¼" tall.

Date: Circa 1858.

Casework: Gilt brass with less engraving and hatching than usual, but with rivetted bezel. The pendant is not cranked. The winding hole is not shuttered. A sliding shutter near the top of the back of the case gives access to the regulation index.

Collection: Private Collection, Australia.

Movement: This is wholly consistent with the style of work most usually found in Thomas Cole strut clocks. The movement has an oval front plate and a clipped oval back plate. The escapement platform is screwed and steady-pinned to inside of the front plate. The right-angled English lever pointed-tooth escapement has a single roller. It is oversprung with a flat steel balance spring and it is provided with a plain steel balance. The platform is neither signed nor numbered. The balance staff runs in jewelled holes with endstones and so does the 'scape pinion. Apart from the impulse pin and pallets, this is the only jewelling used in the clock. The pallet arbor and 'scape pinion are run in the same cock screwed to the "upper" side of the platform (which works on its side).

	Train Count	Pinion
Great Wheel	96	
Intermediate Wheel	75	12
Centre Wheel	63	10
Third Wheel	60	8
Fourth Wheel	64	8
'Scape Wheel	15	7

(16,200 beats per hour)

The minute wheel and "nut" are kept in place by means of a shoulder screw. The cannon pinion is also pinned. The ratchet wheel, click and click-spring all work together under a cock. A stopwork of the so-called Maltese Cross type and allowing a fraction over four turns of the mainspring to be used, is accommodated between the great wheel and the front movement plate. The mainspring is at present set-up one turn (this may or may not be the correct amount, but it probably is). The mainspring has 13¾ turns un-wound. It is about .015" thick and about .180" deep. The internal diameter of the barrel is a fraction under 1.5". The barrel arbor has both its pivots the same size.

Illustrations: (1)   Rear of clock with back of case removed. (2) Front of clock.

1

Item 20

Item 20

ITEM 21

A high numbered oval strut clock with a typical Cole bezel of continuous engraved arches separated by lines. The support system has changed to the later type, design-wise this is not as pleasant for the back of the support protrudes outside the case when shut. The gilding and silvering of this particular clock are in fine original condition and give a good impression of how attractive these clocks looked when new. The scrolling rope twist border to the interior of the chapter ring is also a Cole peculiarity found in the higher numbered clocks.

Movement: 24 hours watch movement, vertical lever escapement.

Hands: Hour hand Fleur de Lis, minute hand plain.

Dial: Silvered with painted numbers, centred by a good floral panel depicting roses and tulips.

Additional Features: Nil.

Duration: 30 hours.

Signed: London and Ryder, 17 New Bond Street, London at this address from 1859.

Number: 1602 212. The number 212 indicates the number of this model made to date and would tend to prove that this was one of Cole's best selling designs.

Dimensions: 12 cm high × 8½ cm wide.

Date: Circa 1860.

Collection: Private Collection, Australia.

ITEM 22

Large circular strut clock, the dial divided into four florally matched panels separated by rope twist borders. The strut has a pleasant refinement in that a little circular wheel attached to the end of the strut prevents the strut from scratching the surface when the clock is moved or set up.

Movement: Specially constructed movement designed to fit in the case signed Thomas Cole, London. The vertical lever escapement with uncompensated balance.

Hands: Hour hand Fleur de Lis, minute hand plain. In the larger strut clocks, Cole seems to have utilised the long plain minute hand.

Dial: Silvered, florally engraved, divided into quarters. Painted numbers.

Additional Fitments: Nil.

Duration: Eight days.

Signed: C.F. Hancock, 39 Bruton Street, London.

Number: 1613.

Dimensions: 35 cm high × 30 cm wide.

Date: 1860.

Collection: Private collection, Australia.

ITEM 23

Another small strut clock with the standard method of support. The dial surround layer has been further simplified, the centre of the dial plate has been left blank, presumably to allow for a crest or monogram which never eventuated. Remarks as to the simpler form of case, as for item No. 19 apply. This clock may be fairly accurately dated in that Henry and Edward Tessier took over their father's business in 1859 from the number, 1614, we can date the clock to circa 1860, the start of line and ball decoration to the bezels of Cole's clocks.

Movement: Vertical lever escapement with uncompensated balance.
Hands: Fleur de Lis.
Dial: Silvered with painted numbers.
Additional Features: Nil.
Duration: Eight days.
Signed: Thos. Cole for H. & E. Tessier, 32 South Audley Street, London.
Number: 1614.
Dimensions: 16 cm high × 11 cm wide.
Date: Circa 1860.
Collection: Private collection, Australia.

ITEM 24

A fine late strut clock with a cast border and a blue porcelain dial. These two features are indicators of Cole's latest period. The border is cast in sections joined at the corners by screwing them to a base plate. The rear of the clock has six different layers of construction to allow for the movement and the strut. The front, including the base plate behind the cast border comprises five layers including the dial. The cast border is accentuated in that it is left ungilded whereas the bezel and cover plate for the dial are gilded. Porcelain dials occur in various Cole strut clocks but must be considered rare. The bezel exhibits Cole's late line and ball decoration, a further indication of the high number of the clock.

Movement: The movement is stamped Thomas Cole, London and numbered as per the case 1700. It is of standard Cole format as per item 23 with a vertical uncompensated balance to a lever escapement.

Hands: Fleur de Lis.

Dial: The blue porcelain dial maintains a frosted appearance as it is decorated over biscuit fired procelain, probably Minton. The dial is painted with finely executed roses, musical instruments and music intertwined with floral decoration.

Additional Features: Nil.

Duration: Eight days.

Signed: W. Payne & Co., 163 New Bond Street, the firm not adopting this title until 1852.

Number: Cole's number 1700, Payne's number 1683.

Dimensions: 20.5 cm high × 17 cm wide.

Date: Circa 1862.

Collection: Private collection, Australia.

See colour plate opposite p. 80

ITEM 25

A general description taken from a photograph, the clock not being seen by the author.

A magnificently conceived desk clock including in its design the aces of clubs, hearts and spades. From the engraving and the strut, which, when folded breaks up the outline of the case, this is a Cole clock. Date circa 1862-64 and probably numbered between 1700-1850 and signed Thos. Cole.

Item 25

*Photograph courtesy of
Daniel Desbois & Sons,
51 Carey Street London*

ITEM 26

A general description taken from a photograph, the clock not being seen by the author.

This is a late example of a strut clock and it is, as if Thomas Cole had at long last run out of ideas. The wired border and feet are unexpected and unusual. The dial again has been left blank for monogramming, this time filled with a simple bunch of flowers.

Date circa 1860   Number between 1650-1750

ITEM 27

A general description taken from a photograph, the clock not being seen by the author.

A unique design of top quality. The case appears to be cast in one unit with the layered construction retreating inwards instead of outwards, a most unusual feature. The central bunch of flowers to the dial and lined background to the rest of the dial plate are accentuated by a most unusual pierced dial cover.

Date circa 1862-64   Number 1750-1850

Item 27

Item 26

ITEM 28

A general description taken from a photograph, the clock not being seen by the author.

A composite strut clock, whose case tells a story.

The clock may have been completed on or after Cole's death in 1864 from various leftovers in the workshop. The dial is an early period dial with the centre left blank for monogramming. This has been engraved instead with the last style of dial engraving with no lined background and it is weak in its execution. The cast applied border has been noted by me on two late strut clocks and is very much a late period feature.

Date 1864   Number 1841

STRUT CLOCKS IN THE MANNER OF THOMAS COLE

ITEM 29

An eight day quarter striking musical strut clock fitted with rotating engraved strut at the base and catch operated alternative strut to the rear which allows the clock to be tipped back at an angle. The heavy cast brass and gilded case constructed in layers with a typical Cole handle. This clock, in my opinion, was not constructed in the workshops of Cole but may have been designed by him in his capacity as an ornamental clock case designer. It certainly has the features which we associate with Cole. The engraving is only of an average standard to the case and dial but exhibits the typical Cole lined background decoration.

Movement: A Savage two pin escapement with jewelled pallets, compensated balance planted on top of the movement.

Hands: Fleur de Lis.

Dial: Silvered, Arabesque engraving. Painted numerals.

Additional Features: Strikes the Whittington quarters on the music box principle and the hours on a gong.

Duration: Eight days.

Signed: Payne & Co., 163 New Bond Street, which means that the clock must have been made after 1852 when the firm changed its designation to "& Co."

Number: Nil.

Dimensions: 18 cm high × 12 cm wide.

Date: 1852-55.

Collection: Collection, M. Kerry Esq. Australia.

Item 29

ITEM 30

A very late and unusual lyre shaped strut clock built up in six layers to include the strut on a cast brass body. The bezel to the dial and the outer border to the lyre have Cole's very late line and ball engraving as a main feature. This clock may well have been designed by Cole and only partially constructed on his death. It bears no number but has a specially designed Cole type movement of eight days duration made to fit in the case. The clock has been completely taken apart and is not stamped with his secret signature in any place. It bears many similarities to the cake basket clock item No. 51.

Movement: Eight day, with a lever escapement in the vertical position, and with a compensated balance.

Hands: Fleur de Lis.

Dial: Porcelain; Cole made clocks with porcelain dials but only towards the latter end of his career.

Additional Features: Nil.

Duration: Eight days.

Signed: No signature.

Number: No number but the movement is stamped with impressed punches D E E 123.

Dimensions: 19 cm high × 13 cm wide.

Date: Circa 1865-70.

Collection: Private collection, Australia.

ITEM 31

This small strut clock, very much a Cole in its feeling, lacks the attention to detail associated with him whilst alive. The execution of the castings is not flawless as would be the case if Cole had supervised its construction himself. The strut to the rear is numbered 13 and the dial bears the painted inscription "Dent, 34 Cockspur Street". Bearing in mind the low number and the style, I am willing to attribute this clock to Thomas Cole, Jnr. and date it circa 1875. The typical Cole lined engraved background is deficient, but the layered construction and the rope twist border inside the chapter ring are typical Cole features.

Movement: 30 hr. watch movement with uncompensated balance, vertical lever escapement.
Hands: Fleur de Lis.
Dial: Silvered and florally engraved, painted numbers.
Additional Features: Nil.
Duration: 48 hours.
Signed: Dent, 34 Cockspur Street.
Number: On the case 13, on the watch movement 22*8 7389   CS.
Dimensions: 21 cm high × 15 cm wide.
Date: 1870-75.
Collection: Private Collection, Australia.

MANTEL CLOCKS

This series of three mantel clocks of similar format, are illustrated and described in what I consider to be the correct order of manufacture, they are all later than the design would initially suggest.

The first one described is numbered 1550, this would date circa 1858-60, the coromandel wood cased mantel clock would date circa 1860-62 and the final example, circa 1864-67 being finished on or about Cole's death and not sold.

They are interesting in that stylistically one would date them circa 1820/30 as Regency mantel clocks with the last vestiges of Napoleon's incursions into Egypt stylistically mounted on the top. Cole must be considered an innovator in many fields, his designs having very much a feel of art nouveau to them. In this particular case, he has reverted to the designs of the past, an unusual departure from custom.

ITEM 32

A fine large mantel clock of superb quality in a cast brass and gilded case. The construction of this case is so designed as to facilitate the removal of the movement for maintenance and repairs. By unscrewing the four finials, the top cover over the clock, may be removed. The whole movement, complete with the barometer, which is attached to the front plate and bezels, can be slid up from between the pillars. By simply laying this flat on the bench, the movement may be easily taken apart.

The columns are cast in one section as distinct from the tripod clock, item No. 39 where the columns are cast in two sections, the division occurring at the top of the engraved decoration to the main tapering column. To my mind, the finest indication of quality is the riveted border on the last layer of the top between the finials. Each little rivet is a perfectly executed half circle and runs right through the plate for security. This applies to all three mantel clocks, and may be noted on strut clock item No. 20.

Movement: Standard eight day chronometer escapement that has been removed from its gimballed box and specially fitted into the clock so that the winding square appears to the front between the barometer dial and the dial of the clock. This is achieved by two large wheels as illustrated p. 34. The movement is signed Murray and Strachan, Royal Exchange.

1817-18   Murray and Strachan, Chronometer, Watch and Clockmakers, 19 Sweetings Alley, Cornhill.
1819-22   Murray and Strachan, Watch and Clockmakers, 30 Cornhill.
1823-47   Murray, James, Chronometer, Watch and Clockmaker, 30 Cornhill.
1848-49   No entry.
1850-59   Murray, James & Co., Chronometer and Watchmakers, 30 Cornhill.
1870-1908 (last) Murray, James & Co., Watch, Clock and Chronometer Makers, 1 Royal Exchange.

The movement was probably bought in by Cole from James Murray & Co., the successors to Murray and Strachan (1819-22) 30 Cornhill, it being made circa 1820 and being old stock in that business.

Hands: Hour hand Fleur de Lis, minute hand plain, chronometer seconds hand, painted numerals.
Dial: Silvered dial with quartered Arabesque engraving design on a partially lined background.
Additional Features: Aneroid barometer and manual weekly calendar operated from underneath the clock.
Duration: Eight days.
Signed: On the dial Thos. Cole, on the movement Murray and Strachan.
Number: 1550.
Dimensions: 40 cm high × 28 cm wide.
Date: Circa 1858.
Collection: Private collection, Australia.

Item 32

ITEM 33

An extremely unusual mantel clock by Cole of superb quality. The veneered coromandel wood case is of particularly well chosen timber giving the maximum amount of figure so as to enhance its decorative aspect. The edges of the side panels and dial are cross banded in kingwood.

Stylistically, this clock with its sphinx and winged caryatids to the sides would appear to be circa 1830. Despite being unnumbered, it must date circa 1860 for the bezels to the dial have Cole's late line and ball border. The winged caryatids occur not only to the front but to the rear of the clock and are superbly finished. The engraved frets to the sides with their large urns mounted on plinths have a very Moorish feel to them, this form of decorative style being in vogue circa 1860. Nevertheless, the combination of styles is remarkably successful. This may have been one of Cole's exhibits in the 1862 London exhibition.

Movement: Month movement with up and down indicator above the manual calendar, the movement divided into two sections with the dead beat escapement outside the recessed backplate. Fitted jewelled pallets and maintaining power to the fusee. This is, I am sure, a Cole movement and bears many similarities to the movements to be found in tripod clocks. When put to the test, Cole could obviously make a clock movement as fine as any other London maker.

Hands: Hour hand Fleur de Lis, minute hand plain.

Dial Silver Arabesque engraved dial divided into quarters. Another departure from the normal is that the numerals are engraved both in the calendar and chapter ring.

Additional Features: Manual monthly calendar, up and down indicator and thermometer in degrees Fahrenheit.

Duration: One month.

Signed: No signature or secret stamp or retailers signature. The clock dials have been resilvered and the panel between the up and down indicator may well have borne Cole's signature.

Number: Nil.

Dimensions: 45 cm high × 28 cm wide.

Date: Circa 1860.

Collection: Private collection, Australia.

Item 33

ITEM 34

Another fine eight day mantel clock with chronometer escapement. The columns in both clocks are of identical overall length but although they look the same, on closer inspection, they are found to be completely different. On this example, the columns are not only thicker but the capitals are of a differing proportion and shape. The overall engraved design is identical, both on the side panels and the dial of both clocks. The panels are not transferable from one clock to another.

Each of these clocks weighs slightly over 35 lbs. which is a colossal weight and is a further indication of the outstanding quality of Cole's engraved metal work.

Movement: Standard eight day chronometer movement with subsidiary platform which has at some stage, been removed from its box and gimbals and fitted into the clock. To enable the winding to take place from the front, a special system of two gears has been employed to bring the winding square between the clock and barometer. Another indication that this clock is later in its construction is that these gears are specially mounted on a carrying bracket, deficient in item No. 32 this provides a more substantial system of transferring the wind into the clock.

Hands: Hour hand Fleur de Lis, minute hand plain. This system is common to all mantel clocks of this form. The magnificent wafer thin barometer hand should be noted.

Dial: Silvered dial with quartered Arabesque engraving design on a partially lined background. It is unusual for two dial designs to be identical. The barometer dial is unusual in that the numerals and letters are engraved. The chapter ring has painted numerals.

Additional Features: Aneroid barometer.

Duration: Eight days.

Signed: The Goldsmiths Alliance Ltd., Cornhill, London. This designation for the firm who were the successors of Savory, was only in use between 1867-93, the firm being incorporated as a limited company in 1866. This clock, which bears no secret signature or number, must have been completed on or after Cole's death and sold to this firm circa 1866/67 as the dial writings are original.

Number: Nil.

Dimensions: 40 cm high × 28 cm wide.

Date: 1864 sold circa 1866-67.

Collection: Private collection, Australia.

Item 34

TRIPOD CLOCKS

The Horological Journal of November, 1896, page 35, provides an excellent introduction to the subject of Cole's tripod clocks. It is headed "Cole's Spring Remontoire Escapement" and the original author is not known.

"I have just met with a description of a clock by the late Thomas Cole which would, I think, be interesting to many readers.

The escapement consists of an escape wheel, A, of five teeth only, but may be made of any number suited to the respective train employed, and which wheel acts alternately on two linear steel springs, B B; each spring being formed with a shoulder or pallet, C, near the free end, for locking the wheel teeth at every vibration of the pendulum in both directions of its motion, showing half seconds on the dial by its present arrangement, or full seconds where a seconds pendulum is employed. See line drawing page 103.

The wheel tooth, when locked on either side, holds the respective spring in tension, until unlocked by the pendulum rod coming in contact with the projectile end of the spring, so raised by the previous action of the wheel, which being at the same time released the wheel advances, and instantly raises the opposite spring into tension, and locks thereon, while the force of the first spring is exerted in giving impulse on the pendulum, at the commencement of the descending arc.

The arcs of vibration produced by this principle are invariable in any determined condition of the springs, but will admit of being made greater or less by opening or closing the projectile ends of the springs.

The employment of springs in this escapement instead of weights for impulse on the pendulum, has the following advantages —

1st.   There being no pivots, there is no friction, and no oil required.

2nd.   There is no liability in this escapement to trip on the lockings, by the most extreme difference of power on the train from a going barrel.

3rd.   Springs for impulse on the pendulum have the advantage of preserving a more uniform condition of strength, relatively to the strength of the pendulum suspension spring, irrespectively of the error on time by dilatation, which is corrected by the compensation for temperature; the three springs being under the same influence are better calculated than weight would be, for producing uniform results.

The pendulum bob is made of a spherical form, 1st, for concentrating the weight of matter in the smallest space; 2ndly, for reducing atmospheric resistance; and 3rdly, for preventing the tendency to rotate with the axis of the rod.

The compensation for temperature in this clock is effected by a modified combination of two or more laminated plates of steel and brass; those plates sustaining the weight of the bob, either above or below the bob, and forming part of the mass.

These laminated compensation plates are formed as triangular arms from a centre through which the rod passes, the plates having perfect and frictionless contact with each other by three points of bearing, those points of contact being adjustable to or from the centre for increasing or diminishing the compensating power.

The general plan of supporting the clock on three or more columns has the advantage of stability, and affords the convenience of removing the movement when necessary without disturbing the pendulum.

This clock is intended to go eight days by once winding; and the calibre of the wheel work is so arranged as to bring the winding square outside the diameter of the dial, which prevents injury to it, or interference with the hands, which may be set by a button at the back of the dial without opening the glass."

This description, the source of which is not stated by the writer in the Horological Journal, may well have been a contemporary description by Cole explaining his ideas. The description of the compensation for the temperature system is difficult to follow and it would require an example of the clock described to ascertain the exact method of action.

Cole produced a considerable number of tripod clocks with certain variations. Four of these design variations are shown but I am sure that more will come to light. The design must have been popular, the highest number recorded for a tripod being 1836 69, which would approximate to the end of Cole's working life. I would think that no more than 75 of them were made. The tripod item No. 36 must rank as one of the finest English 19th century decorative clocks in existence.

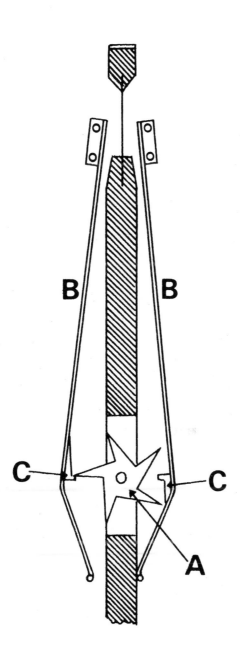

ITEM 35

An early tripod clock, the three supports being beautifully engraved and of unusual shape. This clock has features not evident in the later productions in that the dial is securely attached to the two pillars in such a way that it is not easily removed and the pendulum locking device is of a much cruder form. Although standing on the six sided rating nuts, no plum line attachment for levelling is in evidence. The pendulum is independently suspended and a pleasant refinement of detail is, that the suspension spring is screwed through to the suspension point for ease of repair rather than pinned. The engraving is very much in the manner of the compendium item No. 52. The strut clock Item No. 9 is also obviously by the same engraver.

Movement: The clock employs a variation on Cole's escapement instead of two steel springs acting on the pendulum, only one, operated via an extension rod, acts against the pendulum, this being counter balanced on the inside plate of the clock so as to keep pressure on the rod at all times. The escape wheel has six teeth and acts on the pallet of one steel spring and a roller instead of a pallet on the bar opposite. The steel spring is tripped by a roller in the 6 o'clock position below the escape wheel as shown in the photograph.

Hands: Hour hand spade, minute hand plain. Standard tripod hands.

Dial: Silvered dial, superbly engraved with a mixture of Arabesque and floral engraving. Painted numerals.

Additional Features: An early form of pendulum locking device and a sliding circular disc that can be moved up and down the pendulum rod above the bob for final rating.

Duration: One month.

Signed: Hunt and Roskell but with secret signature underneath the front right hand pillar, Thos. Cole, London.

Number: 939 12.

Dimensions: 46 cm high × 24 cm wide.

Date: Circa 1852.

Collection: Private collection, Australia.

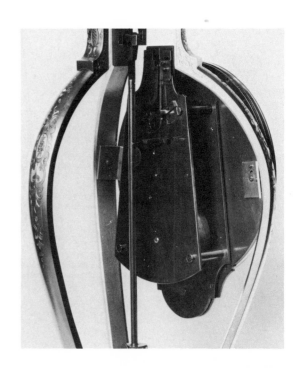

Item 35

ITEM 36

A very interesting and unusual complicated three-sided clock standing under a glass shade on a six-sided ebonised wooden long case with six shaped glass windows. On the meantime (front) dial is inscribed the name of the vendor:

LONDON & RYDER
17, NEW BOND ST.

However the signature of Thomas Cole appears on the movement thus:

THO^s COLE
LONDON
No 968
2

and on the metal base the further signature

THO^s COLE
LONDON
DESIGNER
and
MAKER

Hands: Cole fleur de lis.
Dials: Silvered with engraved decoration. The meantime dial shows hours, minutes and seconds.
Additional Features: Top plumb-bob for setting up clock vertically in two planes.

One subsidiary dial with aneroid barometer and with thermometers for Fahrenheit and Réaumur.

On the third dial a 31-day calendar showing the date of the month and a 29½ day lunation, both driven by the clock.

Amplitude scale on "dish" below the pendulum.

The clock is set to time by means of a square outside the bezel at chapter II, and the clock is wound by a square beneath the bezel at chapter VI.
Duration: Eight days.
Signatures: As above.
Number: $\frac{968}{2}$. (sic) engraved at the centre of the bottom of back movement plate below the signature.
Dimensions: 5′ 6½″ to top of shade.
Casework: As above.
Movement: This clock has a very peculiar dead-beat remontoire escapement showing seconds and employing a 30-toothed 'scape wheel. The escapement is apparently another form of, or derivation from, Thomas Cole's spring remontoire escapement which is described and illustrated in the *Horological Journal* of November 1896 where it is shown having a five-toothed 'scape wheel and where it is mentioned in connection with a tripod clock having a short pendulum. Cole's five-toothed escapement is also mentioned in the *Revue Chronométrique,* April 1856 where the French writer says that Cole exhibited it in the Paris *Exposition Universelle* of 1855 and that Cole's escapement was derived from that published by Prior in 1812. The escapement in this clock, which at the moment is rather sticky and oily and therefore perhaps not working properly, is something in the nature of a gravity escapement with a single arm. Unfortunately the position of the escapement in the clock is so inaccessible that it is impossible to photograph it unless the two subsidiary dials are removed. In a way the modus operandi of the escapement is somewhat analogous to that of Thwaites & Reed's six-legged gravity escapement in the sense that impulse is given to the pendulum at each alternate vibration only.

Cole's fondness for the use of a going barrel persists even in this long-pendulum clock. In the train, to obtain his duration, he employs a wheel and pinion between the great wheel and the centre arbor, but his wheel work generally is notable for the absence of the vehement changes in pitch that are so characteristic of the vast majority of Cole's clocks. Above the centre pinion is a third wheel and pinion followed by the 'scape wheel and pinion (no doubt in Cole's five-toothed escapement an extra wheel and pinion were required). The pendulum is a round-section brass rod with a rating nut beneath the spherical (steel?) pendulum bob and with an additional device for fine adjustment half way up the rod. There is no compensation.

Collection: Private Collection, England.

Illustration: Front view of the clock.

Compiled by C.R.P. Allix

Notes by J.B. Hawkins

With the style number 2 we know that at least one other of those superb clocks exists. From the series number 968 it was commenced circa 1852 but may not have been completed for many years.

Item 36

ITEM 37

Standard size tripod clock suspended from three circular pillars, these pillars standing on a circular engraved stepped base, the base supported on three adjustable nuts for levelling. The nuts are rotated by the spanner fitment on the end of the key so as to put the clock in beat. The clock is fitted with a silver plaque "fecit for the Great Exhibition, London 1851". However, the clock does not appear in the list of exhibits entered for the Great Exhibition by Hunt and Roskell. This fact, combined with the number, 1437 49 suggests that the plaque has been added at a later date.

Movement: Dead beat escapement, the pendulum being independently suspended from the top of the tripod. Fitted with going barrel, a peculiarity of Cole's work as one would normally expect to see a fusee drive.

Hands: Hour hand spade, minute hand plain, the seconds hand of typical chronometer format of the highest quality.

Dial: Silvered with Arabesque engraving and painted numbers.

Additional Features: Thermometer in degrees Fahrenheit (0° - 120°), aneroid barometer. Cole devised a special system for catching the pendulum so that the clock could be moved without damage. The base of the pendulum rod being cut into a square, which, on adjusting the nuts in the catching apparatus, fits into a silvered bar thereby securing it fast. A plum line fitted at the top of the clock terminates in a silvered ball to match the pendulum and ascertains when the clock is level. Original key, see illustration. Page 39.

Duration: One month.

Signed: Hunt and Roskell, London.

Number: 1437 49.

Dimensions: 51 cm high × 23 cm wide.

Date: Circa 1857.

Collection: Private collection, Australia.

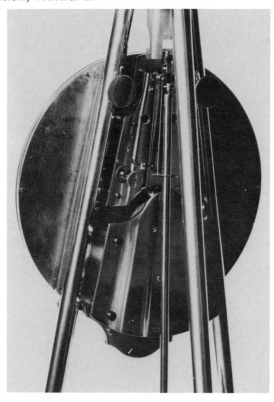

Item 37

ITEM 38

A most unusual tripod clock of the 'naturalist' school of design. In "The Analysis of Ornament" by R. Wornum, London 1856, Wornum, Keeper of the National Gallery, London and Secretary to the Trustees states: "There is a class of ornament which has much increased of late years in England, and by way of distinction, we may call it the 'Naturalist' school. The theory appears to be that as native is beautiful, ornamental details derived immediately from beautiful natural objects must ensure a beautiful design. This, however, can only be true where the original uses of the details chosen have not been obviously violated; and one peculiar feature of this school is that it often substitutes the ornament itself for the thing to be ornamented."

This clock is obviously an effort by Cole to keep in the height of fashion and is extraordinary by any standards.

The tripod holding the clock is made of cast brass silvered as imitation logs, these suspend by way of the pendulum, a lidded cauldron over a simulated log fire. The whole is executed to the very highest standard and whether one approves or disapproves, it must be considered as a premier example of the Naturalist School of Design.

Movement: Brocot jewelled escapement signed Thos. Cole London. The train of standard tripod form.

Hands: The hands are original and the gothic hour hand differs in form from that normally found on tripod clocks.

Dial: Gilded with painted numbers and divided into four quarters.

Additional Fitments: Nil.

Duration: One month.

Signed: No retailers signature, however, the movement is punched Thos. Cole London.

Number: 1642

Dimensions: 21" high × 9" wide.

Date: Circa 1861 and may well have been exhibited at the 1862 London Exhibition.

Collection: P. Hamilton, Esq. Christchurch, England.

Item 38

ITEM 39

Large standing tripod clock suspended on three tapering square pillars. The format for these pillars is the same as that used in the two chronometer escapement mantel clocks, items No. 32 and 34. The whole standing on a stepped shaped base adjusted for levelling on three knurled nuts in the base plate.

Movement: The movement is fully encased and the clock was constructed for use with or without a dome. Fitted with a dead beat escapement, and pendulum with silvered bob. The rating nut sliding up and down above the bob on the suspension rod is deficient.

Hands: Hour hand spade, minute hand plain.

Dial: Silvered dial, florally engraved with painted numbers.

Additional Features: Thermometer in degrees Fahrenheit (0-120), barometer. The plum line hangs in the centre of a small cupola and provides a very pleasant finish, architecturally, to the design of the clock. Cole's pendulum locking system.

Signed: Boxell, Brighton 1052.

Number: 1797. The lack of an alternative number may indicate that this in Cole's mind was to be considered a once only production, or that it was completed after his death and the style number was forgotten.

Dimensions: 59 cm high × 32 cm wide.

Date: Circa 1864.

Collection: Private collection, Australia.

Item 39

ITEM 40

Standard size tripod clock suspended from three circular pillars, these pillars standing on a circular engraved stepped base, the base supported on three adjustable nuts for levelling. These nuts are rotated by the spanner fitment at the end of the key so as to put the clock in beat.

Movement: Dead beat escapement, the pendulum being independently suspended from the top of the tripod. Fitted with going barrel, this is standard instead of fusees to all Cole tripod clocks.

Hands: Hour hand spade, minute hand plain, the seconds hand of typical chronometer format of the highest quality.

Dial: Silvered with floral engraving of a very high standard depicting roses and tulips, the lined background, by this late stage, being no longer used, the edge to the chapter ring having a rope twist border, the edge to the bezel a line and ball border, all late features of dial decoration that tie in with the number. Painted numerals to the chapter ring.

Additional Features: Thermometer in degrees Fahrenheit (0-120°), aneroid barometer. Cole's pendulum locking system and a plum line to ascertain when the clock is level.

Duration: One month.

Signed: Thos. Cole, London.

Number: 1831 67. This high numbered clock must have been made at the end of Cole's life.

Date: Circa 1864.

Dimensions: 51 cm high × 24 cm wide.

Collection: Private collection, Australia.

Item 40

CLOCKS OF UNUSUAL SHAPE OR DESIGN

The clocks shown in this section may be considered a small representation of the large number of unusual clocks designed and constructed by Cole. They are completely original in their design and format and owe their inspiration to Cole alone. The metalwork of the cases, engraving and attention to detail set a standard rarely, if ever, exceeded.

Cheval clocks must exist in considerable numbers being a variation on a theme. They were not allocated a style number, the three known to me although they adopt the same principle, are completely different in case design. I have termed them cheval clocks in that the clock replaces a mirror in the standard cheval mirror format; like the mirror, they are adjusted to suit the eye of the viewer.

The cake basket is a very novel idea and a miniature version of the one illustrated has been noted on the London art market in 1975.

The candlestick clock with its three dials and movement in the base must have been a design nightmare. The drive is transmitted from the base of the clock requiring a specially constructed movement and the castings have not yet appeared in another form on any other clock.

In correspondence with George Daniels, he admirably summed up the Cole problem and I quote - "The subject of Cole is fascinating because so little is known of him except what he made. His circumstances are remarkable because the construction of a clock of the complexity he liked is a considerable undertaking requiring the confidence of practice and about one year's concentrated and skilful work. If he did the work himself, he would need either an alternative source of income during the manufacture of a very extended programme of manufacture. If he employed other workers either inside or outside his workshop, he would need considerable finance during the manufacture to pay his men." Research into workshop practice, numbers employed, costs, etc. in Victorian horology, has hardly started. The unusual clocks would have required considerable liaison between the designer, manufacturer and those employed to do the physical construction. From their complexity in case work, I have no doubts that these clocks took many years to complete under constant supervision to ensure the incredibly high standard attained.

ITEM 41

A well constructed cheval clock with stop to the rear to prevent the clock swinging too far back, hence obscuring the dial to the onlooker. The specially made movement is designed to fit neatly inside the case which is numbered both at the bottom of the stand on the main cast body of the clock and on the dial plate.

The back cover is beaten out as in silversmiths work so as to allow for the regulation shutter and the shutter for the winding handle. Nowhere on the clock can be found the secret impressed punch of Cole, however, there is no doubt that this is a Cole clock.

Movement: Early vertical lever escapement with uncompensated balance.
Hands: Fleur de Lis.
Dial: Silvered, florally engraved, painted numbers
Additional Features: Original travelling case.
Duration: Eight days.
Signed: Nil — probably obliterated when the dial was cleaned.
Number: 1107.
Dimensions: 18 cm high, handle up, 10 cm wide.
Date: Circa 1853.
Collection: Private collection, Australia.

ITEM 42

A small striking mantel clock inscribed on the inside of the back door:

Howell James & Co.

London

Hidden within the case structure appears the secret punched sign of "THOˢ COLE".

Hands: Breguet-style moon hands.

Dial: Typical silvered English watch-type dial with painted chapters and with scalloped engine-turned pattern in the centre.

Additional Features: None.

Duration: Eight days.

Signature: The punched secret signature "THOˢ COLE" appears twice within the structure of the case. The first signature is on the top of that plate sandwiched between the ornamental cupola and the top plate of the clock case proper. This latter plate also carries the punched signature "THOˢ COLE".

Number: None, as the clock is pre-numbered.

Dimensions: 4 ³⁄₁₆ ".

Casework: Gilt brass with corner pillars, feet and finials. The ornamental cupola top is surmounted by a further turned finial. The side panels and the front of the case are engraved but the back is plain.

Movement: The movement is most peculiar. The going train is wound from the front of the case through a hole near chapters I and II. The striking train is wound from the back plate, the winding square being accessible only when the door is open.

The trains are arranged one in front of the other with a common middle plate. The going train is to the front of the clock and the striking train to the rear. The fusees are planted high up in the frames. The going fusee is provided with Harrison's maintaining work. The external striking work is planted on the outside of the back plate of the clock, the twin hammer arbors being vertical. The clock strikes hours and ting-tang quarters on two bells housed below the movement in the base of the clock.

The escapement is an English lever with plain gold balance and flat steel spring. The 'scape wheel and pallets are below the platform.

Conclusions: The link of Thomas Cole with this clock, if only by the use of his punch, is undeniable. It is true that certain features of the ornamental case work, for example the top cupola and the shape of the plate upon which it rests, are somewhat in the Cole idiom; but the dial and hands certainly are not, while the engraving does not seem particularly reminiscent of Cole either. As for the movement, nothing could be more unlike the work now attributed to Thomas Cole and typified by his strut clocks. In Cole movements the work style is highly characteristic, containing proportions, techniques and practices not normally associated with anybody else and utterly dissimilar from the arrangements found in the present clock. Even the lever platform escapement is not at all in the usual Cole style.

Collection: Private Collection, England.

Illustration: (1) Front view (the engine-turning in the dial unfortunately does not show). (2) Detail of the underside of the clock showing the pierced and engraved base designed to let out the sound of the bells.

Compiled by C.R.P. Allix

Notes by J.B. Hawkins

From the style of the engraving, this clock shows a correlation with item No. 43 and would date circa 1840-42. The movement was definitely not constructed by Howell and James who, in this case, acted purely as the retailers. By whom the movement was constructed is open to conjecture.

Item 42

ITEM 43

An ornate and complicated four-sided architectural clock made in the form of a neo-classical temple with eight columns and cupola top. The temple stands on an ormulu base of acanthus leaves presumably intended to represent a rocky outcrop. The movement signed

French

Royal Exchange

LONDON

The case with the punched signature

THO^s COLE

on the upper side of the first lamination under the cupola top.

Hands: Cole-type fleur de Lis on all dials.

Dial: Gilt and not silvered. Florally engraved. All chapters painted.

Additional Features: Top plumb bob and finial (missing).

Lunation dial below the cupola.

Calendar on two sides of the clock; one dial showing the days of the week, another the date of the month.

Thermometer.

Non-original mahogany plinth.

Duration: Eight days.

Signature: As above.

Number: None as the clock belongs to the pre-numbered period.

Dimensions: 9¼".

Casework: Gilt brass engraved virtually all over.

Movement: The clock is not going well at present; but there are eight bells with their associated hammers concealed in the base of the clock. Presumably an eight-bell tune is played at the quarters. The hand-setting knob is arranged like a "typsy" key so that the clock cannot be damaged by turning the hands backwards. There are three trains; one for going, one for striking hours on a circular section wire gong, and the third apparently for quarters on eight bells housed in the base. One fusee visible from beneath the clock. It seems probable that the movement was made by French rather than by Thomas Cole.

Collection: Private Collection, England.

Illustrations: (1) Front of clock. (2) Rear of clock with the thermometer door in place. (3) Right side of clock showing calendar for days of the week. (4) Left side of clock with calendar showing date of the month.

Compiled by C.R.P. Allix

Notes by J.B. Hawkins

This, in my opinion, is an example of a clock case designed and manufactured by Cole, the movement constructed by J.M. French, the whole completed by 1845. Cole returned to the horological trade, circa 1840 and J.M. French was out of business by 1846. Under dials and engraving, the thermometer panel from this clock shows a close stylistic similarity with that of the early mantel clock item No. 42 which I date circa 1842.

1

2

3

4

Item 43

ITEM 44

An upright table clock with thermometer and compass, the silvered dial engraved with flowers and wreaths and bearing the painted inscription:

HUNT & ROSKELL

Hidden within the case structure appears the secret punched signature of Thomas Cole.

Hands: Ordinary blued-steel hands of a type not normally associated with Thomas Cole. Spade hour hand. Plain minute hand.

Dial: Silvered and engraved all over. Chapters and signatures painted in black.

Additional Features: The thermometer is housed inside the pinnacle with the temperature shown against a scale visible from the front of the clock. The pinnacle itself consists of four main upright pieces secured to the top of the clock and joined together at the top of the pinnacle beneath its finial.

A compass is housed in the base of the clock in a stretcher bracing the four splayed feet.

Duration: Eight days.

Signature: The signature "THO^s COLE" is punched into the upper side of the top plate of the clock case immediately beneath the pinnacle. The signature is entirely covered by the base of the pinnacle and cannot be seen unless the entire pinnacle and thermometer unit is removed.

Serial No: Probably pre numbered circa 1846.

Dimensions: 8⅝"

Casework: Gilt brass, some of it engraved and some of it plain, and comprising a multiplicity of castings screwed together. The clock is four-sided. At the front is the dial. At the back is a rear door opening downwards and latching at the top. At the sides are silvered and pierced decorative panels visible behind bevelled glasses. No doubt originally this clock was provided with an elaborate fitted and shaped travelling box.

Movement: The movement has rectangular plates. It is wound with a key and is provided with a fixed button for setting the hands. Although the back plate of the movement bears the engraved inscription "HUNT & ROSKELL" it gives every superficial indication of being typical of the type associated with the work of Thomas Cole. It was not, however, dismantled and it was not possible to examine the movement in detail without taking the clock completely to pieces (which was not done). The escapement platform is on the outside of the back plate. It is an English pointed-tooth right-angled lever with single roller and flat blue steel balance spring allied to a plain steel balance.

Origin: Private collection, England.

Illustrations: (1) Front. (2) Rear to show movement. (3) Side to show door opening downwards and also to show side panel.

Compiled by C.R.P. Allix

Notes by J.B. Hawkins

This clock may not be numbered however, it was not completely stripped. Stylistically, the engraving of the dial would date it circa 1845-50 and with closer inspection it may well transpire to be a prenumbered Cole of circa 1846.

Item 44

Item 44

ITEM 45

Three sided diamond shaped clock, thermometer and manual calendar. To date, I have only seen this shape in the form of the Ace of Diamonds, however, it would be improbable if it was not continued with the Ace of Spades, the Ace of Hearts and the Ace of Clubs. This is the miniature version; for the larger version, see next item.

In a little compartment behind the dial Cole has fitted to the standard watch movement, a going barrel, plus sufficient gearing to allow it to run for eight days. The thermometer denotes the temperature in degrees Fahrenheit and on the Reamur scale. A small thermometer tube to the rear is fitted with a beautifully made brass cover to protect the fragile bulb of the thermometer. The manual calendar may be adjusted by setting the day of the week against the first of the month, it then being correct for the complete month. From the dial engraving this is a very early clock and may be considered to be pre-numbered.

Movement: Standard 24 hour watch movement converted to eight days by the provision of special train encased behind the dial plate.

Hands: Fleur de Lis.

Dial: Silvered with Arabesque and floral engraving, painted numbers.

Additional Features: Thermometer and manual monthly calendar.

Duration: Eight days.

Signed: "Made by Thomas Cole for R. & S. Garrard & Co., Panton Street, Haymarket". The firm used this form of address from 1843-1848.

Number: The clock from the Retailers inscription is pre-numbered.

Dimensions: 11 cm high × 9 cm wide.

Date: Circa 1846-7.

Collection: Private collection, Australia.

Photograph indicates the precise fit of the layered construction looking down on top of the clock.

Item 45

ITEM 46

Three sided diamond shaped clock, barometer and thermometer. This particular clock is interesting in that it obviously took a long time to sell. The numbers on the clock are 1876 856 6. 1876 is the movement number. This is to be found stamped plainly on the movement which is specially designed to fit in the small space available and signed "Thos. Cole, London". The number 856 is the series number, that is, when the clock was initially made it was numbered in Cole's production series 856 and the 6 indicates that it was the sixth of that shape or model produced.

The barometer of the standard aneroid barometer type. The thermometer, unlike the previous item, has been fully encased between the plates and gives temperatures in Fahrenheit (0-130) and Reamur (10-30).

Movement: Eight day, vertical lever escapement, uncompensated balance, going barrel.
Dial: Silvered with Arabesque and floral engraving, painted numerals. Circa 1863/64.
Hands: Spade.
Additional Features: Thermometer and barometer.
Duration: Eight days.
Signed: Movement signed Thomas Cole, no external retailer's signature.
Number: 1876 856 6.
Dimensions: 24 cm high × 14 cm wide.
Date: Date commenced circa 1851, date finished circa 1864, possibly after Cole's death.
Collection: Private collection, Australia.

Item 46

ITEM 47

A clock set in an urn standing on an ornamental plinth. The dial bears the painted signature

Thos Cole

in gothic letters.

Hands: Cole-type fleur de lis.

Dial: Silvered and engraved with characteristic designs.

Additional Features: On the front of the plinth is a Cole-type calendar.

   The clock is wound by means of a conventional key which is inserted through a hole in the back of the urn and which hole was originally concealed by an engraved shutter (now missing). The calendar is set from below the base of the plinth.

Duration: Eight days.

Signature: "Thos Cole" on dial.

Dimensions: 7¼″ tall.

Number: Not located.

Casework: Gilt brass, the urn engraved all over and having a cover topped by the cast and tooled figure of a putto with a globe. Both glasses are bevelled. The back of the urn releases by means of a catch to give access to the movement.

Movement: The train is arranged on the expected Cole eight-day principle. The escapement is a lever.

Collection: Private Collection, England.

Illustrations: Front view.

Compiled by C.R.P. Allix

Notes by J.B. Hawkins

This clock is slightly earlier from the engraving than the next item and it is interesting that they are both signed Thos. Cole and unnumbered. Date circa 1850.

Item 47

ITEM 48

Urn shaped Cole clock on square plinth with stepped base. The urn with two handles, terminating in cherub masks and surmounted by cherub figure pouring wine from a jug. The body of the urn is beaten and raised from the flat in the manner of a silversmith. Detaching completely from the plinth, it is finely engraved with scroll decoration.

Movement: Comprising of split plates for the going train and striking train, the vertical lever escapement on a separate shaped platform, the half hour striking activated by the going train on a small gong, the hour striking independently on a large gong.

Hands: Fleur de Lis.

Dial: Silvered, Arabesque engraved decoration. Painted numbers.

Additional Features: Original key, see illustration page 39.

Duration: Eight days.

Signed: Thomas Cole, London.

Number: Nil.

Dimensions: Maximum width 14 cms. Height 32.5 cms.

Date: Circa 1850.

Collection: Private Collection, Australia.

Item 48

ITEM 49

An outstanding striking vertical table clock signed on the dial:

THO^s COLE

LONDON

and embodying barometer, thermometer, calendar, moon and compass.

Hands: Thomas Cole-type fleur de lis.

Dial: Silvered and florally engraved. Arched top.

Additional Features: In the base of the clock is an Aneroid barometer. In the top pinnacle is a thermometer. In the campanile immediately below the top pinnacle and above the calendar stage is a compass. The compass ring turns on a vertical spike. The calendar is of the same type as that sometimes found in strut clocks, but this time Thomas Cole has set the days of the week horizontally instead of vertically. Immediately above the calendar is a dial showing the age and appearance of the moon. The calendar is set manually by a square to the right of the roller as seen from the front. The moon work is driven by the clock.

Duration: Eight days.

Signature: The signature "THO^s COLE LONDON" appears on a cartouche on the dial below chapter VI.

Number: None seen but neither the clock case nor its movement were dismantled at all.

Casework: Superb by any standard, and owing its tremendous vigour and sharpness of profile to the enormous number of parts and layers of which it is comprised. Being a table clock, the casework is engraved on all four sides and almost literally all over except for the steps at the base and those steps connecting the various stages.

Movement: In the Cole idiom and striking hours on a deep-toned wire gong. The platform lever escapement has a cut brass and steel balance and flat steel spring. The compensated balance may well be a later modification. As usual, Cole employs going barrels.

Dimensions: 23 $^3/_{16}$ " to top of finial.

Collection: Private Collection, England.

Illustrations: (1) Front. (2) Side. (3) Rear.

Compiled by C.R.P. Allix

Notes by J.B. Hawkins

This clock would have taken many years to construct and contains many of Cole's ideas in its construction. The stepped base can be seen on the urn clock, item No. 48. The pillars to the sides surrounding the compass are from the strut clocks similar to item No 2. I think that time will show that the case is constructed from three carriage clock cases of varying sizes, one case containing the barometer, one case containing the clock and one case containing the calendar and moon work, superimposed to do different jobs, one on top of the other. The thermometer to the top occurs as the finial to item No. 44.

As it was impossible to take the clock apart, no number could be located but I would estimate the series number to be between 1300 and 1500 and according to the length of time it took to construct. The clock commenced circa 1850 may well have been exhibited in the Paris Exhibition of 1855.

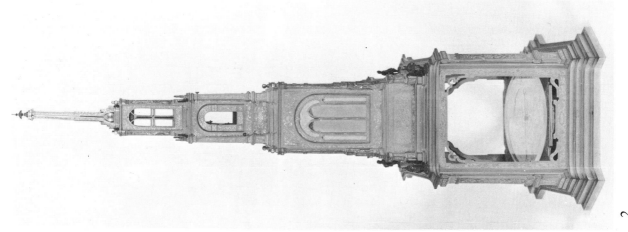

Item 49

ITEM 50

A candlestick clock having three sides, one with a clock dial, one with a thermometer, and one with a calendar for day of the week and date of the month. The clock retains its original sexagonal travelling box covered in red morocco leather and lined with red velvet. The original winding key rests in a velvet loop inside the door. This key is single-ended and fits both the winding and the hand-set squares.

Hands: Thomas Cole fleur de lis.

Dial: Silvered with engraved floral centre and foliated surround.

Additional Features: Here is yet another form of the Thomas Cole calendar requiring to be altered weekly. It will be seen that in this candlestick clock the days-of-the-week are set out in a vertical tabulation, while the date-of-the-month from 1 to 31 are painted in succession on a ring partly visible through an aperture. The calendar is set by means of a toothed wheel moved with the fingernail and accessible beneath the calendar dial. On the third side of the clock there is a thermometer graded in Fahrenheit.

Duration: Eight days.

Signature: None that could be seen but the clock was not completely stripped.

Number: No number in an obvious position.

Dimmensions: 9¼″ high.

Casework: Gilt brass, the engraved parts alternating and contrasting with others deliberately left plain and burnished. The base comprises three stepped laminations with ornamental profiles and surmounted by a scalloped layer on top of which is a circular plinth with beaded base. The stem of the candlestick is built up of six separate engraved castings each with a splayed foot. The "clock tower" consists of a complex build-up of castings. Above it is the engraved candlestick in which the six-sided theme is maintained.

Movement: The movement is housed in the base of the clock with the arbors vertical. The "centre pinion" is not in the centre of the movement. It drives through gearing a lead-off mechanism consisting of a vertical arbor running upwards inside the multi-piece waist of the candlestick. At the top of the vertical arbor is a brass wheel driving (incredibly) an ordinary watch-type contrate wheel which serves the purpose of a spur gear to effect transmission of the motion through 90°. On the same arbor as the contrate wheel is a cannon pinion which drives conventional motion work behind the meantime dial. The circular movement is 1⅞″ in diameter. It is arranged as shown with the going barrel and also the intermediate wheel and pinion in the main frames.

The movement is typically in the Thomas Cole idiom, with going barrel and a train with many changes of pitch. The winding square, hand-setting square and regulation index are accessible through shuttered holes in the base of the candlestick.

The escapement is a right-angled pointed-tooth English lever with single roller, flat steel balance spring and plain gold balance. The clickwork is rather rough, and click and click-spring are almost certainly replacements.

Collection: Private Collection, England.

Illustrations: (1) Front showing clock dial. (2) Side view showing thermometer. (3) Side view showing calendar. (4) View from underneath the clock with two base plates removed in order to show movement.

Compiled by C.R.P. Allix

Notes by J.B. Hawkins

This clock probably has concealed on it somewhere a number between 1500 and 1700. The supports from the base to the clock that make up the stem of the candlestick are very similar to cupola supports on the tripod clock item No. 39 and would date circa 1858.

The key in the travelling case is another example of an unusual and beautifully constructed Cole key.

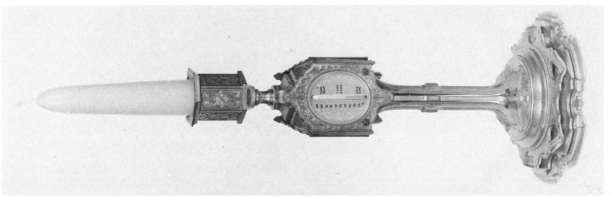

4

3

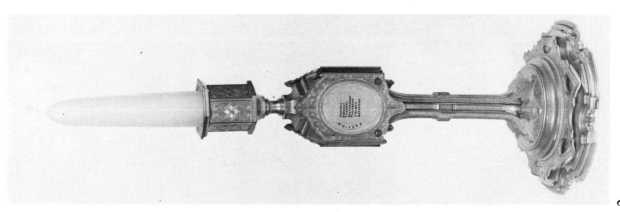

2

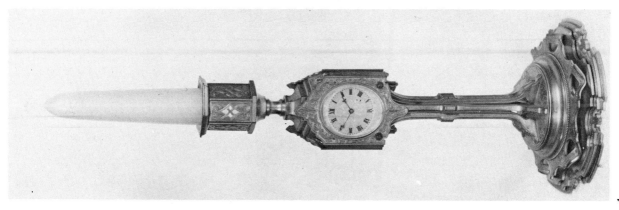

1

Item 50

ITEM 51

A clock in the form of a cake basket with folding carrying handle and with the concave dial set under a dished glass. On the underside of the base of the clock appears the name of the vendor:

JENNER & NEWSTUB
33, ST JAMES'S ST

Hands: Typical Cole-type Fleur de Lis but shaped to the dished contour of the dial.
Dial: Brass gilt and engraved. Chapters painted.
Additional Features: Fixed fold-flat winding key. Hinged shutter covering hand-set square. In the back of the shutter casting are cast the initials AJD.
Duration: Eight days.
Dimensions: Approximately 9" square.
Signature: Jenner & Newstub as above.
Serial No: None visible but the clock was only stripped to reveal the back plate of the movement. See postscript.
Casework: Gilt brass engraved in a far more bold and open pattern than is usual with Thomas Cole clocks. The Cole lamination system is apparent in the side view.
Movement: Typical Thomas Cole style movement with going barrel, the expected changes of pitch, screwed-on platform escapement, right-angled pointed tooth English lever escapement with single roller, plain steel balance and flat blued steel balance spring.
Origin: Private Collection England.
Illustrations: (1) Eye level view showing shape and profile. (2) A view of the underside of clock showing signature and winding arrangements. (3) View downwards showing dial and handle.
In May 1975 the clock was further stripped in the hope of discovering the signature of Thomas Cole, particular attention being given to the laminations outside the dial. No signature or numbers were found. I do, however, think that this is a Cole clock and it certainly has a Cole-type movement evincing his usual peculiarities. On the other hand the engraving of the casework is not very like that usually associated with Cole and there is the clue of the initials AJD (whoever he was) who must have had a hand in the work.

Compiled by C.R.P. Allix

Notes by J.B. Hawkins
This clock has many stylistic similarities with item No. 30 both in the dial engraving, the engraving to the border of the basket and the line and ball decoration to the outside edge of the chapter ring. It is unnumbered as is the lyre strut clock and both lack a secret signature. It may well have been finished and engraved after Cole's death from one of his designs, circa 1870. A miniature cake basket clock retailed by Hancock and numbered 839 22 is known to the author.

1

2

Item 51

COMPENDIUMS FOR THE WRITING TABLE

To my mind, these attractive little desk clocks are amongst the most beautiful of all Cole's designs. It would appear that in all cases, the clock could be removed and used as an independent unit, a pleasant refinement of detail.

From the Art Journal Illustrated Catalogue of the Crystal Palace Exhibition,[1] I extract the following —

"An inkstand or to designate it more correctly according to its varied contents a compendium for the writing table made and contributed by Mr. Cole of Clerkenwell, is a most useful and elegant work of manufacturing art, novel in character when the variety and arrangement of its 'fittings' is considered and most elaborately engraved and richly ornamented." See illustration of engraving.

It would appear from the engraving shown that the inkstand is fitted with malachite mounted compartments for the ink, key and pen. The small handle to the right hand side rear of the inkstand may be manipulated so as to remove the clock. A similar clock retailed by C.F. Hancock was sold by Sothebys in 1969, Lot 30, and I quote from the catalogue —

"C.F. Hancock. A fine mid 19th century gilt metal desk stand incorporating a temple clock, the clock case and stand finely engraved with sprigs of flowers and leaves, and panels of diaper on matt ground. The clock with blue numerals and a subsidiary calendar dial, signed on the back plate, C.F. Hancock, a Successor of Storr and Mortimer's by appointment to HM Queen Adelaide, 39 Bruton Street, London. The stand with an ink and sand well, the lids release on spring catches at the left hand side and in the drawer in the base. 6" × 7" wide."

Reading between the lines, this is another variation on the Great Exhibition compendium by Cole. However, this clock was retailed by Hancocks and had a subsidiary calendar dial as distinct from two separate dials giving the date and the day.

[1]Reprint by Dover Books page 111.

Item 51

ITEM 52

A small compendium for the writing table in a very finely engraved case, the clock being completely detachable from the inkstand by the removal of one knurled brass stud to the rear. As the engraving continues over the top of the stand, where it is normally concealed by the clock, the clock was obviously made to be removed. The base is fitted with two drawers and an ink pot, the right hand drawer contains a finely engraved gold pen, the left hand drawer takes the original engraved key.

   The complexity of construction of this clock is amazing. Exclusive of the movement and screws, the case of the inkstand and the clocks breaks down into 53 separate pieces, see illustration page 35. The drawers all fit flush by the use of tempered steel springs so that they do not move in any way when closed. The pen drawer is fitted with a spring which, on opening the drawer, presents the pen to the hand of the writer. Two gilt roses on the top of the inkstand prevent the clock when lowered to the horizontal position, from breaking its glass on the top of the inkwell.

Movement: 24 hour Lepine calibre Swiss watch movement with a cylinder escapement and uncompensated balance, signed Aine, Geneve.

Hands: Hour hand Fleur de Lis, minute hand plain.

Dial: Silvered with Arabesque engraving incorporating two masks of human faces at 12 o'clock and 6 o'clock. Painted numbers.

Additonal Features: Pen drawer, key drawer and glass inkwell with screw top.

Duration: 24 hours.

Signed: R. & S. Garrard & Co., London and bears an inscription "The Duke of Rutland, Obt Jany 27th 1857." This was presumably engraved at a later date as His Grace must have left this specifically to someone on his death who had it suitably inscribed.

Number: Pre-numbered, and from the designation R & S. Garrard & Co., must date between 1843-48.

Dimensions: 11 cm wide × 12 cm deep × 10½ cm high.

Date: Circa 1845.

Collection: Private collection, Australia.

Item 52

CARRIAGE CLOCKS

As a maker specialising in portable clocks, Thomas Cole must have made a considerable number of carriage clocks, very few however have been noted by the author.

Item No. 53 is the only example of Cole's work known to me that has survived from the first period at 3 New Bond Street. However, I know that another silver gilt carriage clock signed J.F. & T. Cole does exist but at present its whereabouts are unknown.

Illustrated and described are two miniature carriage clocks of considerable complexity.

In *'Carriage Clocks'* by Charles Allix, illustrated by Peter Bonnert, on page 240 there is illustrated a carriage clock retailed by Hancock and manufactured by Thomas Cole for which the following description applies. (see below)

"A timepiece carriage clock with lever platform escapement and silvered panels either side of the case, one with a thermometer and one set with a handset perpetual calendar. The back movement plate is signed C.F. Hancock but Cole's name is engraved on the left hand side panel deliberately concealed by the applied framing."

From the style of the engraving and the cast handle, this could well be a pre numbered Cole clock. If not, the number could be no higher than 800 and the clock be no later than 1850.

The fourth and final carriage clock illustrated has a case that in my opinion may well have been designed by Cole in his capacity as a clock case designer.

ITEM 53

A portable astronomical clock signed J.F. & T. Cole, London, in a silver gilt case bearing the London hallmark for 1825, see colour frontispiece.

On the evidence of this clock, the two brothers were in partnership from 1825 to 1829 at 3 New Bond Street, as noted from the Trade Directories. This is the only clock known to me bearing their joint names but I have reason to believe that at least one other clock exists similarly signed.

The silver gilt case bears the following marks as in illustration 1. Makers mark W.B. badly struck and not rubbed, probably for William Bateman who entered his mark in 1815. The lion passant, indicating the case is of Sterling Standard. The leopard's head, the London Assay mark. The date letter 'k' for 1825. The Sovereign's head indicating that duty had been paid on assaying.

The door bears the makers mark W.B., the lion passant and the date letter 'k' for 1825, see illustration 2.

Illustration 3 shows the hallmarks on the handles. The maker's mark J.A. possibly for John Angel, see Jacksons English Goldsmiths and Their Marks, page 228, last line, the duty mark, the lion passant and the date letter 'h' for 1823.

The two handles are of great interest in that they bear date letter 'h' and predate the rest of the clock by two years. It would, by deduction, appear that J.F. Cole planned a series of clocks on this format and as a result, ordered a number of handles in advance, possibly from a specialist handle and chain maker with the initials J.A.

The British Museum has on loan a similar clock without alarm, signed J.F. Cole and numbered D. Where are A, B, and C? The Horological Journal Vol. I for 1859, pages 134 and 135, gives a description of the clock numbered D and the Editor's Note concludes "Seven similar clocks and pocket watches containing the above and other properties were constructed and made by Mr. Cole about 30 years since, at prices varying from 100-300 gns. each." This note, and the handles from the J.F. and T. Cole clock leads one to the conclusion that a series of clocks were planned rather than constructed at random.

When Thomas Cole joined his brother in business circa 1825 at 3 New Bond Street, he was entitled to have his name inscribed on the clocks produced. The extent to which he participated in their construction, however, can only be conjectured.

Carriage Clocks by C. Allix and P. Bonnert, Plate IX/2 on page 236 shows a view of the J.F. & T. Cole clock whereas the movement, Plate IX/3, page 237, is of the J.F. Cole clock D. This provides an opportunity for comparison between the two clock movements and the similarities are obvious.

On the advice of Mr. B. Hutchinson, Research Assistant at the British Museum, the description of the movement of the J.F. Cole clock D in the Horological Journal, Vol. I, 1859, pages 134 and 135, applies equally well to that of the J.F. and T. Cole clock. The only difference is that the J.F. and T. Cole clock is fitted with an alarm mechanism, the setting dial for which is below the main dial.

Movement: This section is extracted from the Horological Journal mentioned above and provides a good mid 19th century description. It may even have been written by J.F. Cole, then a member of the British Horological Institute.

"The general design or calibre of the movement of this Clock is an arrangement so disposed as to admit the largest amount of power in the smallest space, as shewn by the unusually large diameter of the great wheels and double acting barrel which drives the two trains of the going and striking parts, giving hours and quarters regularly on bell springs, by mechanism resembling in some particulars clocks of the justly celebrated M. Breguet.

This Clock also repeats the hours and quarters, at pleasure, by touching a projectile stop at the top of the case.

The dial plate, also of silver, is quite an original design as regards arrangement of the various indications on the several circles, and scales of figures on segments drawn from three excentric points surrounding the true centre of the hour circle. Hours, minutes, and seconds are shewn by the principal steel hands, and the time is governed by a compensation balance and spring, as usual; the escapement being a detached lever, with a flat steel wheel having the impulse angles formed wholly on the wheel teeth, in the manner of Graham's horizontal wheel, without columns; the pallets acted on by the planes of the teeth being two arms of equal length, with ruby pallets set to represent the edges of a ruby cylinder scaping over three teeth. The wheel in this is a tempered one, and has performed well for 30 years, without the slightest injury from action.

On the dial plate, the small circle at the right shews the days of the week; the corresponding circle at the left shews the months; and the segment below shews the days of the month, by a gold indicator hand, which is governed by the mechanism seen at the right of the back view. This particular mode of shewing the perpetual day of the month is an original improvement, constructed to correct the unequal months of 30 and 31 days, for the 28th day of February, and the 29th day in leap year. Below the centre is a semicircular indication of the Moon's age and phases; and above the centre is a similar aperture, enclosed by the second's circle. Within the circle is a blued steel plate, carrying a disc of silver representing the apparent motion of the Sun. This small disc will appear above and disappear below the moveable horizon daily, through all seasons of the year; the smaller segments at the left and right with gold indicator hands, shew the time of sun rising and setting.

Outside the circular rim of the dial are two apertures — one where the key is inserted for winding the clock, and the other for setting the hands as marked on the gold tablets. The key applied at this point commands all the motions, which are always correct, unless the clock is allowed to go down. On the side of the silver case is a sliding stop, which may be set to strike hours and quarters, or quarters only with the hour at the proper time; and if the stop is set to the lowest point, at the mark "Silent", the power of the striking part is transferred to the going part, and by this the period of going will be prolonged to nearly a month."

The alarm mechanism is operated from a spring loaded barrel, seen at the bottom right of the rear of the clock and wound by pulling a cord.

Additional Features: The key is unusual in that it is double ended, the winding train being activated by the male end and the hands set by the female end. The clock retains its original travelling case, this key fitting into its inside base.

Duration: Eight days.

Signed: J.F. and T. Cole.

Number: The J.F. Cole carriage clock bears the serial letter 'D' and is hallmarked for 1823. The joint venture carriage clock appears to have no form of identification with relation to any series.

Dimensions: 6¼" high.

Date: 1825.

Collection: The British Museum, London.

Other illustrations: (4) Side view to show going barrel with dual drive for striking train. (5) Side view to show alarm mechanism. (6) Front view of clock, dial removed. (7) Rear view, in case, to show striking and alarm system. (8) Signature, J.F. & T. Cole.

1

2

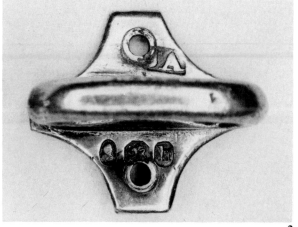

3

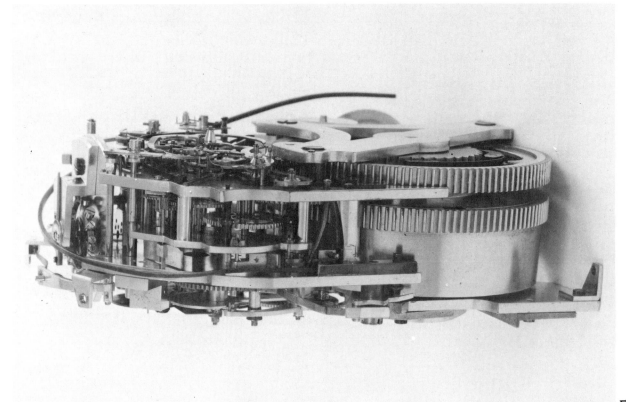

Item 53

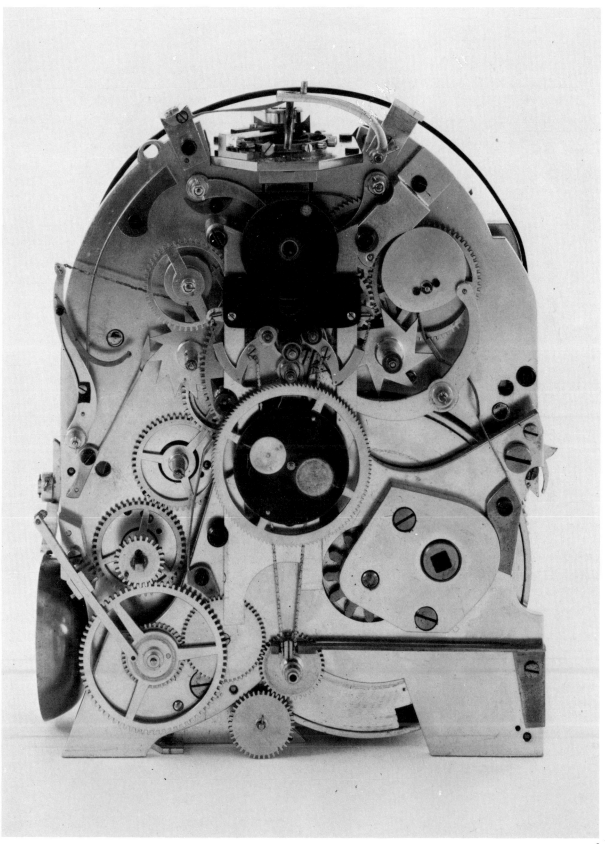

Item 53

7

8

These photographs and frontispiece courtesy British Museum.

Item 53

ITEM 54

A fine and rare miniature carriage clock set with malachite panels to the sides and top. The rear door engraved with a panel of fuschia and roses on a lined background. The dial of the early period, floral engraving, with a fine dial mask signed Garrard.

Movement: Vertical lever escapement with uncompensated balance set outside the backplate.
Hands: Spade, but not original.
Dial: Silvered with painted numerals.
Additional Fitments: Nil.
Duration: Eight days.
Signed: R. & S. Garrard & Co., Panton Street, Haymarket, London, made by T. Cole.
Number: Pre numbered and from the designation, R. & S. Garrard, must date between 1845-48.
Dimensions: 8 cm high × 5 cm wide × 2.25 cm deep.
Date: Circa 1845.
Collection: Private collection, England.

ITEM 55

A fine, rare and unusual eight day striking miniature carriage clock with a lapis lazuli panel to the top. The panels to the sides being engraved on a lined background with vases of flowers containing fuschias and roses. The engraving of the case and dial is of the early period, circa 1850.

Movement: The eight day striking movement is fitted with a vertical lever escapement with uncompensated balance. The striking train is wound by a male key from the front and the going train by a female key from the rear. The clock strikes the hours on a gong coiled between the plates. The two going barrels are planted in tandem but have independent action.

Hands: Fleur de Lis.

Dial: Silvered with arabesque engraving, painted numerals.

Additional Fitments: Nil.

Duration: Eight days.

Signed: "Eight day striking clock constructed and made by Thomas Cole London 1862." Originally the dial bore the name, C.F. Hancock. It is my opinion that this clock was commenced as early as 1850 and completed by Cole, circa 1861/62 in time for the London Exhibition of 1862. This is further confirmed by the fact that the carriage clock item No. 56 also bears the date 1862, they both presumably being exhibited in that year.

Hancock may have purchased it after the 1862 Exhibition and put his name on the dial.

Number: 1862. This is I am sure the date of completion, not the serial number.

Date: Circa 1850, completed circa 1862.

Dimensions: 6 cm high × 4.5 cm wide × 3.2 cm deep.

Collection: Private collection, England.

Item 55

ITEM 56

A superb and richly-decorated clock signed on the dial below the chapter ring:

THOₛ COLE, LONDON

The clock retains its fine original shaped travelling box covered in red morocco leather and lined with green velvet and with off-white silk. The box is furnished with two glazed windows so that not only the time but also the moon dial may be seen during journeys.

Hands: Cole-type fleur de lis.

Dial: Both dials are silvered and engraved. The black painted dial writings are original and unrestored.

Additional Features: The dial showing the state of the moon was a very useful feature in the period when the clock was made. Even in late Victorian times most country roads were still narrow and also un-metalled. Travelling in the dark on moon-less nights could be a dreadfully difficult and dangerous business. The moon dial is worked by the clock and can be corrected from behind by means of a key. The winding and moon setting holes are not protected by shutters. Note the key drawer in the front of the clock above the dial.

Duration: Eight days.

Signature: THOˢ COLE, LONDON on dial.

Number: None was seen; but no dismantling was done.

Dimensions: 7⅝" tall.

Casework: Gilt brass of a most unusual and beautiful form. For instance, the side panels and radiused canted corners are engraved with representations of vases of flowers against a background of parallel horizontal hatched lines, while the upper part of the clock is decorated with tulips and other flowers. A charming feature of the casework is the pillared porch framing the lunation dial.

Movement: Typical Thomas Cole-type of movement with going barrel, train with many changes of pitch terminated in a single roller right-angled lever escapement with plain gold balance and flat blued steel balance spring.

Collection: Private Collection, England.

Comment: The number 1862 engraved on the inside of the back door is almost certainly a date and not a serial number. I suggest that this clock was one of those models noted in the literature of the 1862 London Exhibition as having been displayed by Thomas Cole.

Illustrations: (1) Front. (2) Rear view plus door.

Compiled by C.R.P. Allix

Notes by J.B. Hawkins

From the late style of the dial engraving and the incorporation of the line and ball border to the bezel, this clock is a very late example of Cole's work. It was impossible to take the clock apart but it should bear somewhere a series number between 1750 and 1850. The number 1862 as per Item number 55 is the date of completion as distinct from the serial number.

Item 56

Item 56

ITEM 57

Large and important eight day quarter striking and repeating carriage clock fitted with a chronometer escapement. This clock was exhibited in the 1851 exhibition and is described in the Official Descriptive and Illustrated Catalogue, Vol. I page 417, under the retailers name of W. Payne of 163 New Bond Street, as follows —

"Astronomical clock with chronometer escapement, perpetual day of month, moons age, noon and night, day of week, repeats hours and quarters, zodiacal signs, in engraved gilt case." *See Appendix A.*

The movement of this clock was constructed by Samuel Bartholomew Gaze being signed with punches stamped into the centre plate "S.B. Gaze, London 1850". Samuel Bartholomew Gaze's history may be ascertained to a certain extent from the obituary notice of his son, James Gaze, in the Horological Journal, Vol. 55 (10 June, 1913) page 164 which is more informative about S.B. Gaze than his son. James Gaze died 26th May, 1913 at 385 Holloway Road, London in his 88th year. He was the last surviving son of Samuel Bartholomew Gaze, watch and clockmaker of Spitalfields. S.B. Gaze appears to have moved from Norfolk to Spitalfields and during the middle of the last century his clock manufacturing business was considerable for he had five sons all working in the business manufacturing for the leading makers and opulent private patrons interested in all types of clocks. It was a deep source of disappointment to the late Mr. James Gaze that new methods of manufacture had made their old methods obsolete. Their speciality was the making of clock interiors of the best workmanship and quite a number of these in various stages of completeness and certain of the machines, Mr. Gaze could never persuade himself to part with. In the old days it was part of his duty to climb the tower of Spitalfields Church, once if not twice a day, to wind the clock. He and his brother, Peter (who died in 1892) were among the best clockmakers of their period. They carried on business for many years in Liverpool Road North and were members of the British Horological Institute.

S.B. Gaze first appears in the London Directory (Critchett and Woods) in 1816 at 5 Primrose Street, Bishopsgate, Without. In Johnstons Directory of 1817 his address is 26 Princes Street, Spitalfields and at this address the business continued until the last appearance in 1861. First described as "clock and watchmaker" by 1840, he is "turret, musical and house clock and ship dial manufacturer" adding lever clock in 1846 and church clock in 1853 (up to 1861) to his manufactures.

S.B. Gaze does not appear in the Clockmakers Company apprentices, nor his children. He did not exhibit in his own right at the 1851 or 1862 London exhibitions.
The construction of the clock and the design of the decoration owes a great deal to the inspiration of Cole. We know that he advertised as an ornamental clock case designer also that he exhibited designs in the 1851 exhibition. The small vignettes of flowers in the panels to the rear door and the sides bear the typical Cole lined decoration to the background and provide a clue to their source of inspiration. However, the engraving itself is stylistically similar to the musical strut clock, item No. 29 they both being by a different engraver to that employed in the workshop of Cole. The construction of the clock in such a fashion that the acorn finials unscrew, thereby allowing the top plates covering the escapement to be lifted out leaving the side panels which are grooved into the pillars, to be slid up to expose the movement, is a system used by Cole, see item nos. 32, 34. The whole standard of this clock is such that it may be truly termed an exhibition piece.
Movement: Chronometer escapement fitted with bi-metallic balance and timing screws.
Hands: Breguet Style.
Dial: Silvered with engraved numbers and ancillary information, otherwise plain.
Additional Features: In addition to hours and minutes and seconds, gives the day, the date, the age in days of the phase of the moon, the visual phase of the moon (Halifax Moon), noon or night, strike, not to strike. In the aperture below the figure 12 and read by a cursor, we have a yearly

Item 57

calendar, the month, the sign of the zodiac and a group of figures running from nought to thirty at the bottom end of the aperture to which I am unable to attach any significance. The clock strikes and repeats the quarters.

Duration: Eight days.
Signed: Payne, 163 New Bond Street (see p. 28) on the backplate and stamped S.B. Gaze London 1850.
Number: Nil.
Dimensions: 27 cm high handle up × 17 cm wide.
Date: 1851.
Collection: M. Kerry, Esq., Australia.

Item 57

IMITATORS OF COLE'S WORK

It is not always pleasant when a person's original ideas are plagiarised. It is a good indication of the impact Cole's work made that other makers were tempted to copy his ideas. His work was copied by at least two clockmakers, White and Vasel, after 1900. For this reason, they are noted separately from the other retailers of Cole's work.

In Cole's lifetime, his ideas may have been copied by E.W. Robins and also by the firm of Payne of 163 New Bond Street. Cole advertised as a clock designer, so the benefit of the doubt has to be given to these two retailers, Cole may well have designed the cases of the clocks for them to manufacture.

With both White and Vasel, however, it can be firmly established that they copied Cole's work as their businesses do not correlate with his lifetime.

E. WHITE, LONDON

The three clocks illustrated in this section are stylistically similar and all three of them have their original travelling boxes.

The first item No. 58 was sold by Messrs. Carrington & Co. Ltd. and does not bear White's name as a retailer. Item No. 59 is in its original 'Asprey' box, the firm using this form of designation between 1901 and 1906 tying in neatly with Charles Allix's remarks with regard to the movement in item No. 58 it is signed E. White, 19 Jermyn St., London. Item No. 60 in its original box with no retailer's mark on the box, bears the designation E. White, 19 Jermyn Street, London W.1, it being reasonable to assume, therefore, that they actually sold it.

The firm of White was not at 19 Jermyn Street until 1923 and the address 19 Jermyn Street occurs on two of the three items. However, Aspreys were only using the designation 'Asprey' from 1901-1906. This poses a problem. The clocks could not be earlier than 1905 from the movements, and from White's address, earlier than 1923. It is my opinion, therefore, that the clocks were constructed circa 1905 to 1914 but sales from White's business to the various retailers were restricted by the war and the depression and the clocks themselves gained their final sale in the period 1920-30.

1861-69   White, Edward (from Dents) (sic) Chronometer, Watch & Clockmaker, 20 Cockspur Street (1869 entry adds "Prize medals London 1862, Dublin 1865, Paris 1867")

1870-1900 White, Edward (with similar trade description) 20 Cockspur Street

1901-1922 White, Edward (with similar trade description) 32 Haymarket

1923-1939 White, Edward (with similar trade description) 19 Jermyn Street (last entry)

ITEM 58

A strut clock with mechanically-operated calendar showing day of the week and date of the month. The clock is complete in its fitted travelling box lined with apricot-coloured velvet and covered in morocco leather of the same colour and with gilt ornamental tooling. The double-opening doors are lined in off-white silk. Printed on the silk is the name of the vendor:

CARRINGTON & CO. LTD. 130, REGENT STREET, W.

together with a crown under which appear the words:

BY APPOINTMENT

The travelling box is provided with an external strut so that the clock can be used in situ. The strut of the clock latches into a rectangular recess so that the clock is always held firmly in position. In addition, a recess is provided for the key used for setting the clock to time and for advancing the calendar.

Hands: Typical Cole-type fleur de lis in blued steel.

Dial: Silvered and florally engraved all over in a close symmetrical pattern. Chapters, days of week, date of month all painted on in black.

Additional Features: The calendar is set right by means of a key inserted through two holes in the back of the clock case and marked respectively "WEEK DAYS" and "DAYS OF MONTH". There is a further hole for setting the clock to time. There is also a small square aperture giving access to an index for "FAST" and "SLOW". Each hole is protected from the ingress of dust by means of a shutter operated by a lever projecting through the back of the case above the fixed winding key. Even the lever operating the shutters incorporates its own dust-exclusion device.

Duration: Eight days. The winding key is a fixture and folds flat.

Signature: Apparently none. The clock case was not reduced to its individual component parts. The clock was sold by Carringtons of Regent St. as evidenced by original travelling box.

Number: None apparent on the clock so far as it was stripped. The number "33236" visible on the Swiss movement is a *Brevet* number and not a serial number.

Dimensions: 7⅝" approximately with pendant up.

Casework: Gilt brass. While this casework was clearly made in emulation of the Thomas Cole style, it is in fact of very much simplified construction involving less parts and fewer laminations than are found in a typical Thomas Cole clock. Note the unusual and un-Cole-like bowed double strut support, and also that the clock has no turnbuckle foot.

Movement: The "modern" 24 ligne DOXA Swiss eight-day watch-type movement is of a type first shown to the world on 25th March 1905 and covered by the Swiss Brevet No. 33236 in the name of Georges Ducommun of Le Locle. Ducommun seems to have been a proprietor of DOXA.

Conclusions: Thomas Cole died in 1864; so this clock was made at least 41 years after his death. There can be no doubt whatever that the present movement is the first and only one ever given to the clock as proved by the way in which the movement fits snugly into a circular recess in an internal plate. The same plate also holds the two cocks in which run the two arbors of a very non-Cole-like calendar. The movement is held in place by two steel screws with interrupted heads. The movement is kept from turning in its recess by means of a pin which registers in a slot cut in the plate supporting the movement.

It is also worth re-iterating that the very much simplified case construction is un-Cole like, although superficially it greatly resembles his work.

Collection: Private Collection, England.

Illustrations: (1) Side view to show decoration and also strut support. Note simplified case construction. (2) Front. (3) Clock in travelling case. (4) Rear to show back of clock case. (5) Rear with back removed to show watch-type Swiss movement.

In May 1975 Messrs. Camerer Cuss & Company had the clock in for overhaul at which time it was completely dismantled. This firm confirms all the conclusions reached above, and it confirms that nowhere on the case of the clock is there either a name or a number.

Compiled by C.R.P. Allix

Notes by J.B. Hawkins
This clock, identical in almost every respect to the next two items, thanks to Mr. Allix's researches, cannot be manufactured earlier than 1905.

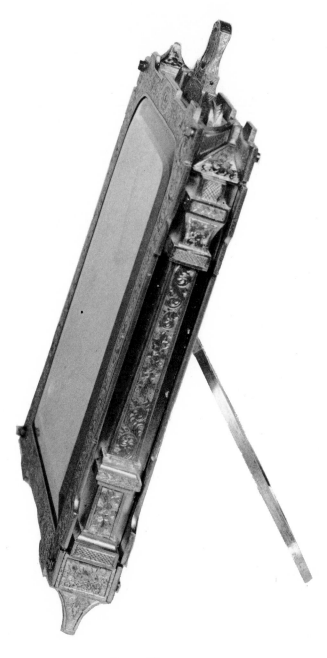

Item 58

Item 58

3

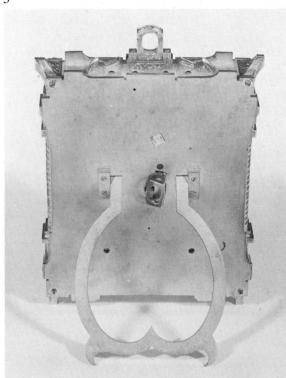

4

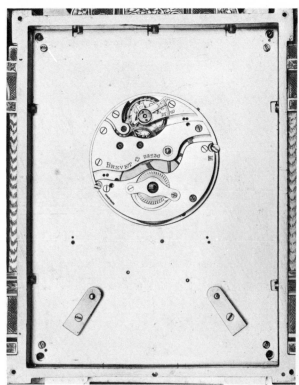

5

Item 58

ITEM 59

Eight day strut clock with mechanically operated calendar showing day of the week and date of the month, in its original travelling box with no retailer's name.
Hands: Fleur de Lis.
Dial: Silvered and engraved with a symmetrical pattern similar to the previous item.
Additional Features: As per the previous item.
Duration: Eight days.
Signature: E. White, 19 Jermyn Street, London W.1.
Serial No: Nil.
Collection: Private Collection, Australia.

ITEM 60

With minor variations to the engraving, this clock is identical to the previous two items, the dial covers are the same and the four leaf engraved pattern occurs somewhere on the dial of each clock. They all have the same method of support, and identical backs with a similar method of shutter operation to keep the dust out of the movement. This particular clock is slightly more complicated in that it has a monthly calendar, a date calendar and a day calendar, all operated from the movement. It still retains its original fitted travelling box with the retailer's name, Asprey, which indicates that the clock must have been constructed between 1905-06. Signed E. White, 19 Jermyn St., London. SW.
Collection: J. Altmann, Melbourne.

W. VASEL, LONDON

ITEM 61

Vasel was a late Victorian clockmaker of repute. Illustrated are two clocks very much in the manner of Cole but lacking his attention to detail. Vasel's working dates are given below.

1886 (first entry)	Vasel, Wilhelm, watchmaker, 21 Howland Street, Fitzroy Square
1887-88	Vasel, Wilhelm, watchmaker, 41 Howland Street, Fitzroy Square
1889-1907 (last entry)	Vasel, Wilhelm, watchmaker, 32 Brewer Street, Golden Square

This clock signed W. Vasel London is a copy of the clock on the compendium for the writing table see page 138. It is stamped W. Vasel, London and the original travelling case bears the retailers name Frazer and Haws 31 Regent Street. Standing 5½″ high, it would date circa 1900.

ITEM 62

The cheval clock illustrated is a direct copy of Item No. 41 both in the dial shape and the supports for the clock movement. However, it completely lacks the finish imparted by Cole. It is interesting that on both the dial plate and concealed on one of the construction plates, may be found stamped the name of W. Vasel in much the same way as the secret stamps of Cole are hidden somewhere in the construction. The standard of the engraving is quite high, however, the layered construction to the body of the clock is deficient, there being only one plate to cover the movement whereas in Item No. 41 there are four. The little drawer in the base with a well engraved interior must, I am sure, have been designed to take the key which, however, is not required in such a late clock.

Movement: A lever escapement eight day movement, from its design and construction made circa 1900.
Hands: Fleur de Lis.
Dial: Silvered and engraved with bunches of flowers, painted numbers.
Additional Features: Nil.
Duration: Eight days.
Signed: Secret signature, stamped twice, W. Vasel, London.
Number: Nil.
Dimensions: 21 cm high, handle up × 15 cm wide.
Date: Circa 1900.
Collection: Private collection, Australia.

Item 62

E.W. ROBINS, LONDON

I stated under E.W. Robins on page 29, that there may in the future be an interesting connection between this maker and Cole. The strut clock illustrated in the March 1974 edition of the Antique Collectors Guide has only just come to hand and the notes concerning this clock form a last minute addition to this book.

Stylistically, there are many similarities between the work of Robins and that of Cole. It is my opinion that Robins purposely set out to imitate the work of Thomas Cole.

The strut clock illustrated has the two methods of support used by Cole, the angled strut to the rear and the turn buckle foot to the base. The pierced dial cover is not a design Cole would have used at this period, however, it is reminiscent of the large pierced borders to standing strut clocks. The case engraving with the lined background is very Cole in feeling as is the use of the bracketed carrying handle to the top and the fleur de lis hands.

The use of Germanic Gothic chapters has been noted on a small carriage clock with up and down regulator. The signature on the dial reads 'Charles Frodsham, 84 Strand, Clockmaker to the Queen', the movement being signed Arnold and Frodsham, see illustration. These two clocks bear many similarities and it is my opinion that they were both made by Robins, one sold under his own name, the small carriage clock being retailed by the firm of Charles Frodsham.

In 'Carriage Clocks' by Allix and Bonnert on page 270, Mr. Allix states that "It would seem that Charles Frodsham was able to take over Vulliamy's Royal Appointment with his business in 1854." Robins working dates, see entry under retailers, are from 1857-59 in London. This clock, despite having the movement signed Arnold and Frodsham, falls neatly into this period. It may be that Robins initially worked for Cole before starting his own business circa 1856/57 but found that his previous master's competition was such that he had to retire to Maldon in Essex.

I have seen at least two more strut clocks by Robins, both of which were unsigned. They also had the Germanic Gothic chapters and the peculiarity that in one, the whole of the back of the case was engraved and in the other, the flap which opens to disclose the escapement only was engraved, as per this strut clock. Maybe the engraving of the back of the case in one way or another was a Robins feature. The cases of Robins strut clocks are always rounded at the top, whereas in Cole's work, the top of the clock always terminates in the horizontal.

ITEM 63

Movement: The movement, while superficially like the work of Cole, becomes steadily more unconvincing. The dial is attached to the movement by four feet in the standard English clock practice manner. So far as I know, Cole never did this. There are other detail differences. For instance:

In this clock only the barrel arbor and intermediate pinion run in the main frames. The barrel arbor is a coarse affair contrasting strongly with the beautiful finish bestowed by Cole on this never-seen part. Cole used to make both pivots of his barrel arbor the same size which was most unusual. The two pivots of the Robins barrel arbor are of quite different diameters. Robins attaches his pillars to the back plate and they are pinned in the clear space "under the dial". This space does not exist in Cole strut clocks in order to keep them slim.

Hands: Typical Cole type fleur de lis.

Dial: Silvered with Germanic Gothic chapters.

Additional Features: A much simplified case construction using very few parts. The Robins clock uses steady-pins in the case construction, and in this respect it is easier to assemble than some of Cole's work. Also Robins' bow-strut has a far better designed and more reliable "flip-up" spring than the design favoured by Cole. Robins' back door opens down like Cole's to show the escapement, but

Robins uses his own form of latch and no "flip-up" spring. In addition to the bow strut there is a turnbuckle foot with detent. No. 3033 is punched on the middle of the case, on the back panel, on the back of the dial, on the back of the spacer-plate between the dial and the mask, on the back of the mask and on the back of the bezel. There is no number anywhere on the movement. The silvered dial has the painted inscription "E.W. Robins London, 28 Queen's Road Bayswater". Note how very badly the dial is divided. Steady pins are also used to locate the mask and spacer-plate in relation to the dial, and also to locate the bezel in relation to the middle case casting.

Duration: Eight days.
Signed: E.W. Robins London, 28 Queen's Road, Bayswater.
Number: 3033 — this is not a Cole number.
Dimensions: 18 cm high × 12 cm wide — the standard dimensions of Cole strut clocks of this shape.
Date: Circa 1858.
Collection: Private collection, England.
Illustrations: (Below) Front of clock. (1) Movement. (2) Showing rear of case and engraving, bezel and pierced dial cover. (3) Carriage clock in the manner of E.W. Robins, retailed by Charles Frodsham, 84 Strand.

By courtesy Algernon Asprey, London

BIBLIOGRAPHY

The reference sources for the biography of Thomas Cole and his brother are to be found on Page 16. At various stages, references have been noted in the text; these and the books, periodicals and pamphlets consulted in the production of this book have been consolidated hereunder. Only sources that provided something tangible have been noted so the extent of this bibliography is limited to published material on Thomas Cole which is virtually non-existent.

Allix, C.R.P. and
illustrated Bonnert P.   Carriage Clocks, Woodbridge 1975.

Baille, G.H.   Watchmakers and Clockmakers of the World, London, 1947.

Borsendorf, L.   Un Coup de Loupe a L'Exposition, Universelle de 1855, Paris 1855.

Britten, F.J.   Former Clock and Watchmakers of the World, London 1894. This is the best source reference for London clockmakers 1800-1870. Gives addresses and working dates with fair accuracy.

Buggins, G.T.E. and Turner, A.J.   The article in Antiquarian Horology September 1973, relating to the production, identification and dating of clocks by A. and J. Thwaites. It is interesting to compare Thwaite's rate of production from their numbering system and the number of people employed, with that of Cole. Thwaite's rate of production from 1804 to 1841 would average twice that of Cole's.

Christie, Manson & Woods, London   Auction catalogues, 1964-75.

Sotheby's & Co. London   Auction catalogues. Reading between the lines so as to identify Cole's work as and when it appears in the London Rooms from 1968-75, 21 Cole clocks have been sold under the guise of various retailers.

Clutton, C and Daniels, G.   Watches, London 1965. Three Hunt and Roskell watches — 514-15, 525-6, 537-8 — possibly made by Sylvan Mairet for this firm as retailers. They obviously used the top craftsmen to manufacture for them.

Daniels, G   The Art of Breguet, London 1974. The Cole brothers' carriage clock, bears many similarities to the Breguet clock on pages 251 - 2 and sold in 1826. It is interesting to note that all Breguet hump backed carriage clocks illustrated, have their escapements in the vertical position.

Gould, R.T.   The Marine Chronometer, London 1923. Descriptions of various escapements by J.F. Cole.

Great Exhibition 1851   Official Descriptive and Illustrated Catalogue. The horological sections have been reprinted, Appendix A and B. Note should be made of the large London retailers and their horological stock in compiling information on 19th century clockmakers.

Great Exhibition 1851   The Crystal Palace Exhibition Illustrated Catalogue published by the Art Journal 1851. Reprint, Dover Books, 1970, contains line drawing of Cole's Compendium for the Writing Table, page 111.

Horological Journal   November 1896, Cole's Spring Remontoire Escapement.
                                     June 1913, Obituary Notice of Samuel Gaze's son, James.

International Exhibition, 1862   Illustrated Catalogue of the Industrial Department. The Horological Sections have been reprinted as Appendix D and E. Note should be made of the large London retailers and their horological stock in compiling information on 19th century clockmakers.

London Trade Directories   Johnstons, Critchett and Woods, Pigots. A search of the Rate books was not conducted for the Retailers of Cole's work.

Salomons, Sir David   Breguet (1747-1823), London 1921.

"Tardy" (Henri Langelle)   La Pendule Francaise, Vol. II, page 445. Drawing of Cole's escapement.

Chamberlain, Paul M.   Its About Time. Most interesting section on J.F. Cole, full of tantalising innuendo.

Tallis, John   London Street Views, 1838-40. A fine book for identifying the actual location of many of the retailers listed in this book. The book comprises the frontages as line drawings of the principal West End London streets.

EXTRACTS FROM EXHIBITION CATALOGUES

During research into Thomas Cole's work, I have had recourse to various international exhibition catalogues. These are now to be found only in public libraries and come in vast heavy volumes. To facilitate research and provide a contemporary background for Cole in terms of what other makers were doing, I have extracted photographically the Horological sections and Jurors Reports from the 1851 and 1862 London Exhibitions and the Exhibitors list from the 1855 Paris Exhibition. These are the three major exhibitions at which Cole exhibited.

A complete book could be written around these extracts but the aims of Victorian horology are spelt out in the Jurors Reports.

These appendices for the first time consolidate as an easy form of reference the exhibits, exhibitors and jurors reports of the London 1851 and 1862 exhibitions.

Appendix A — Official Descriptive and Illustrated Catalogue of the 1851 Crystal Palace Exhibition, Volume I Section II, Class 10, p404 to p423.

Appendix B — Official Descriptive and Illustrated Catalogue of the 1851 Crystal Palace Exhibition, "Report on Horological Instruments, Class XB, p731 to p745.

Appendix C — The English exhibitors in the Paris Exhibition of 1855 extracted from 'Paris Universal Exhibition 1855, Catalogue of the British Section Class VIII, Section 2, Clockwork'

Appendix D — Official Illustrated Catalogue of the International Exhibition 1862, British Division Vol. I, Class XV, Horological Instruments, p65 to p86.

Appendix E — Official Illustrated Catalogue of the International Exhibition 1862, British Division Vol. III, Class XV, Horological Instruments, Jurors Reports, p1 to p21.

APPENDIX A

SECT. II. — CLASS 10.

PHILOSOPHICAL, MUSICAL, HOROLOGICAL, AND SURGICAL INSTRUMENTS.

INTRODUCTION.

THE advance of physical science receives its illustration in a variety of directions among the objects collected together under this Class. The progress of experimental philosophy may be gathered, in a degree, from the perfection of the instruments it employs; for while it is certain that in some sciences much has been accomplished by the aid of rude and imperfect means, it is equally true that in others the perfection of the apparatus is essential to that of the knowledge sought to be established by deductions drawn from its indications. The delicacy of a balance is necessary to the accuracy of a chemical experiment, and therefore to that of the facts it is used to develop, as also is the achromatism of a microscope, or a photographic lens to the development of the optical images, and to the results sought to be obtained therefrom: chemistry, microscopical sciences, and photography, are consequently largely dependent for their progress upon the instruments by the use of which they are to proceed. The same cannot be said of surgical instruments, for in their use the operator may command success by his skill, notwithstanding the imperfections of his apparatus. Nevertheless, the present state of surgery, and the attention bestowed upon it, may be gathered from the inspection of the refined and complicated apparatus offered for its advancement. As one of the results of the splendid and enduring system of knowledge, and of its pursuits—promulgated by Bacon in the "Novum Organon," the system since called Experimental Philosophy—objects in this Class wear a peculiar interest, representing the means employed by man for the establishment and development of inductive science.

This Class includes instruments employed for a variety of philosophical purposes; it also comprises musical, horological, and surgical instruments and apparatus. It may consequently be considered under three Sub-Classes. The first comprehends—A. Instruments for the measurement of space, such as Transit Instruments, Quadrants, Sextants, Telescopes, Microscopes, Theodolites, &c.; B. Instruments to measure the effects of mechanical and physical forces, as Dynamometers, Balances, Thermometers, &c.; C. Instruments to illustrate the Laws of Mechanical and Physical Science; D. Application of mechanical and physical science to useful purposes not included in any of the preceding or subsequent sections, such as instruments connected with Mechanics, Sound, Light, Heat, Magnetism, and Electricity; E. Comprehends Chemical and Pharmaceutical Apparatus. The Sub-Class, Musical Instruments, comprises—A. Wind Instruments, in wood and metal, as Flutes, Bassoons, Horns, Trumpets, &c.; B. Stringed Instruments, as Harps, Guitars, &c.; C. Keyed Instruments, with fixed tones, such as Organs, Pianofortes, Accordions; D. Instruments of percussion, as Drums and Cymbals; E. Automatic Instruments; and F. Miscellaneous articles in connexion with musical instruments. The Sub-Class, Horology, contains—A. Great Clocks for Churches and Public Buildings in general, including Electric or Magneto-Electric Clocks; B. Astronomical Clocks; C. Clocks applied in registration; D. Clocks showing different phenomena; E. Clocks for ordinary purposes; F. Clocks of an ornamental description; G. Sundries applicable to Clocks; H. Marine Chronometers; I. Pocket watches of various descriptions; J. Watches for different markets. The remaining Sub-Class, Surgical Instruments, includes a variety of apparatus adapted to the performance of operations in different parts of the human body, together with the philosophical apparatus employed by the surgeon in the investigation and treatment of disease. It also embraces the instruments employed in Veterinary Surgery.

The large astronomical telescope in the Nave, mounted upon a stand, having equatorial movements and complete adjustments, is an interesting member of this Class. It is a refracting instrument, and possesses an object-glass nearly 12 inches in diameter. Telescopes of a smaller calibre, and adapted for different purposes, are also exhibited near it. But the general arrangement of the objects representative of this Class is to be sought in the Central North Gallery. This gallery is reached by ascending the stairs near the North Transept. On entering it, and proceeding past the articles in glass, which are also placed here, the commencement of this Class is met with at Area I. 22. From this point it extends to the western termination of this gallery. The interspace between the North and South Central Galleries is also devoted to it, and a portion of the South Central Gallery, from M. 3 to M. 8, contains various articles included in this Class. Proceeding westward, in the Central North Gallery, musical instruments are first encountered, including a variety of organs, harps, pianos, &c. Succeeding to these are philosophical instruments, electric telegraphs, daguerreotype apparatus, and specimens of photography: beyond are globes and astronomical apparatus. In the South Central Gallery are watches and clocks. A part of the North Gallery, devoted to surgical instruments, and occupying the space between F. 15 and F. 21, also belongs to this Class.

PHILOSOPHICAL, MUSICAL, HOROLOGICAL, &c.
NORTH, NORTH CENTRAL, AND SOUTH CENTRAL GALLERIES.

405

The science of horology is illustrated on the great as well as on the small scale in the large clocks and the minute chronometers exhibited in this Class. The large electric clock, the hands of which are seen projecting over the south entrance of the Transept, is an interesting example of the application of the force of electro-magnetism to move mechanical arrangement for the measurement of time. A small galvanic battery keeps this large instrument, and several other clocks in the Building, in regular movement. The ribs of the Transept have been made to represent the dial, and show the hours from 6 A.M. to 6 P.M. Other electric clocks on a smaller scale are shown, and exhibit various ingenious arrangements intended to effect the same end. Self-registering, astronomical, and other clocks are likewise exhibited. In some of the large clocks for churches and public buildings, one of which is in the Nave, and others are at the termination of the Galleries, new principles of suspension and compensation of the pendulum and of escapement are introduced. Much ingenuity has often been expended upon clocks with a view of communicating to them the power of indicating, in addition to ordinary time, that of different places, and of different periodical occurrences, as the rise and fall of the tide, the day of the month, &c. Several of these clocks are shown, and particularly one which occupied its patient constructor thirty-four years in its manufacture. The watches and chronometers exhibited have also their peculiar claims to attention. The escapements of some of the latter are in part new, and appear to promise favourable results. Several different specimens of watches, adapted for different markets, afford a curious illustration of the variation of natural tastes—the variety of methods in which compensation for the changes resulting from variations of temperature is obtained both in chronometers and in astronomical and other clocks. Extremely small watches, as specimens of minute workmanship, are exhibited. The parts of watches and clocks are likewise included in this Class.

The philosophical instruments exhibited comprise a large number connected with the display of the phenomena of heat and electricity: the aneroid barometer, in which the mercurial column is dispensed with, and various forms of the ordinary barometer are among them. Electric communications are now effected by a variety of apparatus of greater or less facility of application. Printing electric telegraphs, in which a message is recorded by this agency, upon a chemically-prepared paper, appear in various forms with the ordinary needle telegraph. The methods of electric insulation for telegraph uses are also exhibited. Among these will be regarded with interest the wires adapted for submarine communication between this country and the Continent. The magnetic and electric machines, with electro-magnets of great power, are also interesting.

British manufacturers have for some time been making great efforts with a view of producing good optical glass, and a skilful method of working it into the forms desired for optical purposes. These efforts have been so highly successful that the glass produced in England is not unfrequently exported and again re-imported as foreign glass at a much higher price. The production of lenses has also greatly improved; and achromatic glasses of considerable size, as well as of a smaller kind, are made with success in this country. Microscopes, telescopes, and the minor philosophical instruments, are now of excellent quality and highly-wrought character.

Photography is included in this Class, both on plates of silver and glass, and on paper. The most beautiful specimens of sun-drawn pictures are exhibited. Daguerreotypes of every kind, plain and coloured, "enamelled," and "crayon,"—improvements of recent introduction, and applied to a variety of purposes,—are found here. The largest daguerreotype probably yet produced, a group of sculpture, is placed in this Class. The Talbotypes are also very beautiful, and present a charming evidence of the fidelity and artistic effects capable of being produced by the pencil of Nature. Photographic apparatus of various kinds, together with the results of curious photographic experiments, illustrative of the distinct existence of luminous and actinic rays in the solar beam, are also represented.

A great variety of miscellaneous philosophical apparatus, for popular illustration, and for the purposes of the experimentalist, is also displayed, and must attract notice. The musical instruments exhibited, include several powerful organs. That over the West Entrance possesses 80 stops. The organ over the Eastern Entrance exhibits a new and pleasing arrangement of pipes, and possesses a powerful set of stops. The organ over the South Transept Entrance is devoid of a case, and exhibits the internal mechanism; it possesses a powerful reed stop, and other stops. Pianos, harps, seraphines, of new modes of construction, and decorated in a remarkable manner, are likewise found here. The instruments of the surgeon have a purely professional value, and will be sought by those interested in that pursuit.

Regarding this Class as representing the culminating point of mechanical skill, it forms an appropriate conclusion to those devoted to machinery generally. Delicacy and precision of workmanship are absolutely requisite in the industry occupied in producing philosophical apparatus. It will be found, on inspection, that the genius of this country, so remarkably developed in mechanics applied to commercial purposes, is not less successful in its application to the higher pursuits of experimental and practical philosophy.—R. E.

1   BENNETT, JOHN, 65 *Cheapside*—Inventor and
        Manufacturer.

A regulator, which beats half-seconds, with mercurial
pendulum; adapted for reading-rooms, railway stations,
and other places where an exact time-keeper is required
at a small expense, and where economy of space is an
object.

Hall clock—in a carved oak case, of new design;
chiming the quarters, and striking the hours on a gong.

Finished specimen of marine chronometer.

Model watch on a magnified scale; constructed to show
the most compact form of the modern watch, with all
the recent improvements; to which is attached a peculiar
mode of regulation, by which the wearer, with one touch
of the regulator (fixed on an endless screw) can correct
any variation of time.

Model watches in gold cases for pocket use; jewelled
in thirteen holes. Comprising, in a simple form, essentials
for its correct performance in all climates; with a gold
chain of new design. Exhibited to show the introduction of a variety of ornamental detail, coloured by means
of different bases of alloy, without the aid of either
enamel or precious stones.

Time-keeper, for railway guards, constructed to combine cheapness, strength, and exact performance.

Specimens of standard thermometers, with ivory and
box-wood scales.

Bennett's registered illuminated night timepiece, attached to a Palmer's candle lamp, by the burning of
which a spring gives motion to the hands of the dial with
great exactness.

Carriage clock, in rosewood case, with detached lever
escapements and compensation balance.

A regulator, beating dead seconds, with mercurial pendulum, in the simplest form of case and movement com-
patible with strict nicety of performance.

Cathedral clock dial of plate-glass, and of new design;
weather-proof; with a movement in action.

A wind dial in action from a vane above the roof of the
Exhibition Building, with a self-recording machine for
registering the wind's force.

2   ADAMS, F. B., & SONS, 21 *St. John's Square,
        Clerkenwell*—Manufacturers.

No. 1. Gold open-face, double-back, cased watch;
enamel dial, first class, full plate movement, lever escapement, capped, eight holes jewelled, and compensated
balance, &c. This description of watch is used in the
northern states of America.

No. 2. Similar watch, with gold dial. This is made at
one-third the cost of Nos. 1, 3, or 8.

No. 3. Gold watch; enamel dial, first class, three-
quarter plate movement, duplex escapement, ten holes
jewelled, compensated balance, &c.

No. 4. Watch like the preceding; three-quarter plate
movement, lever escapement, five holes jewelled, and
gold balance.

Nos. 5, 6, 7, 8. Gold watches; first class, three-quarter
plate movement, lever escapement, full jewelled, compensated balance, &c.

Nos. 9, 10. Gold watches; gold dial, full plate movement, lever escapement, jewelled, plain balance (for
ladies.)

Nos. 11, 12. Gold watches; first class, three-quarter
plate movements, lever escapement, eight holes jewelled,
compensated balance, cases enamelled, and ornamented
with diamonds.

No. 13. Gold watch; enamel dial, showing seconds
from the centre, without additional train.

No. 14. Gold, engraved, double-back, hunter-cased
watch; first class, three-quarter plate movement, duplex
escapement, twelve holes jewelled, compensated balance.
This description of watch is used in the East Indies,
Persia, Spain, and South America.

No. 15. Silver, open face, double-back, cased watch;
lever escapement, capped, and four holes jewelled.

No. 16. Silver hunter engine-turned watch, vertical
escapement.

No. 17. Silver pair of case watch; vertical escapement.

Nos. 15, 16, and 17, are used by artizans and labourers.

No. 18. A three-quarter plate finished movement lever
escapement; eight holes jewelled, gold balance. This description of movement is adopted for the purpose of obtaining a thin watch.

No. 19. A full plate finished movement, lever escapement, eight holes jewelled, compensation balance, &c.

No. 20. A finished movement, vertical escapement.

The same workmen, in their various branches, were
employed upon No. 1, the largest, and No. 11, the
smallest of these watches.

3   OLORENSHAW, JOSEPH, and Co., 15 *Northampton Square,
        Clerkenwell, London, and Oxford Terrace, Coventry*—
        Manufacturers.

Two-day marine chronometer.

Specimens of gold and silver watches and watch movements in three-quarter and full plates, with duplex, patent
diamonds, and detached lever escapements. Variously
jewelled and finished.

4   ORDNANCE SURVEY DEPARTMENT.—Lieut.-Col. HALL
        —Producer.

Base-measuring Apparatus.—Two compensation bars, and
one connecting compensation microscope.

These compensation bars and microscope form part of
a base-measuring apparatus, invented by Major-General
Colby, Royal Engineers, formerly Superintendent of the
Ordnance Survey.

Description of Compensation Bar.—1. The compensation
bar consists of two bars of brass and iron, 10 feet 1·5 inch
long, 0·5 inch broad, and 1·5 inch deep, placed 1·125
inch apart, supported on brass rollers, at one-fourth and
three-fourths of their length, and firmly fixed together
at their centres by transverse steel cylinders 1·5 inch
in diameter, and being free to expand from or contract
towards their centres independently of each other. At the
extremity of, and at right angles to, each of these bars is
a flat steel tongue, 6·2 inches long, 1·1 inch broad, and
0·25 inch thick; projecting 3·25 inches on the side of the
iron bar, and moving freely on conical brass pivots, rivetted
into the brass and iron bars, each axis being perpendicular
to the surface of the tongue, allowing it to be inclined at
slightly different angles to these bars according to their
expansion from, or contraction to, their centres. The
centres of the two axes are at 0·5 inch and 2·3 inches from
the end of the tongue next the brass bar. On the tongue,
and flush with its upper surface, near the extremity, is
inserted a silver pin, with a dot marked on it, as the compensation point.

The bars are placed in wooden boxes (made of well-
seasoned straight-grained deal), to the bottoms of which
are fixed the plates that hold the brass rollers on which
they are supported, and having in the middle a vertical
brass stay, screwed to the box, and passing upwards between two steel cylinders, to prevent the bars being
moved longitudinally in their casing. To protect the
tongue carrying the compensated point (which projects
beyond the wooden box) from injury, nozzles are fixed to
the boxes, having a small circular orifice with a lid on the
upper side to allow the dot, or compensation point, to be
seen.

On one side of the connecting steel cylinders, and attached to the brass bar only, is placed the longitudinal
level, the lid of the box being furnished with a glass
window and shutter, to enable it to be observed. Over the
rollers which support the bars are two pieces of metal, for
preventing any sudden jar from striking the bars against
the lid of the box. At each end, on the outside of the
bar-box a thick metal plate is screwed, for the purpose of
firmly fixing a three-armed groove-stand, intended to support the tripod of the compensation microscope; and at
each end of the box are two vane sights (which shut
down with hinges into grooves), used for placing the
bars approximately in line.

On both sides, at one-fourth and three-fourths of the length, are brass plates, with holes for receiving the screw which clamps the plate of the tripod-stand (technically called a *camel*) to the box, for the purpose of adjusting the bar in a longitudinal direction. The compensation bars are six in number; the weight of each bar, with its two brass ends, is 136 lbs.

Description of Compensation Microscope.—2. The compensation microscope consists of three microscopes, placed three inches from centre to centre, connected by two bars of brass and iron, 7 inches long, 0·6 inch broad, and 0·375 inch thick, 2·5 inches apart, firmly secured together by means of a brass collar and cylinder, forming part of the tube of the centre or telescopic microscope.

The two bars, carrying with them the outer microscopes, of two inches focal distance, being free to expand from, and contract towards, the central microscope, independently of each other; and thereby forming with it small angles of inclination similar to the steel tongues of the compensation bars. The compensated point of each is so adjusted as to be in the outer focus of its object glass. The microscopes revolve on the axis of the telescopic microscope in a tube fastened to a horizontal plate attached to a tripod-stand with levelling screws, and furnished with longitudinal and lateral adjusting screws. On one side, secured to the brass bar, is the spirit-level, for levelling the microscopes, and on the other, firmly fixed to the centres of the bars by a brass plate, is a telescope, embraced by a brass collar, with a small cylinder projecting from one side, which turns in a socket attached to the plate; thus affording it a vertical motion, allowing objects to be seen in opposite directions. The telescopic microscope is provided with an adjusting screw, for altering the focal distance within certain limits, as well as moveable object glasses of different focal lengths fitting into the lower end of the tube. The compensation microscopes are seven in number, the weight of each being 7 lbs.

[All the methods adopted in the measurement of base lines in trigonometrical surveys which had been in use previous to the survey of Ireland, depended more or less for their accuracy on the knowledge of the temperature of the bars, &c., used in measuring; but as the time which substances occupy in heating or cooling is dependent upon their nature, mass, &c., it did not appear that any application of thermometers would give the true temperature of a bar throughout its whole length, particularly when the temperature of the air itself was undergoing constant change.

This circumstance led to the application of the principle of compensation used in gridiron pendulums, to devising an apparatus for measuring a base line. As metals have different capacities for heat, and their surfaces have different powers of radiation, experiments were made to equalize the effects of varying temperature in the brass and iron bars; and for this purpose the brass bars were bronzed and varnished, and the iron bars were browned, lacquered, and smoked, and the amount of lamp-black so produced was gradually removed, on successive experiments, till the desired effect was obtained. —J. G.]

---

5   AIREY, THOMAS, 67 *Dale Street, Liverpool.*

Two gold centre seconds with compound independent seconds, and only one train of wheels.

---

6   VEITCH, JAMES, 6 *Ovington Square, Brompton*— Inventor.

An invention denominated the medico-chirurgical ambulance, for surgical use on the field of battle, with an operating table attached thereto. The solid structure is 3 feet 4 inches in length, 2 feet in breadth, to which there is affixed an inclined plane to raise the shoulders when required. The flap is 2 feet 6 inches in length, and of the same breadth as the solid structure, and is supported when necessary by a moveable beam that can be promptly projected from under the table, which is 2 feet 11 inches in height. Under the body of the table and in the centre there is a square box of 16 inches in all directions, with 4 exterior and lateral divis ons of 2 inches in breadth each, 16 inches in length, and 8 in depth, for receiving the cases of amputating, trepanning, miscellaneous, and cupping instruments, and they are exteriorly so marked. When amputation of the thigh, or any other extremity is required, the necessary instruments are laid out on the inside of the cover of the box just adverted to, beginning with the letter nearest to the limb to be removed, the first instrument wanted to be placed opposite A, and the second opposite B, and so on, according to the order in which they are required during the operation. If a shoulder is to be removed, the same arrangements are to be adopted as in the amputation of a thigh, with the difference of placing the instruments at the head instead of the lower extremity of the table. The divisions in the centre are intended to receive bandages of 6, of 5, of 4, and 3 yards in length, and 3 inches in breadth, and they are capable of giving accommodation to 200 of the description noticed. The drawers in front marked ligatures are intended to keep these essential agents of surgery in constant readiness. The drawers marked slips of adhesive plaister indicate the propriety of their being at all times in readiness for operations and wounds. The compartment marked fractures is for keeping the splints and bandages necessary for the treatment of such accidents. The department marked dislocations indicates that all instruments required for the reduction of such dislocations are there to be found.

---

7   HUTTON, JOHN, 9 *Lucas Place, Commercial Road East* —Inventor and Manufacturer.

Lady's gold watch, with patent single compensation stud. Gold watch, and silver lever and silver hunting-watches, with the same improvement.

Clock, with patent compensation pendulum and barometric contrivance, to prevent the variation of rate arising from the changes in the density of the atmosphere.

Marine chronometer, with patent pneumatic auxiliary compensation, for obviating errors in extremes of temperatures; this is effected by means of a metallic thermometer, which varies the air space in which the balance oscillates.

Gold first class watch (called Hutton's patent lever chronometer).

Patent lever escapement, showing the parts separately.

Silver pocket chronometer, with improved adjustments.

Gold first class watch, with patent escapement and spiral spring.

Gold watch, with patent double compensation spring, stud and patent escapement; adapted for riding, &c.

---

8   CRAGG, JOHN, 8 *Northampton Square, Clerkenwell* —Manufacturer.

Varieties of gold and silver watches, and a model of lever movement.

---

9   YATES, THOMAS, *Preston*—Inventor, Patentee, and Manufacturer.

Patent clock, on the detached dead-beat principle. The wheel-work is so arranged that each vibration of the balance measures half a second, while in the ordinary detached lever each vibration measures a quarter of a second. The teeth of the escape-wheel are not so much undercut as in the ordinary lever. The pallets from the point of rest are drawn a complete circle to the escape-wheel teeth; so that when the balance returns and unlocks the escapement, there is no recoil. This escapement will carry a heavier balance with less motive power, and consequently will require a stronger balance-spring.

Gold watch, beating dead half-seconds.

10 LOWRY, S., 3 *Lower Charles Street, Northampton Square, Clerkenwell*—Inventor and Manufacturer.

Lever watch, to show dead seconds on the one train only, with the usual number of vibrations or beats. Invented and registered by the exhibitor.

Gold chronometer, with compensation balance, isochronal spiral, spring rated, and adjusted with other modern improvements.

Model of the chronometer, or detached escapement, on an enlarged scale.

Small watch, with compensation balance, hard pendulum spring, &c. Plain lever watch.

Movements of different watches in their rough and finished state.

Marine chronometers, &c., to show dead and complete seconds on the ordinary train.

11 CONNELL, WILLIAM, 83 *Cheapside*—Manufacturer.

Pair of two-day marine chronometers, Earnshaw's detached escapements; compound balance adjusted for high temperatures.

12 LOSEBY, E. T., 44 *Gerrard Street, Islington*—Inventor.

Mercurial compensation balance, exhibiting four modifications.

A regulator, illustrating a new principle in clocks, and showing an improved form of mercurial pendulum.

An arc compensation.

13 HOLL, FREDERICK RICHARD, 8 *Weymouth Terrace, City Road*—Inventor, Patentee, and Manufacturer.

Gold index pocket-chronometer, with short angle-locking spring to the escapement, set-hands at the pendant.

Gold centre seconds eight-day pocket chronometer, independent seconds, train, and stop work, with left-sided, short, angle-locking spring to the escapement.

Silver thirty-hour pocket chronometer, with right-sided short angle-locking spring, &c.

Gold compensated duplex index watch, gold dial, set-hands at the pendant.

Gold compensated lever index watch.

Gold lever index watch (lady's), gold dial.

Silver lever index watch, set-hands on the dial, with a key, locking spring.

The object of the short angle-locking spring is to make the angle of the escapement so short that the balance, being more detached, the chronometer cannot stop in the pocket from the balance receiving a motion.

The index watches are a new invention, intended to answer the double purpose of supplying a lever to bend the main-spring, and also to indicate the number of hours the watch will go before the power is exhausted.

Gold centre seconds eight-day pocket chronometer, independent seconds train and stop work.

Silver thirty-hour pocket chronometer.

Gold compensated duplex index watches.

Gold and silver lever index watches.

Index watches, upon a new principle, kept going from day to day by simply pushing the index.

14 ADAMS, THOMAS, 36 *Lombard Street*—Manufacturer.

Black marble timepiece, of chronometrical movement, blending the Grecian and Egyptian styles.

Black Marble Timepiece, by Adams.

Imitation oak timepiece represented in the following engraving.

Timepiece, with self-acting model of the Royal Observatory, with staff and ball, to rise and drop at one o'clock, as at Greenwich. Marine chronometer.

16 HOWELL, JAMES, & Co., 9 *Regent Street*—Manufacturers.

Large or-molu clock, representing Jupiter, the twelve Hours of the Sun, Apollo, and Diana, and Spring and Autumn strewing flowers and fruit on the earth.

Imitation Oak Timepiece, by Adams.

Or-molu clock, representing the four Ages by female figures, and the Seasons by boys, in basso-relievo, and intermingled with foliage, illustrative of the Seasons.

Both designed and modelled by G. G. Adams, Esq.

17 WEBSTER, RICHARD, jun., 74 *Cornhill*—Inventor and Manufacturer.

Newly-invented train remontoir clock, the novelty of which is the combination of magnetism with clockwork so as to obviate friction.

Black marble Egyptian clock.

18 VENTURA, ANGELO BENEDETTO, 17 *Charles Street, Cavendish Square*—Inventor and Manufacturer.

Harp Ventura, played like the guitar, combining the tone of that instrument and the harp. Lyra Ventura. New British Ventura. The Venturina. Ventura; new English Cetra.

19 DELOLME, HENRY, 48 *Rathbone Place, Oxford Street*—Designer and Manufacturer.

Seven gold watches, and two marine chronometers, with isochronous pendulum springs. The adjoining cut represents one of the chronometers.

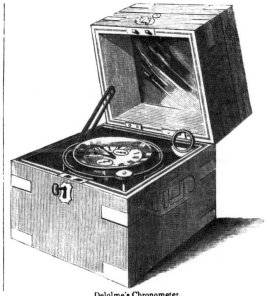

Delolme's Chronometer.

3 M

Specimen of the movements of the preceding, as made in Lancashire to the exhibitor's calibre.

Two specimens of watch movements, to the exhibitor's calibre.

Stethometer, to measure the comparative mobility of the chest in cases of disease of the lungs.

[The effect of most diseases of the lungs is to diminish the extent of the motion of the walls of the chest. It becomes consequently often of considerable importance to ascertain the amount of variation from health in this respect, since this points out, with approximative accuracy, the extent of the disease. The diminished mobility of one side as compared with its opposite thus affords important results. The method of measuring and recording these changes by an index registration was first adopted by Dr. Sibson, F.R.S. The present instrument, designed by Dr. Quain with the same object, is of very simple construction, and consists essentially of a dial-plate with a moveable index. which is acted on by the pressure of the sides of the chest on a cord which is made to extend around, or from one point to another of the walls of the chest.—R. E.]

20   NEWINGTON, S., *Hastings*—Inventor.

Patent clock, or regulator. A common clock with spring and balance-wheel; having the hands and dial-plate removed, and a dial substituted, which revolves in the same way as an hour-hand. This clock is placed in a flat round box, and is arranged to show whether a person has been at a particular spot at any required time.

21   GIBBS, H., 2 *Nelson Street, City Road*—Maker.

Watch, showing double time, with improved stop-work.

22   PHILCOX, GEORGE, 89 *Great Norfolk Street, Borough*—Inventor and Patentee.

Patent marine time-keeper. This time-keeper is intended to give correct time in taking observations, where a chronometer is not at hand, or as a companion to a chronometer. It is adapted for use in locomotive railway engines, to show the engineer the rate of his speed, being the only species of escapement not affected by the motion or tremor of a railway carriage. The construction of the calibre for the train is a going barrel. The advantage is getting the motive power close to the centre, and by an extra wheel in the train taking the escapement further from the centre, the defects or irregularities of the main spring have less effect on the time, consequently the action, or the arcs of vibration, are more regular, and the time more correct. This train is well adapted for chronometers and watches. The timepiece should be wound up every day, though constructed to go two days. The escapement beats dead half seconds.

Model of the patent "diamond escapement," as intended for the use of marine chronometers. It is much less expensive than the detent escapement now in use; it is not affected, as that is, by the sudden motion and tremor of the vessel, and is not so liable to stop in cold climates. The locking is intended to be jewelled. This compensating balance differs from others, having the arms resting on the brass plate.

A model of a new compensating pendulum. This pendulum is adapted for astronomical and other purposes requiring correct time, showing how to correct the error caused by the expansion and contraction of the pendulum rod. The two brass arms, fixed at each end of a bar of hammered steel, will, as they become heated, expand, and increase the arc of the circle, thus taking up the elongation of the steel rods. The brass expanding about two-thirds more than the steel, will show the proportions required; and should the expansion of the arms be found more than required for the steel rod, an adjust-

ment of the two screws will correct the error, and, once adjusted, will always correct itself. This compensating pendulum is more simple and correct than mercurial and other pendulums.

Patent "double spring." This new principle possesses many important advantages: it eradicates an error now existing in the chronometer spring in present use. With the patent spring the balance of the chronometer will at all temperatures remain in the same position unaffected by heat, and at the extremes of temperature make one uniform rate (the patentee in this instance uses the compensating balance), thus removing the great effect produced on the old principle.

23   CHEVALIER, BENJAMIN, 41 *Brunswick Street, Stamford Street*—Manufacturer.

Chronometer cases.

25   BROOKES, JOSEPH, 5 *Berkeley Court, Clerkenwell*—Manufacturer.

A chronometer main-spring for a two-day marine chronometer.

26   FUNNELL, EDW., 2 *Clarence Place, Brighton*—Producer.

Small lever watch, the size of a silver three-halfpenny piece of the present reign.

27   GOWLAND, JAMES, 52 *London Wall*—Inventor and Manufacturer.

Improved free pendulum regulator, for the isochronal division of time.

Patent tourbillon remontoir chronometer, in which the impulse is imparted to the balance through the balance spring, its stud being advanced one degree or tooth of the locking-plate at each oscillation.

Large model of the escapement.

Model of Earnshaw's escapement.

Skeleton clock with improved compensation pendulum.

Model of an improved anemometer and wind-dial and vane; and of an electric clock.

Various specimens of watches, including gold keyless hunting lever watch, winding and setting the hands through the pendant, and also unlocking the cover of the case by the same means. A gold keyless repeater, indicating the hours, quarters, and minutes, &c.

28   TANNER, WILLIAM, 83 *Upper Street, Islington*—Inventor.

The polyhorion (or many hour-clock) exhibits, in addition to the local time, the time at Dublin, Paris, and Edinburgh; it can be made to show the time at any other four places. This clock is simple and not liable to get out of order, as one movement and pendulum regulate the different times. This clock is represented in the following cut.

Lever watch, set to Liverpool and Greenwich time: but it can be set to the times of any two places more convenient.

30   DAVIS, WILLIAM, 37 *Gracechurch Street*—Manufacturer.

Watch, horizontal escapement, made entirely by hand.

Watch movement, duplex-escapement, made entirely by hand. Made by H. A. Davis, 57 New Street, Birmingham.

31   COLE, THOMAS, 2 *Upper Vernon St., Lloyd Square, Clerkenwell*—Inventor, Designer, and Maker.

Inkstand, containing requisites for writing; and showing the time, the day of month, and the day of week, with thermometer. In metal, engraved and gilt, inlaid with malachite.

Tanner's Polyhorion.

Design for a portable eight-day timepiece, showing the months and days of the week and the month.

Design for a flat, portable clock, with calendar; metal, engraved and gilt, inlaid with malachite.

Eight-day night and day timepiece, or horological lantern.

Small eight-day clock. Improved calendar, in metal frame.

Flat eight-day striking clock, to repeat the hours and quarters, in engraved and gilt case.

[The substance here called "malachite" is also known as *mountain green*. It is a beautiful mineral of a fine green colour, variegated in a pleasing manner. It consists chemically of carbonate of copper, and is found native in Cornwall and Cumberland.—R. E.]

32 JACKSON, W. H. & S., *Red Lion Street, Clerkenwell* —Inventors and Manufacturers.

Registered soliclave lever watch: exhibited for cheapness and various improvements. Specimens in gold of various styles; specimens in cases enamelled, set in gems, and painted with designs; the enamelling the work of this district.

A gold three-quarter plate lever watch, with enamelled dial, jewelled in six holes, of the same construction.

Gold lever watch, with compound balance crystal dome, showing the motion of the escapement.

Duplex timepiece with whole or dead seconds from centre; a new calibre.

Lever watch, with whole or dead seconds.

Gold pocket chronometer.

Two-day marine chronometer, and a compensation balance, with adjustment for extremes of temperature.

Parts of watches, showing their construction.—See Plate 34.

33 MOORE, JOHN, & SONS, 38 *Clerkenwell Close*— Manufacturers.

Chiming skeleton clock to go a month. Chiming clock in rosewood case. Skeleton clock.

34 BARRAUD & LUND, 41 *Cornhill*—Inventors and Manufacturers.

Marine chronometer, with a model of a newly-invented compensation balance, constructed for exact adjustment to all temperatures.

Marine chronometer, of ordinary construction.

Very small gold pocket chronometer, a specimen of minute English manufacture.

35 PARKINSON & FRODSHAM, 4 *Change Alley, Cornhill*— Manufacturers.

Astronomical clock, with mercurial pendulum, in mahogany case.

Eight-day chronometer with ordinary compensation.

Lever watches with compensation.

Gold chronometers for pocket.

Gold watch-cases and carriage clocks.

36 FAIRER, JOSEPH, 17 *Bishopsgate Street Without* — Inventor and Manufacturer.

Improved railway guards' timekeeper.

Improved railway station clock, showing the day of the month.

Pocket watch for engineering purposes.

Improved electric clock, to show uniform time, irrespective of distance, from one prime mover.

37 ROBINSON, P., *Bishop Auckland*—Designer and Manufacturer.

Skeleton spring clock, which strikes the hours and quarters on modulated bells; with a compensator for counteracting temperature. The clock and framework are a representation of the clock-tower and entrance to the palace of the Bishop of Durham, at Bishop Auckland.

39 ELISHA, CALEB, 13 *New Bond Street*—Inventor and Manufacturer.

An eight-day timepiece (regulator), to go by a weight, in a mahogany case, with a compensating pendulum. This pendulum has a brass ball, seven inches diameter, and three-quarters of an inch thick, on the face of which is screwed a brass rim, a quarter of an inch thick and one inch broad; on the inside of this is a steel rim, secured to the brass, one-eighth of an inch thick. The outer diameter of this rim, composed of brass and steel, is also seven inches. This rim is divided or separated at the bottom of the ball, leaving two arms of equal length; at the end of each is screwed a brass cup, to admit glasses of a conical shape containing mercury, about $4\frac{1}{2}$ inches high, the lower diameter being about $1\frac{3}{4}$ inch, and the upper about the half. The adjustments for variations in temperature are made by the compensation rim with mercury in the glasses. The escapement of the clock is of George Graham's construction, dead-beat, but the pallets are jewelled. The vibration is made as short as possible.

A silver lever watch, with compensation radii, composed of brass and steel united. The proportions are about 1 of steel and 2 of brass. The bar is screwed on to the upper plate at one end, and at the other end a hole is drilled, to admit the pendulum or regulating spring, where it is pinned in.

A silver lever watch, with compensation radii, composed of brass and steel, fixed on the index on the cock, the two shifting together, and acting up and down the spring as the regulator is shifted. In the outer end of this radii compensation, are drilled two holes for the pins, between which the pendulum spring plays.

Model of a mahogany door, with machinery. In the posts of the inside of the door are fixed two staples. An iron chain, case-hardened, rather longer than two widths of the door, is drawn through the staples, and when on the outside, the chain is pulled, so as just to admit the hand to secure a padlock into the links of the double chain. The chain is then drawn, with the padlock, out of sight. The lock catch must also be case-hardened.

40 BROCKBANK & ATKINS, 6 *Cowper's Court, Cornhill*— Inventors.

A fifty-six hours' marine chronometer, on spring gimbals, enclosed in improved box with glazed sides and front, for the better admission of light.

The same inverted, showing the interior mechanism.

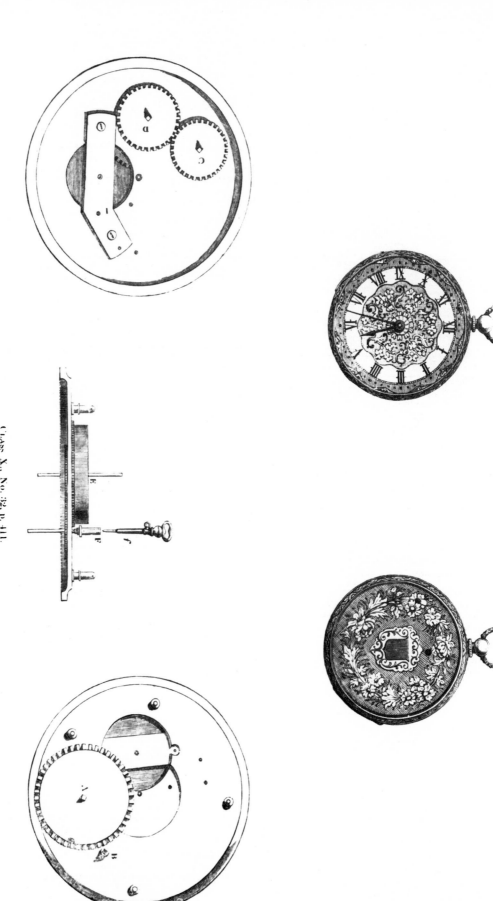

CLASS X., No. 32, p. 411.

SECTIONS OF WATCH MOVEMENTS, SHOWING THE CONSTRUCTION OF THE SOLID LEVER, OR SOLID KEY WATCH.

W. H. & S. JACKSON, Red Lion Street, Clerkenwell.

41   WALTER, FRANCIS, 9 *Devonshire Place*—Inventor.
Agent—Mr. HAWLEY, 123 *Regent Street*.

Model of a new design for giving a moral and religious application to the dial indications of a clock. The subject has been the study of five years.

42   LAMB, J., *Bicester, Oxfordshire*—Manufacturer.

Skeleton clock: to go 400 days.

43   THORNELOE, C., *Lichfield*—Designer and Manufacturer.

Clock, which strikes quarters, and goes 32 days. Design, Lichfield cathedral.

Gothic skeleton clock.

46   GRANT, P., 29 *Lower William Street, St. John's Wood* —Designer.

Timepiece-stand, composed of ivory, tulip-wood, and ebony.

46A   COPLAND, C., M.A., *South Villa, Kennington Oval* —Proprietor.

A watch once the property of Henry VIII.

Silver watch, of same character and date, finely engraved.

Gilt watch, 150 years old, chased, Henri Quatre style.

47   HARVEY, W., *Stirling, Scotland*—Inventor and Manufacturer.

Improvement in horology, dispensing with striking work. Only one wheel is used, which is placed under the hour-wheel, and receives motion from it. This improvement can be applied to almost any other timepieces, especially to skeleton timepieces. The article exhibited is the original invention.

49   BENNETT, GEORGE WEEDON, *Blackheath, Kent*— Manufacturer.

A public clock, showing time on four dials, and intended to be fixed in an ornamental case at the intersections of streets, or the approaches to bridges, entrances to parks, village greens, the quadrangles of baronial halls, in colleges or other public places, in order to supply correct time, independently of church clocks (which are, from their lofty and exposed position, almost always wrong), and to serve as useful ornaments in the streets. It has a two-seconds' pendulum, pin-wheel escapement, lantern pinions, gun-metal wheels, and slate dials; and the whole is constructed with every regard to accuracy of performance. Two designs for cases accompany it; but these would necessarily be adapted to the locality and taste of the purchaser.

52   DONEGAN, JOHN, *Upper Ormond Quay, Dublin*— Manufacturer.

Gold and silver watches, of Dublin manufacture.

Specimens of Irish gold and silver, from Ballycorus works.

52A   AUBERT & KLAFTENBERGER, 157 *Regent Street*— Manufacturers.

Regulator remontoir, and of continual power. The movement consists of two barrels, centre, third, fourth, and escapement wheels: the axis of the fourth wheel traverses the upper plate, and receives a wheel which is fixed on the axis of the pinion above, the object of which is to wind up the weight of the maintaining power; this movement maintains the oscillation of the half-second pendulum.

The escapement wheel, and the second wheel exposed in the dial, form part of the independent train, which has to maintain the oscillation of the mercurial pendulum.

The principal and medial trains are brought into communication by means of the third wheel, seen in the dial: this wheel is fixed in the centre of a rack mounted on an axle, which is pivoted between the frame; a wheel here forms a depth into the rack, and upon the axle on which this wheel is placed, is fixed a double pulley, on one side of which is suspended a small weight, and on the other the half-second pendulum. The weight and pendulum draw contrary ways, and as the weight is heavier, it gives the power to the independent train.

The third wheel of the principal train, which forms the depth with the medial wheel seen in the dial, will displace it from right to left; by which means, if the two wheels, having the same number of teeth, turn equally quick, the intermedial wheel will be set in motion, but its axle will not change in position, and consequently the rack, and also the wheel in which the rack works, will be immoveable, and the hand fixed to the axle of the pulley will point to zero.

The independent train receiving thus a *force constante*, and maintaining the oscillation of the mercurial pendulum, will not be susceptible of variation. Any difference of quickness in the action of the second wheel upon the medial wheel in the dial, can only be occasioned by the principal train, through the action of the half-second pendulum, which, if not perfectly regulated, will occasion an advance or *retarde*.

If the half-second pendulum should advance, the principal train will raise the weight of the *force constante*, and the half-second pendulum, acting in a contrary sense, will cause it again to fall, and consequently the pendulum will then *retarde*. If, on the contrary, the half-second pendulum loses, the principal train will not raise the weight of the *force constante* sufficiently quick, and the pendulum will then drop; but the regulator acting in a contrary manner will again shorten it, which will then cause it to advance.

Two-day marine chronometer.

Repeating watch, in gold case, striking the hours, quarters, and half-quarters; with lever escapement and compensation balance, showing, on the dial plate, the age of the moon, the day of the month, the hours, minutes, and seconds.

Pocket chronometer, in gold case, with enamel dial.

Duplex and lever watches in gold cases.

53   PENNINGTON, JOHN, *High Street, Camberwell*— Inventor and Manufacturer.

Marine chronometer, with improved compensating balance weight, to remedy the defect produced in ordinary chronometers by extremes of temperature.

A A represents levers with weights attached, B B acting on pivots, C C, held against bankings, D D, in middle temperature when not in action, by springs, E E, moved towards centre of balance in extreme heat by point of screws, F F, and the same by shoulder of screws, G G, in extreme cold.

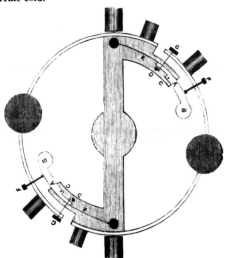

Pennington's Compensating Balance.

54   TAFFINDER, —, *Rotherham*—Manufacturer and
Designer.

An eight-day skeleton clock with lever escapement.
Design taken from Rotherham cathedral.

---

55   DENT, EDWARD JOHN, 61 *Strand*, 33 *Cockspur Street*,
and 34 *Royal Exchange*—Inventor and Manufacturer.

1. Gold "tac" watch. The term "tac" implies that
the time is ascertained by turning round the large external gold hand until it is stopped. The time is then
known by determining the place of the hand with reference to the twelve projecting nibs on the edge of the case
by the touch. The interval of time can be thus determined to about a minute. This description of watch
supersedes the usual striking repeater, is less liable to
derangement, and is less expensive. It is wound up and
the hands set without the usual detached key.

2. Similar watch, with hunting-case, and small opening in the centre to know the time without opening the
cover.

3. Hunting cased watch, with case springs outside, and
to wind up and set the hands without a detached key.
For use in India, and may be considered air-tight, by
which arrangement frequent cleaning is avoided.

4. Gold open-faced watch, with compensation-balance,
&c. A specimen of the best description of English watch.

5. Gold watch, with compensation-balance, &c., and two
seconds' hands in the centre. The under one (as shown
stationary at the 45 seconds or minutes) drops instantly
on pressing a nib at the end of the pendant of the watch.
This auxiliary hand remains still as long as required.
Intended for delicate experiments where small intervals
of time are required to be noted.

6. Chased watch, with compensation-balance, &c., having a drop seconds' hand. It is wound up, and the hands
are set, without the usual detached key; made for the son
of the Viceroy of Egypt.

7. Engraved watch, with compensation-balance, &c.;
a specimen of watches intended for the Spanish market.

8, 9. Watches, with compensation-balances, as specimens for the Turkish market.

10. Watch, with compensation-balance, &c., as a specimen for the Persian market.

11. Watch, with compensation-balance, English style.

12, 13. Ladies' watches, with compensation-balances, &c.

14, 15. Ladies' gold watches of the usual construction.

16, 17. Gentlemen's gold watches, with compensation-
balances, &c.

18, 19, 20. Gentlemen's watches of the usual construction, without compensation-balances.

21. Marine chronometer, with a glass balance-spring,
glass balance, and compensated, for temperature, by
means of platinum and silver. This glass balance-spring
has been tried at the Royal Observatory, and on board
H.M. surveying ship, "Fairy" (for official rates, *see* "Nautical Magazine," xxix).

22. Patent marine chronometer, having the steel balance-
spring, gilded by the electro-metallurgic process.

23. Patent marine chronometer, having a secondary
compensation, by which the compensation weights are
made to move so as to counteract the effect produced by
the changes of temperature.

24. Marine chronometer of the ordinary construction.

25. A compass which can be inverted; the magnetic
needles are placed on a vertical axis, and the divisions
are engraved on both sides of the silver ring (or compass-
card), so that one reading can be made before, and the
other after, inversion. The mean between these two
readings gives the error of the zero on the card; therefore the true magnetic bearing of any observed object
can be determined.

[The ordinary way of fixing the card and needle of a
compass is upon an inverted cup resting on a fine point.
The application of the chronometer suspension to com-
passes, as above, is with the view of avoiding the great
friction upon the fine point, caused by great vertical
oscillations.—J. G.]

26. An azimuth and altitude compass. The principle
is the same as in the former, with the addition of a
telescope carrying cross wires, and a divided arc for
altitudes; the rays from the observed object pass through
the telescope, whilst those from the card, reflected by
the prism, pass to the eye of the observer.

27. A steering compass, with the needles gimballed on
a vertical axis, by means of which the effect of the violent
motions of the ship on the compass-card, and the effect
of variation of dip, are neutralized. The superiority of
this over the ordinary compass, in which the point of
suspension of the card is higher than the centre of gravity,
is most evident in steamers where the speed is great, and
where the motion occasioned by the sea, as well as that
from the vibration of the engine, disturb the usual compass-card, which obeys the laws of a pendulous body;
whilst the compass-card placed on a vertical axis is not
disturbed from any such causes.

28. An eight-day quarter striking turret clock, with
compensated pendulum, 8 feet long, and weighing above
2 cwt.; vibrating half seconds, with pin-wheel, and dead
escapement, but with a small recoil. All the wheels in
the clock are of cast-iron, except the 'scape-wheel, which
is brass, of only 4 inches diameter, containing 40 pins,
and turning in 2 minutes.

The 'scape-wheel is driven by a small spiral spring fixed
to a pinion, which turns on a stud set in the same line as
the 'scape-wheel arbor, and carrying one of the pivot-holes
of that arbor. This spring is wound up a quarter of a
turn by the clock, at every quarter of a turn of the
'scape-wheel.

The dial-work is all driven by the great wheel, without
the intervention of any pinion, and it is consequently
very strong, and capable of working four very large dials.
The dials in the great avenue of the Exhibition are 7 feet
in diameter. The hands are adjustable by means of
hand-screws, and a small regulating-dial set on the clock;
this dial is reversed, in order to provide for the case of
the external dial being on a level with the clock, and the
hands driven directly by the prolonged arbor of the
regulating-dial. The hands are counterpoised outside the
dials; because, when the counterpoises are within, the
force of the wind on the hands is not counterpoised at
all; and the weight of a large hand, when unbalanced,
tends to loosen the hand on its arbor, and so make it
point behind the true time from 6 to 12, and before it
from 12 to 6.

The maintaining power for keeping the clock going
while winding, is of a new construction. Before winding,
the maintaining weight must be raised sufficiently high
to keep the clock going about seven minutes, and when
wound up, it can be thrown out of action immediately.

All the great wheels are set in the great frame, and the
small triangular frames can be taken off without moving
the great wheels and barrel, or the pendulums, which
may also be suspended from the wall. The smaller
wheels will also take out separately. The weights are
hung by wire ropes, and they require a fall of about
40 feet, with a single pulley. The pulleys are 1 foot
in diameter.

The hammers are raised by cams cast on the great
wheels, of such a shape as to raise them with the least
friction. They are strong enough for an hour-bell of
several tons weight, and quarters to correspond, though
the great wheels are only 18 inches in diameter. The
hammers all stand ready to fall as soon as they are discharged by the going part. The 1st, 2nd, and 3rd quarters
begin exactly at those quarters; the 4th begins half a
minute before the hour, and the hour-hammer falls
exactly at the hour.

The object aimed at in this clock, is to combine the
greatest accuracy of time-keeping with great strength,
and the cheapest mode of construction which is consistent
with good work.

29. A patent dipleidoscope, to be used as a fixed meridian instrument. The optical arrangement consists in
two silvered parallel reflecting glasses placed at an angle
of about 60° behind the front glass. The image of the
sun is reflected from the front glass, and the sun's rays

which pass through, impinge first on one plane, and are reflected to the other, they then pass out through the front glass. By this optical arrangement, two suns are visible to the eye of the observer moving in opposite directions, and when they coincide, it is the instant of apparent noon. The time can be ascertained by this instrument with considerable precision. The dipleidoscope allows of three observations of the sun: 1st, when the limbs touch; 2nd, when the images coincide; and 3rd, when the limbs separate.

[The dipleidoscope was invented, a few years since, by G. M. Bloxem, Esq., and, when accurately fixed, the time of apparent noon can be determined by it within one or two seconds. Two bright and sharp images of the sun are seen, which approach each other, and exactly coincide at apparent noon.—J. G.]

30. A dipleidoscope fitted up equatorially, which admits of observations being taken from 9 A.M. to 3 P.M., and is rendered portable by having a magnetic needle. When the instrument is set by the needle, the magnetic declination of the place requires to be allowed for.

31. A superior astronomical clock, with a remontoire dead-beat escapement, invented by G. B. Airy, Esq., Astronomer Royal (*see* paper in "Royal Astronomical Society's Monthly Notices," Nov. 11, 1842, by Mr. Airy.)

A large church clock. (*Main Avenue.*)

---

56   DRURY, JAMES, 16 *North Avenue, North Street, Pentonville*—Designer and Manufacturer.

Clock dial-case in brass, adapted for clocks in hot climates, at sea, and in bakers' shops, as they are not affected by steam and heat.

---

57   FRODSHAM, CHARLES, 84 *Strand*—Chronometer Maker.

1. Astronomical clock, with mercurial pendulum, and Graham's dead-beat escapement.

[Mercurial pendulums, and Graham's dead-beat escapement, are now used in nearly all astronomical clocks. The number of such clocks now in London exceeds 200; about 60 of these, chiefly the property of eminent chronometer makers, are rated on Greenwich mean time, and

it is found that their performance is such as to adapt them for astronomical uses. They certainly reflect great credit on the various artists engaged in the science of horology.

The mercurial pendulum is so called from the circumstance of the bob being of mercury enclosed in a cylinder, screwed to the bottom of a steel rod. Gridiron pendulums were in use before mercurial pendulums were adopted: they consisted of an assemblage of brass and steel rods so arranged that, owing to the difference in the expansion of brass and steel, the brass rods carried the bob up, while the steel ones let it down. The shape of pendulum bobs is important. Until lately they were of the form of a double convex lens, this form offering but little resistance on passing through the air, when its edge was always in the plane of motion; but, as it was liable to be a little twisted, a varying resistance was offered; and which is not the case in the adoption of the form of the cylinder, which probably is the best shape for the bob.

It is usual to call those clocks astronomical which are used in observatories for determining the right ascension of the heavenly bodies, and they are such, including every appendage which contributes to accuracy in the measurement of time under all the changes of atmospheric temperature.—J. G.]

2. Marine chronometers, on a new calibre, with Arnold and Earnshaw's detached escapement; the compensation balance is of the ordinary kind, with Arnold's bar as auxiliary compensation. This new calibre is based upon the plan of the diameter of barrel, fuzee-wheel, and extreme diameter of the balance being the same, namely, one inch and five-tenths. The total weight of the compensation balance is 5 dwts., being as the contents of the barrel. Thus if a barrel, one inch in diameter, by three-tenths of an inch in depth, will carry a balance weighing 20 grains, a barrel of the same diameter, and of double the depth, will carry a balance weighing 40 grains. The balance-spring is 15 inches long; the diameter $\frac{45}{100}$, the thickness of wire $\frac{10}{1000}$ by $\frac{18}{1000}$ broad, and the number of turns 10 to 12. The wheels (escape-wheel included) are each five times the diameter of their respective pinions—that is, the pinion upon which the

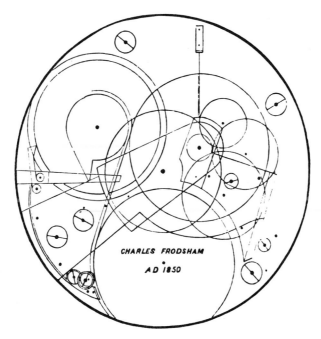

CHARLES FRODSHAM

AD 1850

Frodsham's new Calibre for Watches.

wheel revolves. The fuzee-wheel has 90 teeth, centre wheel 90, centre pinion 14, third wheel 80, third pinion 12, fourth wheel 80, fourth pinion 10, and 'scape pinion 10, 'scape-wheel 15.

3. Specimens of gold pocket chronometers and lever watches, reduced from the calibre of the chronometer; with improvements in the form of the teeth of wheels and pinions, in the balance-springs, and in the mode of attaching the spring.

4. The double rotatory escapement. This is a specimen of a new calibre movement, by which a powerful watch may be made in a flat case; a method which might have been adopted at the period when flat watches were first introduced, as it has all the advantages of a thick watch, by taking the contents of the barrel in diameter and depth as the basis of power.

5. Day-of-the-month watch, with lever escapement and double rollers. The calibre of this watch may be called more simple than the preceding one, only because it more closely resembles that which is daily made. The number of the teeth of the wheels is peculiar. The centre-wheel is much enlarged, with 100 teeth working in a pinion of 10, whilst the third wheel is diminished, which has 60 teeth working in a pinion of 10; the fourth wheel 63 teeth in a pinion of 7. Although this is a good working calibre for a superior watch, yet if power is admitted to be a principle in watch-making, it is impossible to get the same depth of barrel in this watch, unless the calibre of No. 1 is used.

In producing the foregoing calibres, all technical sizes have been rejected, and the common measurement of inches, tenths, hundredths, and thousandths adopted; so that from one calibre, a watch of any size may be made by proportion.

6. Specimen of gold lever watches, with the split-centre seconds-hand movement. This watch, being a complete time-keeper, is capable of determining the precise time of any observation to a quarter of a second, by means of an extra seconds hand, with which it is provided, and which in the ordinary state of the watch lies under the principal seconds hand, and travels with it.

In taking an observation, the observer keeps his eye steadily fixed upon the object, and his finger in readiness to touch a spring, which allows the registering hand to fall simultaneously upon the face of the watch, where it may be allowed to remain upwards of 40 seconds for reading off the time; this being done, the finger is to be immediately removed in order to free the register, which instantly returns to its place ready for the next observation, without having in the least degree interfered with the correct performance of the watch.

7. Specimen of railway watches.

8. Specimen of English pinions for astronomical clocks, showing the true curve of the teeth.

9. Specimen of carriage clocks.

10. Specimen of portable chime clock.

11. Specimen of chronometer and watch movements.

12. Diagrams of calibres of chronometers and watches.

13. Gauges for admeasurement of watch-work to the thousandth of an inch.

14. Specimens of gold watch cases.

15. The new calibre, by means of which the manufacture of watches and chronometers is greatly improved and facilitated, and the expense considerably reduced. The cut in the preceding page represents this new calibre.

16. Five stages of the process of manufacture in the compensation balance.

17. Auxiliary compensation for the adjustments of the extremes of temperature.

[Power being an indispensable element in time-keeping, it is of the utmost importance that the motive force should be transmitted with a constant velocity-ratio from wheel to pinion throughout the train, without its being absorbed by the increased friction and wear consequent upon improper curves.

The correct forms of curve were described, a century ago, by Camus, and recently in a work on the Principles of Mechanism, by Professor Willis, of Cambridge, 8vo, London, 1841.

In watch-work, the wheel is the driver, and the addendum to the tooth beyond the pitch-line is of the epicycloidal form, which, to the general eye, may be familiarly explained as resembling a Gothic arch, or a bishop's mitre. The pinion is the follower, and has the two flanks of its leaf formed by radial lines direct to the centre; and the addendum upon the pitch-line is a semicircle whose diameter is the breadth of the leaf. The specimen will explain the rest.

The new calibre by the exhibitor is shown as a general improvement in chronometers and watches.]

Fig. 2.

60 HALL, GEORGE FREDERICK, *Norfolk St.,* *Fitzroy Square*—Inventor.

An astronomical and meteorological clock for mean time, and for registering the hourly variations of the barometer and thermometer. The escapement of the clock is a new vertical dead-beat escapement; the pendulum has a new micrometrical compensation adjustment for temperature, intended for the self-registration of natural phenomena.

Fig. 1 is a plan of the escapement, half-size. A is a vertical wheel of seven teeth, which move in a horizontal plane. B is a concentric circle, with two ruby pins moving in a vertical plane; if the pins are circular or chamfered, the action is dead during the coincidence of the two planes; but as the pins vibrate, the top of the teeth strike, and escape, and slide, under the circular or chamfered surface of the ruby pins, and give the necessary impulse to the pendulum.

Fig. 1.

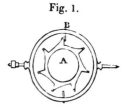

Fig. 2 is the pendulum with the micrometrical adjustment for temperature, which is effected by a compound rod of brass and zinc, in the proportion of 20 brass and 10 zinc, joined just above the bob: a zinc screw is soldered into the top of the brass tube, and a steel screw into the zinc cylinder, both of the same pitch. The length of compensating rod is first obtained by calculation; then, if the pendulum is compensated plus, the rod is turned to the right, which shortens the zinc screw, and increases the steel; the difference between the expansion of zinc and steel is the amount rendered minus in the compensation. If the pendulum is compensated minus, the rod is turned to the left, which increases the zinc, and shortens the steel; the difference of expansion is the quantity rendered plus. The pendulum is made of two glass tubes expanding downwards, and the compound compensating rod expanding upwards; the bob being placed upon studs fastened to the inner glass tube, and passing through the outer. The black line in the drawing is the compensating rod.

Fig. 3 is the elevation of the clock one-eighth real size, with the dial-plate removed, showing the meteorological registering apparatus. A *a* are two revolving cylinders

Fig. 3.

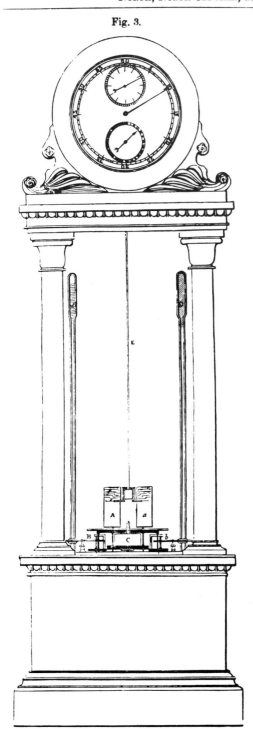

Hall's Astronomical and Meteorological Clock.

fastened to the arbors of the first wheels of the train, and which revolve (upon the average) once in three hours. B *b* are the escape wheels of the train, of the same kind as the clock (the vertical dead beat), of 25 teeth. *c* is the going barrel to impel the two independent trains. D *d* is the thermometer and barometer. E is the rod to which is fixed the marking apparatus in connexion with the revolving cylinders A *a*. F is the escape hour-wheel of 24 pins, with a barrel to receive the chain of the rod E. G is a wheel with a logarithmic spiral, the groove of which receives the pin of the bar H.

I is the clock-frame. The action of this entirely new invention is as follows:—D *d*, the thermometer and barometer, are made to vibrate continually by the escapement B *b*, as inverted pendulums; the radii of the gyrations of which are continually affected, either by the pressure of the atmosphere, or by the change of temperature: thus *d*, the Torricellian barometer, will, if the mercury fall one inch, increase the number of its vibrations per hour by 1,000, every one of which is registered on the revolving cylinder A, which gives a line in length equal to the number of vibrations given by the barometer *d* per hour; a similar effect is produced by the thermometer D, by any change of temperature, and its variation registered on A. The hourly measure is marked by breaking the lines, which is effected by the escape of the wheel F, and the descent of the rod E, with its attached apparatus.

Patent diplometer for railway purposes; the tickets are stamped with the date and the number of tickets issued, with the amount paid.

---

62   HINTON, CHARLES, 10 *Corporation Lane, Clerkenwell*
—Designer and Manufacturer.

English hard white enamel watch dial, with sunk centre and seconds, allowing free motion of the hands, with a flatter glass than usual.

---

64   JONES, JOHN, 338 *Strand*—Manufacturer.

Gold and silver watches of peculiar construction.

No. 1. The Rose Watch, showing Time and its doings. On one half of the margin around the back is engraved, on blue enamel, "Man cometh forth as a flower, and is cut down." On the surface of the richly engraved gold back is a Maltese cross, in white enamel, and on its four limbs are depicted the four seasons of life—in the bud, blossom, decay, and death of a rose. On the other half of the margin is engraved, "It is sown in dishonour, it is raised in glory." The dial represents, in enamel colours, the rose window of Westminster Abbey. On the twelve compartments indicating the twelve hours, are the names of the twelve Apostles. On the bezil that holds the glass is engraved, in blue enamel, "He that taketh not his cross daily is not worthy of me."

No. 2 shows, when viewed through a magnifying power. a series of cubical crystals, that being the primary crystal of gold.

No. 3 is a new and simpler mode than hitherto employed of producing dead seconds, with sunk centre in the dial, also a novelty.

No. 4 shows comparative merits of English and foreign work at equal prices.

No. 5. Centre seconds hunter with compensation balance, isochronal spring, and lever escapement.

---

66   KAISER, JOSEPH, 30 *Park Terrace, Regent's Park*—
—Inventor and Manufacturer.

Improved detector clock, on a novel principle, indicating, at a glance, the days of the week and of the month, also the name of the month. It goes eight days. and requires no attendance after winding.

66A   MOORE, Major W., 3 *Cornish Terrace, Rathmines,*
Dublin—Inventor.

A surgical instrument for use previous to operation for lithotrity, &c.

---

67   MACDOUAL, E. J., 12 *Dorset Place, Pall Mall East*—
Inventor and Manufacturer.

Patent escapement for chronometers, watches, and clocks, without escape wheel. The same spring by India-rubber.

Drill-stocks: Archimedean; centrifugal Archimedean; vibrating; and duplex, simple, and centrifugal.

A new method of converting rectilinear into rotary motion.

A new decomposition cell. Medals made by the process.

68   MACDOWALL, C., 4 Hyde Street, Bloomsbury—
Inventor.

Clock-movement, with a dead escapement of a new construction, in which the escape-wheel consists merely of a
small disc, with a single pin in it. The parts are arranged
for the purpose of exhibiting the action of the escapement.
The advantages claimed are—the impulse takes place at
the middle of the vibration of the pendulum, as in the
common dead escapement; it is given chiefly by direct
action instead of oblique, and requires little oil; the construction is easy, and may be made with a ruby for the
escape-pin as cheaply as with a common recoil escapement.
It is applicable to watches as well as clocks.
    (E. J. Dent, Manufacturer and Patentee, by assignment.)

69   MAPPLE, D. D., 17 Hall's Place, John's Row,
St. Luke's— Producer and Designer.

Registered skeleton timepiece, with improved lever
escapement.
Improved clock-winder.

70   DAVIS, J., 119 High Holborn—Inventor and
Manufacturer.

An instrument, on a new principle, to survey without
calculation.

71   MARCHAND, LUCIEN, 1 Red Lion Street, Holborn
—Manufacturer.

Very small gold lever watch.
Musical clock, with four overtures, independent seconds,
and amusing figures. Size, three feet high, two square.

73   PAYNE, WILLIAM, & Co., 163 New Bond Street—
Inventors and Manufacturers.

Quarter clock, on eight bells, in Amboyna wood, and
or-molu case, made for the Sultan of Turkey.
Timepieces, in buhl and or-molu case; and in tulip
wood and or-molu case.
Clocks, with lever escapement, in engraved gilt case
with patent musical chimes; and in black marble case,
with half dead-beat escapement.
Small carriage clock, with lever escapement.
Astronomical clock, with chronometer escapement,
perpetual day of month, moon's age, noon and night, day
of week, repeat hours and quarters, and zodiacal signs, in
engraved gilt case.
Timepiece, in square buhl case.
Clock, in square rosewood case, with lever escapement.
Lever timepiece, in satin-wood case.
Small clock, in rosewood case, with patent musical
chimes.
Half-regulator, in mahogany case, new style.
Small timepiece, with thermometer.
Clock, in ebony case, with silvered ornaments.
Clock, with or-molu ornaments, old English style.
Patent pedometer, for measuring walking distances;
pedometer attached to a repeating watch, with patent
winding, showing seconds and day of month.
Odometer, for measuring carriage distances.

74   RIX, ISAAC, 21 Conduit Street, Westbourne Terrace
—Inventor.

Skeleton chronometer timepiece, slow motion, beating
only once in three seconds; the escapement so contrived
as to allow the pendulum to vibrate two seconds every
beat without touching anything; a perfectly dead escape.

78   TOBIAS & CO., Liverpool—Manufacturers.

Registered compound-seconds watch movement, a new
configuration produced by combining a quarter-seconds
train of wheels with an independent full-seconds train,
in such a manner as to cause the seconds hand of the
independent seconds train to perform one revolution in
the same space of time that the quarter-seconds train is
performing four revolutions.
Gold watch, dome case, made from similar movement.
Three-quarter plate movement, combining soundness and
utility.
Gold watch, with same movement. Lady's watch, with
ornamental engraving, and engine-turned case.

Gold hunting watch, with ornamented and engine-
turned case.
Silver lever watch, as used in Turkey.
Horizontal movement, jewelled in five pair of holes;
extra chronometer-balance, adapted to all climates.
Left-handed movement, extra-jewelled, gold balance.
Silver hunting and plain watches.
Railway guards' timepiece, secured in case.

79   GILLETT, W. S., Upper Harley Street—Inventor.

Models of a system of thin rings or discs of metal,
which being conical or disked, may by pressure be
shortened, and thereby extended either inwards or outwards; applicable to pistons, stuffing-boxes, and other
similar purposes; also to the construction of hollow
cylinders to bear pressure from within.

80   THOMSON, ADAM, 25 New Bond Street—Inventor
and Maker.

Autochronograph: for the instantaneous marking or
printing of time, giving the month, day, and hour (night
and day), with the minutes and portions of minutes.
The machine requires setting but once a-month. The
clock must be wound once a-week. The register may be
extended to any required length, and the date, with the
exact time, may be stamped or printed in one second of
time.
The attendance of guards and of workmen can be
correctly noted; and the presence or substitution of
particular individuals can be known by their signature
upon the register.
The commencement and duration of any event can be
correctly registered within a few seconds of time, and all
the work of a "time clerk" correctly done. Provisionally
registered.

81   PETTIT, W., & Co., 2 Crombie's Row, Commercial
Road, East—Inventors.

A watch, keeping time, though suspended in a glass
globe, filled with water, and surrounded with gold and
silver fish. The object of the invention is to secure the
protection of time-keeping and other instruments from
water, sea-damp, rust, &c.

85   HARDY, G., 5 Wellington Road, St. John's Wood—
Inventor.

Electro-magnetic motive engine; exhibiting a new
mode of employing electricity as a motive power.

85A   WATKINS, A., 7 Weymouth Terrace, City Road
—Inventor and Manufacturer.

Original eight-day chronometer, striking the hours;
being a self-acting repeater, chiming the quarters upon a
set of five bells, and showing the day of the month; each
set of works detached; the whole comprising 200 pieces
of mechanism in a diameter of not more than two inches.
Chronometers of three-quarter plate construction,
with hard cylindrical springs, jewelled with rubies in
every hole; presumed to be the smallest ever made of
the same construction, the diameter being nearly that of
a guinea.

86   COUSENS & WHITESIDE, 27 Davies Street, Berkeley
Square—Inventors and Manufacturers.

A sporting watch, the novelty of which consists in its
determining the time to one-sixth of a second, by means
of an independent hand acting from the centre, and
detached from all the other hands, with stopping and
starting springs. It has a detached lever escapement, is
jewelled in 14 holes, and is particularly adapted for
racing and other purposes. It may be considerably reduced in size.

87   ALLIS, J. H., Bristol—Inventor and Manufacturer.

Bracket regulator timepiece, with a new description of
compound pendulum, which vibrates seconds, though less
than half the length of a usual seconds pendulum.
Adapted for compensation against the effects of heat and
cold.

90   BARLING, JOSEPH, 90 *High Street, Maidstone*
—Designer.

Dial of a clock, exhibiting a new pattern figure.
Table and dessert spoons and forks, ornamented in a
novel manner, with enamel.

91   VIEYRES & REPINGON, 129 *Regent Street* —
Manufacturers.

Two-day marine chronometer, in temporary gimbals,
for the convenience of exhibition.
Gold and silver watches, of various fashions, for the
home trade and for South America.
Steel for chronometer pendulum springs, by A. Ganeral.

92   BLAYLOCK, JOHN, *Long Island, Carlisle*—Inventor
and Manufacturer.

Motion-work for the hour and minute hands of a turret-
clock with four dials.
Apparatus for turning on and off gas for illuminating
dials, self-acting and self-regulating for each half-year.

94   BOLTON, THOMAS, *Coventry*—Manufacturer.
German silver watches, plated with silver.
Gold-plated watch.

95   MOUILLARD, PIERRE FORTIME VICTOR, 71 *Albany
Street, Regent's Park*—Inventor.

The artificial leech. It is composed of a body of cylindrical form, about three and a quarter inches long, and
about one inch in diameter. Towards the bottom end
is a small cylinder, slightly flattened at its lower part,
containing a small spoon of about two-thirds of an inch
of elevation on its upper part, the opening of which is
slightly oblique, of an oval form. This tube, including the
spoon, is about two inches long by about half an inch in
diameter. The other extremity of the body of the pump
is furnished with a piston, which, on being drawn back,
empties the pump. This piston, being entirely drawn
out to its full length, and pressed by the thumb, releases
an interior spring in which the lancets are fixed, and
these pierce the skin raised by its suction. The operation
is not painful, as the lancets do not remain an instant in
the wound.

95A   BRISCALL, JAMES, 48 *Constitution Hill, Birmingham*
—Designer and Manufacturer.

Self-correcting clock, with a detached lever escapement;
it goes a month; and shows the day of the week and
month. At the end of each month, and in leap-year, it
corrects itself.

96   BRUTTON, CHARLES, *Exeter*—Proprietor.

A clock, in a case, which occupied thirty-four years in
its completion. The movements are as follow :—moving
panorama of Day and Night; Day represented by Apollo
in his car drawn by four coursers, accompanied by the
twelve Hours; and Diana in her car, drawn by stags,
attended by the twelve Hours, representing Night. Two
figures which salute each other, as the panorama revolves,
and the bells are ringing. Perpetual almanac, showing the
day of the month on a semicircular plate, and the equation
of time, regulated only once in 130 years. Circle, the index
of which shows the day of the week, with its appropriate
planet. Circle showing the leap-year, the index revolving only once in four years. The sun in his course,
with the correct time of rising and setting by a horizon
receding or advancing as the days shorten or lengthen;
and the moon, showing her different quarters, age, &c.
Two female figures, one on each side of the dial-plate,
representing Fame and Terpsichore, which move in time
when the organ plays. Movement regulating the clock as
a repeater. Saturn, the god of time, who beats in movement when the organ plays. Circle on the face, showing
the tunes played by the organ every four hours. Belfry,
with six ringers. Bird organ, which plays when required.
This clock is shown in the annexed Plate, 35. It was
made by Jacob Loudan.

99   CHURCHILL, GEORGE, *Downton, near Salisbury*—
Manufacturer.

An eight-day spring-clock, with music attached, playing a tune every three hours: cast and manufactured by
a blacksmith.

100   DELL BROTHERS, *Bristol*—Inventors and
Manufacturers.

Specimens of ordinary clock-work. Transparent timepiece for the bed-room: a small light is placed behind
the dial, showing the time distinctly; the time-piece has
a lever escapement, going two days.
Specimens of iron and brass wheel-cutting, for clock-
work, lathe-work, &c.; and wood-pattern cutting, for
cast-iron and other wheels.
Pianoforte music-box, playing six overtures, made by
Nicole Frères, of Geneva.

102   DRIVER, J., *Silver Street, Wakefield*—Designer
and Manufacturer.

Chime-clock, showing simultaneously upon the dial
the time in any part of the world.
A compensating clock, with a lever escapement, and
without pendulum.

103   EDWARDS, JAMES T., *Dudley*—Manufacturer.
Portable spring time-keeper, to go 426 days.

104   EDWARDS, JAMES, *Stourbridge.*

Large transparent skeleton spring timepiece, made of
a combination of brass and glass: the wheels consist of
cut flint-glass centres, hooped with brass teeth rims, engraved glass dial-plate, and crystal cut pendulum ball;
it goes eight days.
New skeleton quarter-day spring timepiece, made of cut
flint-glass centres, hooped with brass teeth rims, having
engraved glass dial-plate, and glass pendulum ball; it
goes three months, and is kept in motion by a new clock-
movement propeller.

104A GRAY, JAMES, Dr., *Perth*—Inventor.

Medical walking-staff, containing an enema—syringe, a
catheter, a test tube and test paper, a pair of forceps, a
number of wax matches, and a pill-box, divided, containing in each division pills of various medicines.

105   BAGLEY, S., & SON, *Livery Street, Birmingham.*
Clock on carved mahogany pillar.

106   EVANS, WILLIAM F., *Soho Street, Handsworth,
near Birmingham*—Manufacturer.

Gothic skeleton clock, detached lever escapement.
Elizabethan timepiece, chronometer escapement.
Skeleton lever clock, with representation of Sir Walter
Scott's monument, Edinburgh.
Cabin clock, detached lever escapement.

109   GERARD, ALEX., *Gordon's Hospital, Aberdeen*—
Inventor.

"Spherical trigonometer," or an instrument adapted
to the mechanical solution of problems in spherical
trigonometry and nautical astronomy.
Portable, or field transit instrument, for finding the
time on shore, laying down meridian lines, &c.
Water-meter, for registering the quantity without inter-
rupting the pressure.
Clock, with conical pendulum.
Marine clock, with two pendulums.
A centrifugal, or conical pendulum clock; capable of
performing much heavy work with great accuracy.

113   HART, WILLIAM, & Co., *Christchurch, Hants*—
Manufacturers.

Chronometer and watch fusee chains, of different sizes.

115   LAWRENCE, I., *North Curry, near Taunton*—
Inventor.

Sun-dial, to suit any latitude in the northern hemi-
sphere. Hand-drill. Turner's centre, with friction rollers. Spring screw-wrench. Dividers.

117　Pace, J., *Bury St. Edmunds*—Inventor, Designer, and Manufacturer.

Skeleton clock, which goes three years. This period is obtained by the use of six springs, the united force of which is 250 lbs. They are enclosed in six barrels or boxes: three are connected with chains to a fusee on the right hand, and three to one on the left.

Pyramidical skeleton timepiece, which goes three months. The dial is placed at the bottom of the clock to show the motion of all the wheels; with Graham's dead-beat escapement, and the hands moved by a simple mechanism.

Barometer of highly-polished brass, containing three glass tubes supported by scroll-work. The centre-tube is the barometer, and those on each side move an index which rises and falls by turning a nut at the base of the stand: by means of wheel-work, they turn the hands on two dials, one for night and the other for day, indicating the state of the barometer.

119　Radford, Jonas, 339 *High Street, Cheltenham*—Inventor and Designer.

Design and diagrams of a geographical clock or watch; model made by F. Drury, 26 Albert Terrace, Penton Street, Islington.

Two timepieces. Provisionally registered.

121　Wright, William, *Exchequer Row, Aberdeen*—Designer and Manufacturer.

A clock, showing the minutes, hours, days of the month, and months of the year; the time of the sun's rising and setting; the diurnal revolution of the sun and moon; the moon's age; phases; time of her meridian passage and position relative to the sun; the time of high water at Aberdeen, both superior and inferior tides, and its depth at the bar; and the state of the tide at some of the principal sea-ports of Great Britain, Ireland, France, North and South America, Spain, Portugal, Holland, and Germany; it goes twelve months.

[By adding one or two wheels below the great wheel, and by greatly increasing the usual weight of a clock, it can be made to go for a year. Occasionally such clocks are furnished with two barrels, for the purpose of avoiding the great strain upon the teeth of one large wheel and pinion.—J. G.]

122　Broadbent, John, *Ashton-under-Lyne*—Exhibitor.

Peal of small bells to ring changes; worked by springs. Scale for pitching wheels. Timepiece.

123　Roskell, John, *Church Street, Liverpool*—Designer and Manufacturer.

Watch and clock machinery.

124　Rotherham & Sons, *Coventry*—Manufacturers.

Gold and silver watches. Specimens illustrative of the progressive stages of manufacture of a lever watch.

[A large number of watches are made at Coventry, not only for home, but also for colonial trade. The best forms of the common English watch, together with patented and others of a superior manufacture, are here prepared and completed. The manufacture has had its local establishment in Coventry about 80 years.—R. E.]

126　Mapple, H., *Child's Hill, Hampstead*—Inventor.

Machine for saving life on railways, now used in America. Fire alarum, on the principle of the telegraphic alarum now used on the English lines. Resonant spring for English clocks. Compensation pendulum. Supporting telegraph wires on tripods of iron rods. Improved clock escapement; system of railway signals; and mariners' compass needle. Electric telegraph. Specimen of insulated wire for telegraphic purposes. Compensation for pianoforte strings. Improved system of collecting lamp black; and of making permanent magnets. Improvements in electric timekeepers. Implement for shoemakers. Model to illustrate a theory for crossing any expanse of water by electric currents, for telegraphic purposes.

127　Einsle, Edward, 46 *St. Martin's Lane*—Manufacturer.

Syphon douche, invented by Dr. Charles Jones.

Model of an improved syphon, for brewers, distillers, &c., dispensing with the suction-pipe.

Stomach-pump, with several useful adaptations. Complete case of amputating and other instruments. Double-action enema pump, enclosed in bronze. British plate and electro-plated reservoirs; the valves so arranged that they work freely, and are not likely to get out of order.

Double-action enema apparatus, with metallic folding joints, suitable to warm climates; the same with flexible tube. Portable enema apparatus, with metallic joints. Improved enema apparatus, in round reservoir, discharging the contents with one stroke of the piston. Veterinary enema and stomach-pump, with useful tubes and pipes, for hove cattle, &c. Common enema apparatus. Model, to show the action of the double-action enema pumps.

127a　Taylor, G., *Wolverhampton*—Inventor and Manufacturer.

Registered self-correcting eight-day date clock, showing the day of week, day of month, &c.

128　Shepherd, Charles, 53 *Leadenhall Street*　Inventor and Patentee.

Patent electro-magnetic striking clock. From the pendulum of this clock, a number of dials may be worked. The greatest novelty consists in the method of giving the impulse by means of a remontoir escapement, by which the variations of the battery take no effect on the time measured. The novelty of the Large Clock in the Transept of the Exhibition Building, in connexion with the former, is in the method of locking the escape-wheel, to prevent the train from running by the action of the wind on the hands.

Two dials, five feet in diameter each.

A skeleton electro-magnetic striking clock, showing how the number of blows to be struck is regulated.

Small turret bell, illustrating the method of applying electro-magnetism to move the hammer.

The power employed for keeping in continual action the electric clock is one of Smee's batteries in connexion with a powerful horse-shoe magnet. In the case of the mechanism of the great clock now under consideration, a series of such magnets is used, the connexion of which, with their armature, is shown in fig. 1. These are

Fig. 1.

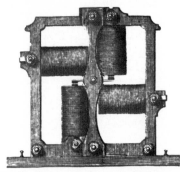

surrounded by 25,000 feet, or nearly five miles of No. 18 copper wire, the total weight of which is about 160 lbs. As weights are entirely dispensed with, the frame containing the wheel-work is much lighter than usual; the escape-wheel, *a, a,* fig. 2, is 10 inches in diameter, and is in two parts, the teeth of each being reversed; the click and rachet escapement, which is moved by the electro-magnets, acts on the teeth of one of the parts, while the teeth of the other part are used for the purpose of locking the train, in order to prevent it running forward from the action of the wind on the extra-sized hands which present a large surface. A central vertical wheel, b, of larger diameter (see fig. 2 and fig. 3), which works into a pinion, c, on the arbor of the escape wheel, gives motion to the wheel-work in connexion with the hands, which are at a height of 40 feet above the pedestal in the South Gallery of the Transept on which the machinery is placed, the communication being effected by a 12-inch bevelled wheel, d, which rotates on the end of the spindle of the great wheel, and works into a horizontal bevelled wheel, e, with which a vertical shaft, f, made of brass tubes of 1½ inch diameter, and

Fig. 2.

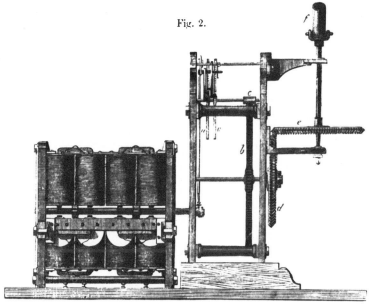

Fig. 3.

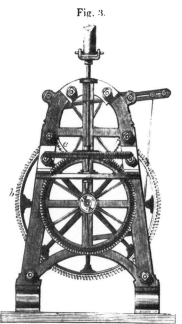

hand side of the semicircle; while on the left side the figure VI. is repeated, and the remaining figures up to XI. inclusive follow in the usual order. In order to render the new form of dial perfectly useful, it was necessary to have two minute hands, and also two hour hands; so that when one of the minute hands, for instance, leaves the figure VI. on the right hand, the other minute hand also points to the corresponding VI. on the left hand. The two minute hands together are 16 feet, and the two hour hands 12 feet in length respectively. Two smaller dials, each of five feet diameter, are fixed up inside the

Fig. 4.

Shepherd's Patent Electro-Magnetic Clock.

screwed together in several lengths, revolves, and which, in connexion with wheel-work at top, gives motion to the hands.

In order that the clock-face might harmonize with the design of the south elevation of the Transept, it was considered that the conventional form of a circle for the dial might be dispensed with; the figures were accordingly arranged in a semicircle, and placed at the intersections of the radial bars with the second semi-ring from the centre of the great fanlight.—(See fig. 4.) As is the case in ordinary dials, so in the present instance, XII. is at the top, I. to VI. following on the right-

building; one in front of the cross gallery at the east end of the central aisle, and the other in front of the south gallery of the transept. All the dials are regulated by one pendulum, represented in fig. 5, and which

Fig. 5.

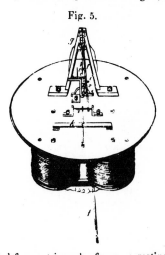

is suspended from a triangular frame, *g*, resting on a bed-plate, to which it is secured by screw bolts in the ordinary way. The pendulum has a mercurial compensation for heat and cold, and is kept in motion by electro-magnetism by a method entirely different to any previously invented. Instead of applying directly the attractive and repulsive forces of electro-magnetism to the pendulum, according to all the previous methods, the power of an electro-magnet is here employed to bend a spring to a certain fixed extent, the reaction of which gives the necessary impulse to the pendulum, by which means the variations which are continually taking place in the batteries have no effect on the time measured. The arrangement of the spring for giving the impulse is represented at *s* (fig. 5), in which *b* is the impulse spring, consisting of a short steel spring, to which are attached two arms, *c* and *d*, at right angles to each other; *e* is the detent, or catch, for holding this spring when bent by the action of the magnet; *f* is the pendulum-rod carrying the two screws, *h* and *i*, which may be called the impulse and discharging pallets. As the pendulum vibrates to the left, the discharging-pallet pressing against the perpendicular arm of the detent, *c*, forces it into the position indicated by the curved lines; the impulse spring is thus liberated and immediately falls against the impulse pallet *h*. As the pendulum returns to the right, the impulse spring by its elasticity urges the pendulum forward with the exact power required to continue its vibration. The spring is limited in its motion by a screw, *o*, by screwing or unscrewing which the length of the stroke of the spring, and consequently the power may be regulated to the greatest nicety. The pendulum continuing its motion to the right, comes in contact with a slight spring tipped with platina, which completes the circuit of the galvanic battery through the coils of the electro-magnet, which is placed immediately underneath the bed-plate in an inverted position, the poles of which pass through the bed-plate. An armature, *k*, consisting of a flat bar of iron, is placed immediately above the poles, being attached to a horizontal arm at right angles thereto, which arm moves freely on an axis, *x*, properly supported at either end on a bracket. On the opposite side of the axis is another arm also projecting at right angles, but considerably longer than the first. The use of the second arm, in connexion with an adjustable weight. is to raise the armature from the poles of the magnet. When, therefore, a current of electricity is made to pass through the coils of wire which surround the magnet, the armature is attracted towards the poles, and consequently the long arm with the adjustable weight is elevated in the opposite direction. It is evident that this arm cannot be raised without lifting the arm, *d*, of the impulse spring, *b*, bending the

impulse spring, and locking the upper end of the arm, *c*, on the detent, ready for the next impulse.

[A point of importance in the construction of this clock is the method of making and breaking contact for the electric currents. When the circuit is broken, a spark is seen to pass between the points of contact. The continued action of this spark causes the points between which it passes to become oxidised; and as the metallic oxides are non-conductors of electricity, it follows that the passage of the electricity will be thereby interfered with and prevented.

In the first clock constructed, a piece of steel-wire was used as a break spring, touching against the side of the pendulum-rod; but the points of contact oxidised so rapidly, that the clock would not go for more than a few days without stopping. The steel spring was then removed, and one of gold substituted, and a small plate of gold was soldered to the side of the pendulum-rod. The difficulty appeared to have been entirely overcome; but in six weeks the quantity of electricity passing was considerably reduced, and at the end of two months the clock stopped.

Platina was next tried, in the same manner as the gold, in a new clock, completed in 1848, since which time the points of contact have never required cleaning, the circuits being completed at the present time with as much certainty as when the clock was first put together. These points of contact present some peculiarities when examined with a lens. With metals having a great affinity for oxygen, a black spot forms immediately at the point of contact; while in the case of platina the immediate point of contact remains perfectly clean, a rim of black forming around it. This black rim has been found to be quite capable of conducting electricity. The probable conclusion, therefore, is, that the black rim is platina in a very fine state of division, and not an oxide of the metal.

The battery best adapted for these clocks is that of Mr. Smee, both on account of its simplicity and the ease with which it is recharged. The amalgamated zinc employed in this battery is subject to rapid local action, by the quantity of impurity which it contains, consisting usually of lead, iron, copper, tin, and cadmium; all these metals having less affinity for oxygen than zinc, become negative when immersed in dilute acid, and form a voltaic circle with the surrounding particles of zinc. The use of amalgamation is to stop this action, which, when the amalgamation is fresh, it accomplishes; but in a few days the local action again commences, and increases until the acid is neutralised, or the whole of the zinc dissolved.

This may be obviated by standing the zinc plate loose in the jar, resting on the bottom, and pouring in an ounce or two of mercury. This plan is found to answer remarkably well; the quicksilver soaking up the zinc plate keeps it thoroughly amalgamated. The zinc may be melted, and after being mixed with mercury, cast in moulds; the quicksilver would then form one of the impurities present: and should local action take place at any one point, the solution of the zinc would not only liberate the other metals present, but liberate at the same time sufficient quicksilver to cover them, and stop the local action.

It is well known that the zinc of a battery is acted upon more severely at the surface of the liquid than elsewhere, by which the lower part is wasted. This appears to depend on the presence of oxygen; for it does not go on, where the battery has been enclosed in a bottle to collect the hydrogen evolved. A double advantage results

---

from making the batteries air-tight; not only is this peculiar action stopped, but the evaporation of the water prevented. In batteries required to act for long periods, one zinc plate should be employed, as when two are used, one of them almost always becomes negative to the other; and although this action is very slight, yet when it continues constantly for several months, its effect is very perceptible.

This clock, although quite equal to that of St. Paul's Cathedral, occupies far less space; the heavy weights, with the room necessary for their descent, being of course dispensed with. One of the most obvious advantages in electro-magnetic clocks is, that precisely similar time will be kept by any number of dials situated in the different parts of a large establishment, and connected with one pendulum. Such a series has been in operation for some time at an extensive commercial warehouse. The whole of the dials are regulated by one pendulum, situated in the counting-house. The wire required to communicate between the pendulum and the dials in the different departments of the warehouse is upwards of a quarter of a mile in length.]

129 SMITH & SONS, JOHN, LANCELOT, & WILLIAM, *St. John's Square, Clerkenwell*—Manufacturers.

Regulator and case, with self-adjusting pendulum, suited to any temperature, by its own action; with barometer, thermometer, &c.

[Astronomical clocks are sometimes made, and yet not used in observation, but kept by clockmakers themselves, for the purpose of being used as a standard by which to adjust other clocks, chronometers, and watches not yet brought to time; and such clocks, when so used, are called *regulators*, from the use to which they are put; and when they have good compensating pendulums, and the best escapements, they differ from astronomical clocks only in the name.—J. G.]

Detector clock, or watchman's timepiece, for indicating the precise time of absence or neglect of duty in watchmen, nightwardens, &c.; forming also a bracket timepiece.

Eight-day office dials. Eight-day church or turret clock. Church clock to chime the quarters.

Skeleton timepiece and almanac, which goes twelve months with once winding, and shows seconds, minutes, and hours, with the days of the week, and the month, on one dial. Skeleton quarter clock, which chimes the quarters on eight bells, and strikes on steel wire gong.

Whishaw's uniformity of time clock and telegraph instruments.

130 ROBERTS, RICHARD, *Globe Works, Manchester*— Proprietor.

Patent alpha (church or turret) clock, the wheels and pinions made of cast-iron, with the teeth retaining the scale; it has only one weight to actuate both the going and striking trains, and the chain or cord, requiring no lateral traverse, can be taken off in any direction. The pendulum (compensation) and the escapement (remontoire) are adapted to keep the clock at an almost uniform rate, whilst the hands being advanced at intervals of thirty (or, if preferred, sixty) seconds, afford opportunity for ascertaining the time to a second.

[The striking of the hour is effected through means by which the blows are given at equal intervals of time, thus avoiding both the irregularity of the fan and the expenditure of power to drive it. The upper part of the case in which the clock stands shows a simple mode of constructing a turret, to consist of four pillars connected together by as many dials, which turret it is proposed should be placed diagonally with reference to the building on which it is to stand, in which position the dial will be better seen in all directions.]

Watch which beats dead (centre) seconds with only one train of wheels, &c.

Patent recorder watch with double hands.

Patent normal drill, for drilling all the pivot, screw, and steady pin-holes in the frame-plates of watches, chronometers, and small clocks. A boy may drill with this machine any number of watch frame-plates, so precisely alike, that the parts that fit one of the frames will fit all or any of the others.

[It will be seen that by varying the distance of the drill from the fulcrum of the graduated beam, any size of watch-plate may be drilled from the same model-plate; and that by changing the model-plate, the arrangement of the holes may be varied at pleasure.]

Patent synchronometer model, to show that by the application of pneumatics, a clock may be made to indicate simultaneously the time of day on dials in various places at a distance from each other.

Patent wheel sector. By this instrument the external and pitch line diameters of wheels and pinions of any pitch and number of teeth are accurately ascertained.

Electro-magnet, $2\frac{1}{4}$ inches square, the iron of which weighs only one pound four ounces and a half; capable of sustaining upwards of 500 lbs.

Electro-magnet, three inches square, the iron of which weighs only two pounds six ounces; capable of sustaining 678 lbs.

131 YOUNG, J., *Knaresborough*—Manufacturer.

Skeleton timepiece.

137 RUSH, G., *Elsenham Hall, Bishop Stortford.* Inventor.

Design for the improvement of the dial-plate, and registering of the aneroid barometer; so that by the addition of a table engraved upon the face, it will enable the traveller to determine approximate altitudes by simple inspection of the dial.

138 GRAY & KEEN, *Liverpool*—Designers and Manufacturers.

Wheel barometer, designed for use in naval establishments.

Gothic wheel barometers.

140 ABRAHAM, JOHN ABURGHAM, 87 *Bold Street, Liverpool*—Inventor.

Barometer, designed to show, without adjustment, the true height of the mercurial column.

141 JONES, W. & S., 30 *Holborn.*

A mountain thermometer.

144 BROOKE, CHARLES, 29 *Keppel Street*—Inventor and Designer.

Photographic self-registering magnetic, and meteorological apparatus.

The object of this apparatus is to obtain a more perfect knowledge of magnetic and meteorological phenomena, by continuous observation of all the changes that occur simultaneously in the various instruments. As the magnetic changes are too minute to actuate continuously any mechanism, however delicate, a record can be obtained by an imponderable agent only, as light.

Even with a staff of assistants so large that the eye of one of them should be constantly applied to every telescope, the results would be liable to errors of observation; besides which, the magnetic changes occasionally occur too rapidly to be continuously recorded by an observer. Since the apparatus has been employed at the Royal Observatory, Greenwich, the number of the staff has been reduced, and the fatiguing process of nocturnal observations in the magnetic department has been entirely superseded. The apparatus consists of—

1. A declinometer.
2. A bifilar magnetometer.

In these instruments, the torsion circle from which the suspension skin hangs is supported by eight brass tubes springing from the four corners of a marble slab (which, when in actual operation, would be cemented on the top of a stone pillar firmly fixed in the ground, and insulated from the floor of the observatory): these tubes, about 4 feet long, converge alternately to four points of the torsion plate; they thus compose a framework possessing great stiffness. To the suspension frame of each magnet, a plane glass mirror and a concave metallic speculum are attached. The plane mirror is for the purpose of making eye-observations with a telescope in the usual manner. A gas-light or lamp is so placed at a distance of about two feet in front of each speculum, that an image of a small slit in the copper chimney surrounding the burner may fall on the sensitive paper attached to—

3. The registering apparatus. This is placed midway between 1 and 2, and consists of a stand supporting horizontally on friction rollers two concentric glass cylinders, round the inner of which is wrapped a sheet of prepared photographic paper: the outer or covering cylinder keeps the paper moist during the 24 hours it remains in action. A bent arm, attached to the axis of these cylinders, is carried round by a fork at the end of the hour-hand of a time-piece specially constructed for the purpose. The horizontal motion of the tracing point of light, combined with the vertical motion of the paper, traces out the magnetic curve, which, when the paper is removed from the cylinder, is developed and fixed by the usual photographic processes. A third light is attached to the registering apparatus, for the purpose of drawing a standard or base line on the paper; by the varying distance of any point of the magnetic curve from this line, the magnetic variation is determined. At the distance at which these instruments are placed, an angle of 1° is represented by 2 inches on the paper; but the scale valve may be enlarged at pleasure, by placing them further apart. This instrument is shown in fig. 1.

Fig. 1.

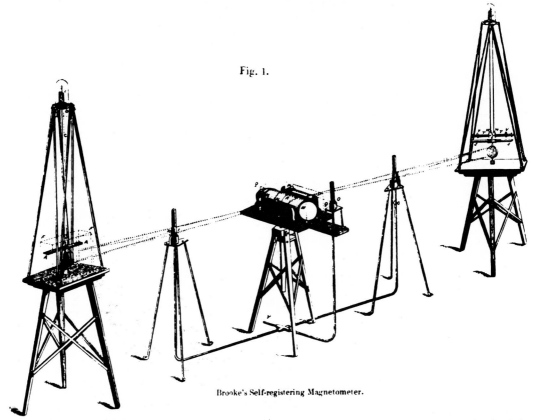

Brooke's Self-registering Magnetometer.

AA, the declination magnet.

B, a concave speculum attached to the magnet.

C, a plane glass mirror also attached to the magnet, for making observations by a telescope, on the old method, when required.

D, the torsion plate, reading to minutes by two verniers.

E, a frame standing upon the torsion plate. A hook capable of being raised or lowered by a screw, is attached to this frame, from which the magnet is suspended by a skein of untwisted silk fibres.

FFF, a glass box, in which the magnet and its appendages are enclosed, to protect them from the air; for the same purpose, the suspension skein is enclosed in a glass tube G, which passes through a stuffing box H, in the lid of the box.

I, a gas-burner enclosed in a brass chimney, from which no light can escape, except a small pencil which passes through a narrow slit K, capable of being adjusted by a screw; on the breadth of this slit, the breadth of the register line depends.

LL, a combination of two plano-convex lenses. The pencil of light passing through K, falls on the mirror B, and is reflected to the cylindrical lenses; by these, the image of the slit is condensed to a point of light on the surface of

MM, the registering apparatus, consisting of two concentric cylinders, between which the photographic paper is placed.

N, the magnetic curve traced by the point of light.

O, a gas-burner, fixed to the stand on which the cylinders rest.

P, a plano-convex prismatic lens, attached to the top of

QQ, an opaque box, which protects the photographic paper from extraneous light. A pencil of light from O passes through P, and is brought to a focus on the surface of the paper.

R, the base line, described by the point of light.

SS, the bifilar, or horizontal force magnetometer.

TT, the apparatus for producing an automatic temperature compensation; this consists of two zinc tubes, which are clamped to a glass rod by two adjustible clamps VV, the suspension skein passes over a pulley X, and the ends are attached to two hooks WW; as the temperature rises, these hooks are approximated to each other by a quantity

APPENDIX B

(731)

CLASS X_{B.}

REPORT ON HOROLOGICAL INSTRUMENTS.

Jury.

E. B. DENISON, M.A., *Chairman and Reporter*, 42 Queen Anne Street. (Juror Class X.)
Baron ARMAND SEGUIER *Deputy Chairman*. France. (Juror Class X.)
Professor DANIEL COLLADON. Switzerland. (Juror Class X.)
E. J. LAWRENCE, M.A., 44 Chancery Lane.

THE marine chronometer may be considered the most important of all machines for measuring time; and it is also the one in which an invariable rate of going is of the most consequence, inasmuch as longitude at sea is determined by means of chronometers, and they have frequently to go for a longer time without the means of being corrected by astronomical observations than astronomical clocks, which are generally accompanied by fixed transit instruments.

It will probably appear strange that we have not awarded any Council Medal for chronometers, of which there are a considerable number in the Exhibition, especially in the English part, some of them by makers of the highest reputation. It is, however, this very circumstance which has rendered it impossible to make any such award; not only because we are directed by the Royal Commissioners to avoid the attempt to distinguish one article from others of the same kind, merely on account of superiority of execution, but because among several of the best makers there really is no one who could properly be so distinguished above all the rest.

The principles of the construction of chronometers have now been settled for some years without any material variation, except in one point, which will be mentioned presently, and there is hardly any visible difference between one good chronometer and another; it was hence obviously out of our power to make such actual trial of them as can only be conducted in an observatory, and must be continued for a considerable time in order to ascertain their relative merits.

We therefore came to the conclusion that the only satisfactory plan on which we can distinguish any among the large number of chronometers in the Exhibition (at least in the English part of it), is to adopt the results of the trials at the Royal Observatory, during the last few years, of chronometers by the same makers as have now sent any to the Exhibition. But it must be understood that the same reports of the Greenwich trials which justify us in awarding prizes to several chronometer-makers who are exhibitors, show that others who are not exhibitors would have been equally entitled to Medals if they had sent any chronometers here. The exhibitors who have been awarded Prize Medals from having obtained high places in the trials at the Royal Observatory in the last few years are—Messrs. DENT, C. FRODSHAM, PARKINSON and FRODSHAM, HUTTON, and LOSEBY; and we should have been glad to have had the opportunity of similarly acknowledging the merits of Messrs. Poole, E. J. Massey, and Eiffe, as the makers of chronometers, which, together with those of Loseby and Dent, have exclusively occupied the first three places in all the trials of the last four years.

Among the foreign chronometer-makers we have had the satisfaction of being able to award Prize Medals to three of the highest reputation in their respective countries, viz., M. VISSIÈRE, of Paris, M. URBAN JÜRGENSEN, of Altona, and M. LOUIS RICHARD, of Neufchâtel; the last of whom has exhibited a chronometer in which the necessity for a fusee is superseded by a remontoire escapement of a more simple construction than usual, the impulse being given to the balance, not by any teeth of a scape-wheel, but by a small spring which is wound up sufficiently for the purpose by the scape-wheel every time it escapes.

The single point in which there is any material difference in the construction of the best chronometers, is the mode of effecting what is called the secondary or auxiliary compensation of the balance, or that which is required in addition to the ordinary compensation, to prevent the chronometer from gaining at mean temperatures if it is adjusted for two extreme ones, such as 20° and 100°, or losing at the extremes of heat and cold if the compensation is adjusted only for temperatures within moderate limits, as from 40° to 80°.

The earliest inventions for this purpose, as well as the discovery of the necessity for a secondary compensation, appear to have been made by Mr. Eiffe and Mr. Dent about the same time, and independently of each other; and their methods are still in use, and evidently very successful. But we agree with the opinion expressed by the Astronomer Royal in a Report made by him to the Admiralty, that the most ingenious contrivance for this purpose, and probably the best adapted to the wants of chronometers—at least of those which are likely to be exposed to extreme temperatures—is Mr. LOSEBY's, in which small curved thermometer tubes are set upon the ends of the ordinary compensation bars, so that the mercury advances along the tubes towards the centre of the balance, and at an increasing rate the nearer it approaches the centre. The effect of this, as of most of the other contrivances for the same purpose, is evidently to diminish the moment of inertia of the balance still more than it is diminished by the bending inwards of the ordinary compensation bars, on the ends of which the mercurial tubes are fixed.

The three makers who have been mentioned in addition to those who have received Medals not being exhibitors, we can give no account of their methods of compensation. Mr. Dent's consists in placing the balance weights on small additional compensation bars set on the ends of the common ones, in such a position that the weights advance and recede in a radial direction more rapidly the nearer they are to the centre, for any given number of degrees of heat. There is also a chronometer exhibited by Messrs. BARRAUD and LUND, with a contrivance which is substantially the same in principle, and perhaps equally likely to answer, though not so simple in form; besides others, which do not appear to us to require particular notice.

We desire to draw attention to a chronometer with a glass balance and balance-spring, exhibited by Mr. Dent, on account of the remarkable fact that such a spring only requires about one-tenth of the compensation of a steel spring, and one-twelfth of a gold one. We have been furnished with a copy of the Observatory Report of the rate of a chronometer with this balance and spring, and the small amount of compensating materials which it requires ; and the variation of rate during the five months it was tried was very small. It is necessary to add, however, that Mr. Dent told us that some difficulties in making these glass springs have hitherto prevented their being generally used, even by himself ; and we mention these facts in the hope that he and other persons may be thereby induced to exert their ingenuity in overcoming these difficulties, so as to bring into use a material for springs which requires so little compensation, and consequently no secondary compensation, and which is also free from liability to rust, a point of manifest importance in instruments to be used at sea.

Astronomical Clocks.

Among these clocks, which are also sometimes called *regulators*, there is little that requires special notice. There are several of the usual construction, with Graham's escapement and mercurial pendulum, by the eminent makers who have already been noticed, as well as by some others, both English and Foreign. But astronomical clocks which will go accurately within two or three seconds a week may now be had of all good clockmakers ; and it would be absurd to give a prize to any one for sending an instrument here, which a hundred other persons could have sent if they pleased ; except in a few cases, such as that of chronometers above mentioned, where the exhibition of an article, not in itself distinguishable from others of the same kind, has enabled us to make a proper acknowledgment of the well-established reputation of the maker.*

Besides these astronomical clocks of the usual construction, there are several with new escapements, chiefly on the remontoire principle, but none that appear to us likely to supersede the old dead escapement. We have nevertheless given Prize Medals to Mr. GOWLAND, of London, and M. GANNERY, of Paris, for gravity escapements, which are substantially the same ; the impulse being given in both of them, not by arms turning on pivots, but by small weights, which in M. Gannery's clock are hung by threads to the pallet arms, but in Mr. Gowland's are still more independent, being small inverted cups resting on the pallet arms, and alternately taken up by spikes projecting upwards from another pair of arms attached to the pendulum : on the other hand, in M. Gannery's escapement there is less tendency to *trip ;* and it ought to be known to the inventors of remontoire escapements, that independently of the risk of actual tripping (or letting two or three teeth slip past at once), any tendency to drive the pallets too far, if the force of the clock happens to increase, is fatal to the accurate performance of such an escapement.

It should be added, that Mr. Gowland claims as an advantage of his escapement (and M. Gannery may do the same, and so may M. Wagner for one of his turret

---

* It is a bare act of justice to the other exhibitors to mention, that in this desire to acknowledge the reputation of makers whose works have been tested by a much better criterion than we had the means of applying, we were nearly misled into giving a Medal to an exhibitor of astronomical clocks and watches on the ground of his being really, as he very conspicuously designated himself, " Maker to the Royal Observatory." We fortunately ascertained from the best authority that the only ground on which this person so distinguished himself from all the other exhibitors was, his having once performed certain services for the Observatory establishment, by no means of a high order, and even those performed in such a way that they have been discontinued, and are particularly unlikely to be resumed.

clocks, which will be noticed afterwards) that the pendulum is independent of the friction of unlocking, because that is done by the little remontoire weight, which is stopped for a moment as it descends on to the pallet arm by reason of the inertia of the pallets and their arms. This was also the case in the late Captain Kater's escapement, which is described in the Transactions of the Royal Society, but is too complicated for use. And indeed the contrivers of all such escapements should remember, that no new escapement has any chance of coming into use unless it is as cheap and easy to make as Graham's, and is really so independent of the force of the train that a common house-clock movement will do as well for it as a well-finished train with high-numbered pinions: an experiment which the makers of remontoire escapements seldom venture upon.

We have also given a Prize Medal to M. DUBOIS, of Locle, the only Swiss maker who has exhibited a pendulum clock, for a regulator, with a gridiron pendulum in which the compensation is adjustable, and an escapement which is a sort of imitation of the chronometer escapement. A construction of much the same kind was suggested by Mr. Airy, in the Cambridge Philosophical Transactions, in the year 1827; and we do not mean, by giving this Medal, to express any opinion on the probability of such an escapement superseding the ordinary one.

Besides these escapements, which are all intended exclusively for astronomical clocks, there is one lately patented by Mr. C. MACDOWALL, which is intended as a substitute, not only for Graham's escapement, but for the common recoil escapement; and we are informed, as a proof of its cheapness, that a tender has been made to supply clocks to a public office, either with this escapement, or the usual recoil escapement, at the same price. Instead of a scape-wheel there is only a small disc, with a single ruby pin set in it, very near the arbor: the disc turns half round at every beat of the pendulum; and the pallets are both together on an arm, which may be the crutch of the pendulum, or may be in the pendulum-rod itself; and they are so formed, that the impulse is given chiefly by direct action across the line of centres, and not obliquely, as in all the anchor escapements, and therefore with less friction. It is also a dead escapement, and by the simple addition to it of two long teeth or arms for the locking part (on the principle of the duplex escapement in watches), the friction on the dead part of the pallets may be reduced almost to nothing, in clocks intended for very accurate performance. Mr. Macdowall is now making a clock with a remontoire escapement, on the same principle, which may evidently be as well applied to such an escapement as to impulse escapements. He has also successfully applied it to a lever-watch.

The greater velocity of the disc than of a scape-wheel renders another wheel in the train necessary; but as the clock, notwithstanding, goes with even a less maintaining force than usual, the friction of this extra wheel is evidently compensated by the diminished friction of the escapement, in consequence of the impulse being given directly instead of obliquely.

We are quite aware that an escapement, in general appearance similar to this was made some years ago, both in England and France; and specimens of it were produced to us from each country. But in both these specimens there was a roller instead of the fixed pin in the disc; and what is perhaps of more consequence, they both had a much larger angle of escape than Macdowall's clock, and consequently, required a larger vibration of the pendulum : and we are not surprised that escapements so made had never come into general use, which was admitted with respect to the French one ; or had been abandoned, as those who produced the English one assured us that it had been long ago. Mr. Macdowall's escapement avoids the *shake* and the uncertainty of a roller, and does not require a larger arc of vibration than a common clock ; and, on the whole, we think that it combines, in a high degree, the several qualities which we are directed to regard in our distribution of prizes, viz., simplicity, cheapness, durability, and at least probable accuracy of performance, and therefore we have given Mr. Macdowall a Prize Medal for what he calls his " single-pin escapement."

Turret Clocks.

After astronomical clocks, those which are intended for public buildings are of the greatest importance. Indeed, in some public clocks a degree of accuracy may now be properly required, as it can be obtained, exceeding that of most astronomical clocks. Considering the number of persons who make turret clocks in this country, the smallness of the number of them in the Exhibition is rather surprising : and those which deserve any favourable notice are still fewer. It is remarkable, too, that the only ones in the English Department which appeared to us to deserve such notice, are two clocks with cast-iron wheels ; and they are both of them such as ought to convince anybody, that the prejudice against cast-iron clock wheels is altogether unfounded, now that they can be made so well that the teeth do not even require touching with a file after they come out of the mould. Both of these clocks also have a remontoire apparatus in the going train, the effect of which is, that the escapement is driven, not by the great clock weight, but by a small weight, or a spring, wound up at intervals by the train, which is discharged like a striking part, or in some other way, at every minute or half minute, by the revolution of the escape-wheel. Most of the turret clocks in M. WAGNER's collection, which will be noticed presently, are also on the remontoire principle. And there can be no doubt that, since it can be applied at a moderate expense, all turret clocks of high character, at least if they have large external dials, ought to be so made, because it renders the escapement independent of all variations in the force of the train, which are sometimes very considerable, and also allows a sufficient weight to be applied to the clock to drive the hands in all weathers, without making the pendulum swing too far ; and moreover, as the hands of a clock of this kind do not move an almost invisible quantity at every beat of the pendulum, but by a very sensible jump at every letting off of the remontoire, the time can be taken from the minute-hand, at a considerable distance, as accurately as from the seconds-hand of a regulator ; and for the same reason the striking part is also discharged more exactly at the right time.

As regards the going part, the principal advantage of cast-iron wheels over brass or gun-metal is their much greater cheapness. But in the striking part they have the further advantage of greater strength, which, in large clocks, is the chief thing to be attended to, and the thing in which they are most frequently deficient. In Mr. ROBERTS's clock the striking is done on a new plan, with a very light hammer ; but the clock has only a small hemispherical bell attached to it, and we have no proof that this very ingenious contrivance, in which neither fly nor hammer-

5 D

spring is required, would answer for a large bell, such as that on which Mr. DENT's clock strikes, or even a much smaller bell of the usual form. In the latter clock the hammer is raised by broad cams cast on the great wheel of the striking part, and of such a shape, and with the lever so arranged, that there is the smallest possible waste of power : in fact, very little more than one-fourth of the force of the great striking weight is lost in friction, the resistance of the air to the fly, and in the necessary interval between the fall of the hammer and the beginning of its next rise,—a proportion which is much less than usual.

Both Mr. ROBERTS's and Mr. DENT's clocks have compensated pendulums. The former has a steel and brass compensation, which, Mr. Roberts says, is made in accordance with his own experiments on the relative expansion of the two metals ; though it differs from the result of all the ordinary tables of expansion, the length of the brass compensation-tubes being much less than usual. Mr. Dent's pendulum has an iron and zinc tube compensation, made according to the usual tables, and agreeing with his experience of the Royal Exchange clock pendulum, which has a similar one, and has now been sufficiently tested for several years.

Mr. Roberts's escapement is a new one of his own contrivance : the pendulum only receives its impulse on a roller at every alternate beat. The remontoire is on the endless chain plan, which is described in Reid's book on clockmaking, except that the mode of letting off is different. The form of the clock-frame is pyramidal, with the pendulum hung from the top ; and it is consequently very steady, provided the floor it stands on be so ; though the plan of fixing turret-clocks on beams let into the wall for the purpose, is, in most instances, steadier than any fixing to a floor can be. All the wheels are made to take out separately, as they should always be, and the Jury were particularly struck with the goodness of the casting and the form of the wheels. Mr. Roberts is well known as an eminent engine-maker at Manchester, and by the application of his machinery to the manufacturing of these clocks he is able to sell them at a much lower price than usual. On the whole, without expressing any opinion on the supposed advantages of the escapement, or the mode of striking, or some other peculiarities of this clock, we consider it well deserving of a Prize Medal.

The escapement in Mr. Dent's clock is the ordinary pin-wheel dead escapement, but the wheel is smaller than usual, being only four inches in diameter, and it contains forty pins. It is driven by a spiral spring, which is merely part of a large watch-spring, and is wound up a quarter of a turn after every quarter of a turn of the scape-wheel. The pinion, or small wheel to which one end of the spring is fixed, does not ride on the arbor of the scape-wheel, in which case there would be considerable friction between them, but on a stud fixed into the clock-frame ; so that the scape-wheel is driven by the spring without any friction whatever, except that of its own pivots, and the very small friction which is due to the upward pressure of the ends of the remontoire fly on the arbor of the scape-wheel. The consequence is, that there cannot possibly be any variation in the force on the pendulum, except that which may arise in the escapement itself, if the pallets are not properly oiled,—as in all other anchor or pin-wheel escapements. It may be worth while to state that the variation of force in the spring due to changes of temperature, if it were ten times as great as it is, would produce no sensible effect upon the pendulum. And as this pendulum is 8 feet long, and weighs above 2 cwt., such a clock may be reasonably expected to go as well as any astronomical clock; and in fact it has gone since the opening of the Exhibition, at least as well as a highly-finished astronomical clock, which was placed by the side of it, and every week compared with the time brought from Greenwich.*

The maintaining power for keeping it going while winding is of a new construction; as the common spring-going barrel is difficult to construct with both sufficient play and sufficient power for large clocks of this kind, which take several minutes to wind up. This maintaining power is of the "bolt-and-shutter" kind, but not requiring any click, and so made that it is impossible to begin winding without raising the maintaining weight high enough to keep in action for seven or eight minutes, and yet it can be thrown out of gear as soon as the winding is done. There is another point in which the arrangement is different from usual: the great wheel and barrel of the going part, and of both the striking parts, are set in the great frame, and the smaller frame, which carries all the other wheels of the going part, can be taken off entire, without disturbing either the great wheel or the pendulum. Mr. Dent uses wire ropes, because by that means he obtains the advantage of many turns of the barrels in the eight days, without the inconvenience of long barrels, or the bad practice of letting the rope go twice over them.

A Council Medal has been awarded to Mr. DENT for this clock, on the recommendation of all the members of this Jury, except the Chairman, who declined to express an opinion upon it, on account of having himself furnished the design. But as it contains hardly anything which had not been either previously used by Mr. Dent, or suggested in print, and therefore equally open to the adoption of any other maker, he is entitled to full credit for it, as well as for his enterprise in attempting to introduce a new description of clock, possessing both greater accuracy and greater strength than usual, and one which can be made for less money than equally large turret-clocks, of the common construction and of good quality.

We have already referred to M. WAGNER'S (of Paris) collection of turret clocks, which displays great fertility of invention; and we have awarded him a Council Medal for the collection, but especially for his clock with a continuous motion, intended for the purpose of driving equatorial telescopes, so as to keep them pointed at any given star, and for all other purposes for which a continuous, instead of an intermittent, motion is required. The mode by which this is effected is particularly ingenious as well as simple. In this, as in several others of M. Wagner's clocks, there is a gravity remontoire apparatus, on the bevelled-wheel principle, on the arbor of the wheel below the scape-wheel. For the construction of these remontoires we must refer to books, as it would be difficult to give an intelligible description of them without drawings; but assuming that to be understood, the arm which carries the remontoire weight is in this clock prolonged to a convenient distance, so as to carry a kind of bell hung to it by a couple of wires, and within the bell a fly is driven by a train of wheels connected

---

* Since the close of the Exhibition, we have been informed that the accumulated error of the large clock, from the 8th August to the 15th October, was – 2·8 seconds; or, in other words, the pendulum lost not quite two beats in the four millions of vibrations it performed during that period.

with the great wheel of the clock. This fly is so adjusted, that the velocity with which it allows the train to move is equal to the *average* velocity which it would have if connected with the pendulum, or to the velocity of a train with a revolving instead of a vibrating pendulum of the same period. If the force on the clock be too great, the remontoire arm becomes raised above its average height, and the bell rising with it lets in more of the external air upon the fly, which reduces its velocity, and *vice versâ*. In this way, the hand, or telescope, attached to that part of the train which has the continuous motion, is always made to keep pace with the average velocity of the scape-wheel with its vibrating pendulum.

M. Wagner has exhibited a movement of this kind applied to a long vertical barrel for measuring the force of gravity, as in Attwood's machine. The barrel revolves in a second, and by the side of it a weight descends freely in a groove, with an inked brush attached to it; and as the barrel revolves, the falling brush traces a curve on the surface, which exactly indicates the space descended in any given portion of the time which the barrel takes to revolve.

Two of M. Wagner's turret clocks have this same bevelled-wheel remontoire in the train, only with a provision for letting it off at every half-minute, instead of a continuous motion; and one of them has a remontoire escapement also, but by no means incapable of tripping, if the force be increased.

There is another clock in the same collection, which deserves particular notice on account of there being a remontoire in it, without any additional wheel in the train. This is managed by setting the second-wheel in a swinging frame, having its axis in a line with the arbor of the scape-wheel, and so allowing a little play sideways to the arbor of the second-wheel. In this clock, also, the pallets are set in the pendulum without any crutch, the scape-wheel being put outside the frame.

Another of M. Wagner's clocks has an escapement with a direct recoil, as in Harrison's once famous but long-ago abandoned escapement; and in this clock, also, the pallets are set on the pendulum without a crutch. It is certainly a superior contrivance to Harrison's; although, as in his, the recoil is necessarily very great and sudden.

All the smaller clocks in this collection have cast-iron striking parts, though the two large ones are of brass, probably for the sake of appearance; and they all strike from the great wheel, like Mr. Dent's clock; but most of them have two hour-hammers, striking alternately, and none of them appear to have barrels of sufficient length, in proportion to the number of striking pins, to go a week without the rope going twice over the barrel. They have also compensated pendulums, all on the lever principle; in some cases applied to the pendulum rods, and in others fixed to the bar at the top of the clock frame, so as to draw up the pendulum spring through a slit in the clock. The lever compensation seems to be the only one used in France, except occasionally the gridiron pendulum, with nine bars of brass and steel. In English clocks, hardly any compensation is now used, except the mercurial cylinder in the best astronomical clocks, and the zinc tube compensation in clocks where the mercurial pendulum would be too expensive.

We have given a Prize Medal to M. GOURDIN, a maker of some celebrity in France, for a small well-executed turret clock, with a train remontoire of a different construction from any of M. Wagner's, the remontoire wheels being employed in changing velocity, or as part of the clock train, and not merely in changing direction, which is the case in the bevelled-wheel remontoire.

There are also some small turret-clocks, both by M. CHAVIN and by M. BAILLY COMTE, which we mention on account of their extraordinary cheapness.

Electricals clocks may be considered as connected with turret clocks, especially in this Exhibition, in which the experiment has been made of working three large dials by electricity, not merely as a means of connection with one large clock driven by a weight in the usual way, but using electricity as the motive power. It is needless to inform any one who has frequented the Exhibition, how far that experiment has been successful; but whenever the practical difficulty is overcome, of obtaining unfailing electrical action, i. e., of securing perfect contact of the wires at every proper epoch, there is no doubt that some kind of remontoire action will be the proper way of maintaining the motion of the pendulum, as has been attempted by Mr. SHEPHERD in these clocks, and by several other exhibitors. The other plan, of making the pendulum drive the train, cannot possibly avoid such variations of force as will be fatal to the isochronism of any clock pendulum.

There is no instance in the Exhibition of a large weight-clock driving dials at a distance by electrical connection, either galvanic or magnetic; although there is not found to be any difficulty in doing it by the latter method, by a strong permanent magnet, such as in Henley's magnetic telegraph, set on an axis, so that it can be twisted out of contact with the armature by the force of the great clock, whenever the remontoire is let off. The wires are coiled round the armature, in the well-known manner which is employed in telegraphs of this kind; and they make and unmake the temporary magnets placed behind every dial, of which the hands are to be kept in motion with those of the great clock by means of ratchet-work, or pallets, worked by the alternations of the temporary magnets, just as in the two electrical dials in front of the South and West Galleries.

House Clocks.

In what are called by the French civil clocks, or clocks for domestic use, there is not much room for difference, except in the merely ornamental parts, which we have nothing to do with. There are many such clocks, of various shapes, in the English part of the Exhibition, as well as the foreign, and most of them sufficiently good for their purpose. But it is impossible to distinguish any of the English ones as manifesting such superiority over the rest as would justify us in giving Medals for them; because such Medals could only mislead the public into the belief that there are not many other makers from whom equally good house clocks may be obtained: indeed, some of the best makers have not thought it worth while to exhibit any.

Among the French Exhibitors, however, we have given a Prize Medal to Messrs. DETOUCHE and HOUDIN, who exhibit a very handsome collection of well-made clocks, of various sizes, some with compensated pendulums and uncommon escapements, and with what is called *equation work*, or a hand to show solar as well as mean time. They also exhibit some of their pinions separately, which are very well made. Altogether, their collection is well worthy of notice.

We have also given a Prize Medal for small clocks to M. Brocot, the originator of an elegant and popular form of a nearly dead escapement in ornamental clocks, in which the pallets consist of semi-cylinders of jewels, at right angles to the plane of the scape-wheel. These clocks are generally made with the escapement in front of the dial, so as to be visible, and also to allow the scape-wheel to be taken out without disturbing the rest of the clock.

In addition to these Medals, which we have awarded chiefly on account of the good execution or arrangement of the movements, we have given one to Messrs. Reyder and Colin, who exhibit a number of house clocks of various kinds, all remarkable for the lowness of their price, and sufficiently well executed for the ordinary uses of such clocks. And in speaking of cheap house clocks, of course the American clocks ought not to be unnoticed, though we have thought it unnecessary to attempt to distinguish any of them by a Prize Medal, as they are all substantially alike; and they are now so universally known for their cheapness—a quality which generally receives its own reward—that the additional distinction of a Medal on that account would be more than usually superfluous. There is, however, one quality for which they are entitled to greater credit than is generally known, and that is, the small weights or moving force which they require, showing that there is much less power wasted by friction and the inertia of the train than in most other clocks. The small amount of inertia is caused by the lightness of the wheels; and the small friction (which certainly cannot be attributed either to the high finish or high numbers of the pinions) is accounted for by the use of lantern pinions, which (when driven by the wheels) have much less friction than leaved pinions of such low numbers, and are also less liable to be clogged with dirt, and are less affected by the wheel-teeth being inaccurately cut, as they generally are in clocks of much greater pretension than these.

To this class of domestic clocks belong the various forms of striking and chiming clocks, and alarums, and also tell-tale or watchmen's clocks, and clocks going a long time without winding, and perpetual almanac clocks, whatever be the number of phænomena which they profess to show. There is now so little difficulty in making these things, and so little use in most of them when made, that we do not think it necessary to distinguish any of them by a Medal, although in some instances they display ingenious contrivances for effecting their different objects. The Jury, however, agreed to mention some small alarum clocks by M. Pierret, of Paris, on account of their cheapness, and because alarums really are, for certain purposes, useful articles of household furniture.

Watches.

The only horological instruments which remain to be noticed are watches, in which term are included carriage clocks, since these are, in fact, only large watches, set in cases like those of small clocks, and with the balance placed at right angles to the rest of the wheels, so that its axis may stand vertically, because it vibrates with less friction in that position—a fact of which some of the exhibitors do not seem to be aware.

Watches like house clocks, are so much an article of general manufacture, and there is so little difference in the quality of those of several of the best makers, that it is difficult to establish any principle on which prizes can be given for them, except with reference to the general reputation of the exhibitors of articles which appear in themselves to be good.

The three principal places in England where watches are made, are London, Liverpool, and Coventry. Among the London makers, several who have received Medals for chronometers or other articles, would have been entitled to receive them for their exhibition of watches alone. There is a very beautiful collection of carriage clocks and watches, of various kinds, by Mr. DENT; some of them exhibiting, besides the compensated balance, which all first-rate watches now possess, a contrivance (different from most others for the same purpose) for winding up and setting the hands without a key, by turning the knob in the handle or *pendant*; and others having what is called a split seconds-hand, that is to say, two seconds-hands, which travel together, and appear as one, till you move a pin in the case, whereupon one of the hands separates from the other, and stops until you move the pin again, when the hand starts forward and rejoins the proper seconds-hand, after any length of stoppage; and this is done without the use of an independent train to drive the extra seconds-hand. There are various contrivances, of different kinds, for the same purpose, among the other watches in the Exhibition. Mr. Dent also exhibits a night watch, or a watch for blind persons, technically called a *tac*-watch, with an external hand, which moves round with the hour hand, and the position of which can be felt with tolerable accuracy, with reference to twelve studs set round the rim of the case, for the twelve hours, reckoning of course from the handle. There is also a watch similar to this among the Swiss ones; but Mr. Dent's has a special provision to prevent the position of the hand from being altered by the act of feeling it. He is to be considered as entitled to a Prize Medal for his collection of watches, independently of the Council Medal awarded to him for the large clock.

In like manner the Prize Medals awarded to Mr. C. FRODSHAM, and Messrs. PARKINSON and H. FRODSHAM, for chronometers, are to be understood as awarded also in respect of their exhibition of watches.

The former of these exhibitors states that his watches are made on a certain *caliper* (as the watchmakers call the working plan of a watch), in which the sizes of the wheels are determined according to a set of rules, partly arbitrary and partly founded on experience, according to the size of the barrel, or in other words, according to the power of the mainspring. All makers of watches on a large scale must have some such system of their own; but Mr. Frodsham proposes that a general system shall be adopted, in which the sizes of the various pieces of a watch shall not be expressed by the usual conventional numbers, known only to those who have to use them, but in decimals of an inch, and according to certain tables of proportion with reference to the size of the barrel, as above mentioned. It would probably be convenient if some such system were adopted, either according to Mr. Frodsham's rules (so far as they are arbitrary), or any others which might be generally agreed on.

Such a system as this is still more completely carried out by Mr. ROBERTS's watch-plate drilling machine, a most ingenious and apparently successful invention, by which any given caliper or proportion of the parts of a watch of any size can be at once transferred, by a mere mechanical process, to any other watches of any other sizes; piercing all the holes required for the pivots of the wheels, and other purposes with unfailing accuracy. And in connection with this machine there is a *sector* for proportioning the sizes of wheels for any required number of teeth, also by a mechanical operation without the necessity of calculation. The Prize Medal before mentioned, as given to Mr. Roberts for his cast-iron clock, is therefore to be considered as awarded equally in respect of his watch-plate drilling machine.

It should be mentioned also that he exhibits some watches with a remontoire escapement, and one, which he calls a *recorder* watch, with two seconds-hands, of which one can be stopped to denote the exact time of any observation, as is done in various other watches in the Exhibition. Indeed, the number of them is so great that we have not been able to give a Prize Medal to any maker solely on account of such a contrivance, except to M. Rieussec, a well-known watchmaker of Paris, for his watches with a seconds-hand, which, on touching a pin at the time of observation, makes a black spot on the dial; and this can be repeated at very close intervals, so as to record the exact epochs of a number of observed phænomena succeeding each other very closely, without the necessity of taking the eye off the object to be watched for in order to look at the dial.

What are called the *movements* of watches and small clocks are made by machinery on a very large scale by Messrs. Japy, of Paris, to whom we have awarded a Council Medal; although the objects themselves, as they appear in the Exhibition, are by no means striking, inasmuch as these watch movements are in fact only the two plates and some of the larger wheels of the train, and the clock movements are the internal parts of the clock without the escapement. The most, indeed the only remarkable quality in these movements, is their extraordinary cheapness. They are, however, at least as good as any others of the same kind made in the usual way by hand; and Messrs. Japy, we are told, sell no less than half a million of them to watch and clockmakers in the course of a year. The great cheapness of these articles being obtained by means of a peculiar process of manufacture, it was considered that Messrs. Japy might properly receive a Council Medal for their watch movements, as a specimen of the produce of such improved mode of manufacturing.

Messrs. Rotherham, of Coventry, exhibit a large collection of watches in all stages of manufacture, for which we have awarded a Prize Medal. We have also given one to Mr. Roskell, of Liverpool, an eminent maker, who exhibits a handsome collection of watches and small clocks, some of which are so constructed as to show the action of the various forms of watch escapements in general use; and to M. Redier, of Paris, for a cheap kind of watch alarum, of which a great number are sold both in France and in this country.

It may be mentioned here that M. Kralik, of Pesth, exhibits a set of models, in which thirteen different escapements can be fitted to one clock movement, by merely unscrewing the part containing the escapement. This is apparently intended for illustrating lectures on watchmaking, or for experiments on the effects of different escapements.

Mr. Jackson exhibits what he calls (with some disregard of etymology) a *soliclave* watch, whereby he means a watch with a solid key. However, his invention of the thing fortunately deserves more credit than his name for it. Most people are aware that the pipes of watch-keys wear out; and in so doing, they wear off the corners of the winding square on which they act. The shorter this winding square is, the sooner of course this will happen; and in thin watches of the common construction the winding square cannot but be short. With the view of avoiding this, Messrs. AUBERT and KLAFTENBERGER'S watches, and several foreign ones in the Exhibition, which have no fusee, have the arbor of the barrel hollow and squared for a solid key to fit into it the whole depth of the barrel. But this will not do for watches with a fusee, because the fusee arbor has to turn while the watch is going, though the barrel-arbor of a watch without a fusee only turns while it is being wound up; and a hollow fusee arbor would be much too thick. Mr. Jackson, therefore, winds up his fusee by a small auxiliary wheel, analogous to what is called a jack-wheel in turret clocks; and the arbor of this small wheel is made hollow and squared to receive the solid key. As the little wheel has nothing to do, and no pressure on it, when the watch is going, the friction of its thick arbor is inconsiderable, even supposing it not to be thrown out of gear, as it might be. This also allows the fusee arbor to be smaller, and therefore to turn with less friction than usual. We have consequently given Mr. Jackson a Prize Medal for this invention.

We have also given a Prize Medal to M. MONTANDON, of Paris, for his mainsprings, of which he is a maker of high reputation; and it is unnecessary to say that the goodness of the mainspring is of great importance to the accurate performance of watches, especially of foreign ones, in which there is generally no fusee, and so the spring must be capable of acting with nearly uniform force for four or five turns of the barrel.

We agreed to mention the names of two other French watchmakers: M. LE ROY, for a collection of well-finished clocks and watches: and M. LAUMAIN, who exhibits some well-made pocket chronometers, with the escapement part made to take off separately; as well as the name of Mr. BOLTON, an English exhibitor of some very cheap watches in German silver cases.

The Swiss exhibition of horology consists entirely (with the single exception of a clock before mentioned) of watches and watchwork; and, as is well known, a large proportion of the watches of the world, especially the small and cheaper ones, are made in Switzerland. But in this instance, as in some others, it is not to be inferred that we intend the superiority of the works of one nation over another, in any particular department, to be measured by the number of Medals which have been awarded to each, as they were given on no such consideration.

We have given Prize Medals for watches to the following Swiss exhibitors:— Messrs. AUDEMARS, GRANDJEAN, GROSCLAUDE, LECOULTRE, MERCIER, PATEK and PHILIPPE, and RETOR, except that for the last a grant of money has been substituted.

M. AUDEMARS exhibits a watch with a contrivance for winding up the train which is required for driving what is called an "independent seconds-hand," as well as the ordinary train, by the handle or pendant, so that when either train is fully wound up the winder acts on it no longer, but proceeds with the other train alone. He has likewise a watch with several dials, one of them indicating one-fifth of a second, and with provisions for stopping the different hands independently. It may be mentioned here that Messrs. COUSINS and WHITESIDE, of London, also exhibit a large watch with a stop seconds-hand, indicating one-sixth of a second.   M. Audemars' collection contains various other watches, with different kinds of escapements and other peculiarities, which cannot be particularly described here.

M. GRANDJEAN exhibits some pocket chronometers, *i. e.* watches with the chronometer escapement ; and one of them has a balance-spring of a spherical form instead of a flat or a cylindrical one.

M. GROSCLAUDE has sent some watches with "independent seconds-hand" and only a single mainspring.

M. LECOULTRE's watches are remarkable for the good execution of the wheels and pinions.   He is stated to make all his watches with the corresponding wheels of the same size, so that when any wheel is damaged, it can at once be replaced by a new one without any other trouble than that of putting it in.   And he, like some other makers, has a method of winding up and setting the hands without a key, and with a provision to avoid the risk of a slight derangement of the hands in the act of putting their adjusting work in gear, to which some other methods are said to be liable.

M. MERCIER exhibits, among other well-made articles, a watch with a new recoiling escapement with a double scape-wheel, which is ingenious and simple ; but we do not profess to give any opinion on the probability of its success.

MM. PATEK and PHILIPPE exhibit a large and valuable collection of watches and pocket chronometers.   Their articles are generally of moderate price, besides being well made, and some of them are highly finished.   They have a repeater with two barrels, both winding in the handle, and a watch for the blind.   They are the makers of the very small watch, only ·35 of an inch in diameter, which attracted much notice as the smallest in the Exhibition.

We have recommended M. RETOR for a reward in money instead of a Prize Medal, as we understand that he is a person of very small means, who has had some difficulty in getting up the articles which he has sent to the Exhibition, and that he is also engaged in making experiments in watchmaking, which are of course at present unremunerative.   He has exhibited a pocket chronometer with an ingenious escapement.

We conclude the notice of the Medals to the Swiss exhibitors of watches with the award of a Council Medal to M. LUTZ, of Geneva, for his watch balance-springs. On the balance-spring, more than any other single piece of a watch, its isochronism depends ; and these springs present a marked difference in some of their qualities from those of any other exhibitor (even of some who specially directed our attention to the alleged superiority of their springs), inasmuch as they bore the tests both of heating and stretching out nearly straight without at all altering their permanent form, which was not the case with any other springs which we tried.

Besides these, we agreed to make Honourable Mention in our Report of the following Swiss exhibitors of watches :—ELFROTH, the maker of the small watch in the end of a pencil-case ; BOCK, COURVOISIER, MERMOOZ, and Messrs. BARON and UHLMAN ; also of M. FAVRE BRANDT, on account of his ingenious instrument for tracing out (not cutting) the teeth of watch-wheels in the epicycloidal form.

And lastly, we have awarded a Prize Medal to M. BENOIT, of Sardinia, for his watches and watch movements, and for a machine for rapidly polishing the teeth of the scape-wheel of a horizontal or cylinder escapement.

The following is a summary of the awards in this Class :—

COUNCIL MEDALS.

Nation.	No. in Catalogue.	Name of Exhibitor.	Objects Rewarded.
United Kingdom	55	Dent, E. J. - - -	Great clock and collection of other articles.
France - - -	275	Japy Brothers - -	Cheap clock and watch movements, made by machinery.
Switzerland -	94	Lutz, C. - - - -	Hair springs.
France - - -	736	Wagner, J. (Nephew) -	Continuous motion remontoire, and collection of turret-clocks.

PRIZE MEDALS.

Nation.	No. in Catalogue.	Name of Exhibitor.	Objects Rewarded.
Switzerland -	22	Audemars, L. - -	Watches and watch movements.
Sardinia - -	33	Benoit, A. - - -	Watches and tooth-polishing machine.
France - - -	411	Brocot, A. - - -	Half-dead jewelled escapement.
France - - -	1589	Detouche and Houdin	Collection of clocks.
Switzerland -	9	Dubois, F. William -	Astronomical clock.
United Kingdom	57	Frodsham, C. - -	Chronometers and watches.
France - - -	516	Gannery, V. - - -	Astronomical clock.
France - -	525	Gourdin, J. - - -	Small turret-clock.
United Kingdom	27	Gowland, J. - - -	Astronomical clock.
Switzerland -	8	Grandjean, H. - -	Pocket chronometers.
Switzerland -	24	Grosclaude, C. H. -	Ditto.
United Kingdom	7	Hutton, J. - - -	Chronometers.
United Kingdom	32	Jackson, W. H. and S.	Watches, solid key.
Denmark - -	17	Jürgensen and Sons -	Chronometer.
Switzerland -	25	Lecoultre, A. - -	Watches, movements, and pinions.
United Kingdom	12	Loseby, E. T. - -	Chronometer compensation balance.
United Kingdom	68	MacDowall, Charles -	Clock escapement.
Switzerland -	96	Mercier, S. - - -	Watches.
France - - -	–	Montandon Brothers -	Watch mainsprings.
United Kingdom	35	Parkinson & Frodsham	Chronometers and watches.
Switzerland -	99	Patek, Philippe, and Co.	Chronometers, watches, &c.
France - -	1425	Redier, A. - - -	Cheap watch alarums.
Switzerland -	101	Retor, F. (money prize, 50l.)	Pocket chronometer with new escapement.
France - - -	984	Reydor Brothers & Colin	Cheap house clocks.
Prussia - -	142	Richard, Louis - -	Chronometer.
France - - -	1685	Rieussec, N. - - -	Watch with hand printing seconds.
United Kingdom	130	Roberts, R. - - -	Turret-clock, and watch-plate drilling machine.
United Kingdom	123	Roskell, J. - - -	Collection of models and watches, and small clocks.
United Kingdom	124	Rotherham and Sons -	Collection of watches.
France - - -	733	Vissière - - - -	Chronometers.

HONOURABLE MENTION.

Nation.	No. in Catalogue.	Name of Exhibitor.	Objects Rewarded.
United Kingdom	52A	Aubert & Klaftenberger	Watches.
France - -	407	Bailly-Comte and Son	Cheap turret-clocks.
Switzerland -	74	Baron and Uhlmann -	Chronometers and watches.
United Kingdom	34	Barraud and Lund -	Compensation balance and watches.
Switzerland -	31	Bock, H. - - -	Watches.
United Kingdom	94	Bolton, T. - - -	Cheap watches.
France - - -	450	Chavin (Elder Brother)	Cheap turret-clocks.
Switzerland -	34	Courvoisier, F. - -	Chronometers and watches.
United Kingdom	–	Cousens and Whiteside	Stop-watch.
Switzerland -	78	Elffroth, D. H. - -	Watch in pencil-case.
Switzerland -	23	Favre Brandt - -	Watches and tooth-tracing machine.

APPENDIX C

PARIS UNIVERSAL EXHIBITION 1855
CATALOGUE OF THE BRITISH SECTION,
CLASS VIII, SECTION 2,
CLOCKWORK

371 Adams, F.B., and Sons, 21 St. Johns Square, London, watches, *Hon. Mention*

372 Cole, Thomas, 6 Castle Street, Holborn, London, Clocks, *Hon. Mention*

373 Davis, W. and Son, 37 Gracechurch Street, London, watches

375 Frodsham, Charles, 84 Strand, London, Watches and chronometers, *Medaille d'Honneur*

376 Frodsham and Baker, 31 Gracechurch Street, London, watches and chronometers

376a Funnell, E. Brighton, small lever watch ⅛" thick, *Hon. Mention*

377 Gerrard, Alex. (Teacher) Gordons Hospital, Aberdeen, Clock Barometer Spherograph

378 Hall, George Frederick, 15 Norfolk Street, Fitzroy Square,
Clock pendulum and mechanical apparatus

379 Lozeby, E.T., 44 Gerrard Street, Islington, Chronometers and watches, *Silver Medal*

380 Nicole & Capt., 80 Dean Street, Soho Square, London
Watches for astronomers, engineers and physicians, Watches, self-adjusting, without key

382 Poole, John, 57 Fenchurch Street, Chronometers, *Bronze Medal*

383 Watkins, A. 67 Strand, Watches

384 Webster, Richard, 74 Cornhill, Chronometers and Watches

385 Aubert & Klaftenberger, Regent Street, London, Watches and Clocks, *Bronze Medal*

386 Bennett, John, Cheapside, Turret Clock and Watches

APPENDIX D

Class XV.

HOROLOGICAL INSTRUMENTS.

[3218]

ADAMS, F. B., & SONS, 21 *St. John's Square, London.*—Patent reversible chronometer; duplex and lever watches.

[3219]

AGAR, WILLIAM, *Bury, Lancashire.*—Specimens of working men's watches and independent centre seconds, manufactured in Bury.

[3220]

ARMSTRONG, THOMAS, Inventor and Manufacturer, *Manchester.* — Armstrong's improved watchman's detector clocks, steam or speed clock, &c.

The following are exhibited :—

	£ s. d.		£ s. d.
ARMSTRONG'S IMPROVED WATCHMAN'S CLOCK is an ordinary office Timepiece and Watchman's clock combined, for indicating punctuality and registering the neglect of it. It is entirely self-acting, portable, simple in construction, and requires little attention. Price, in plain mahogany case, dial 14 inches diameter	4 15 0	ARMSTRONG'S IMPROVED WATCHMAN'S CLOCK, same as the above, but in a more highly ornamented case, dial 12 inches diameter . ARMSTRONG'S IMPROVED STEAM OR SPEED CLOCK indicates the amount of work done in all establishments where steam-power is used. It also compels the engineer to work at the required pressure, by indicating any neglect. In mahogany case complete, for fixing .	5 10 0 2 15 0

[3221]

AUBERT & LINTON, 252 *Regent Street.*—Watches with recent improvements; ornamental clocks for the table and mantelpiece.

[3222]

BAILEY, JOHN, & CO., *Albion Works, Manchester.*—Improved turret clock in tower, suitable for a market-place, &c.

[3223]

BARRAUD & LUND, 41 *Cornhill, London.*—Chronometers and watches.

[3224]

BAYLISS, WILLIAM, *Finmere, Oxfordshire.*—Model of new remontoire escapement, as put up in Finmere church clock.

[3225]

BENNETT, JOHN, F.R.A.S., 64 & 65 *Cheapside, and* 62 *Cornhill.* — Marine and pocket chronometers; public and private clocks; every description of gold and silver watches.

[3226]

BENSON, J. W., *Ludgate Hill.*—Gold and silver watches and clocks, highest quality, magnificently decorated with artistic designs.

[3227]

BLACKIE, GEORGE, 24 *Amwell Street, E.C.*—A new compound balance to correct the errors in chronometers, and new auxiliary to balance.

[3228]

BROCK, JAMES, 21 *George Street, Portman Square.*—Marine chronometers.

[3229]

BROOKS, S. A., *Northampton Square, London, E.C.*—Watch jewels; sets of jewel gauges for watchmakers and material dealers. (*See page* 67.)

[3230]

CAMERER, KUSS, & CO., 2 *Broad Street, Bloomsbury.*—1. A three-part quarter skeleton on ten bells. 2. A trumpeter clock. 3. A cuckoo clock.

[3231]

CAMPBELL, ANDREW, 63 *Cheapside, E.C., and* 43 *Tottenham Court Road.*—A selection of gold and silver watches.

[3232]

CHEVALIER, BENJAMIN, 4 *Red Lion Street, Clerkenwell, E.C.*—Chronometer and watch cases.

[3233]

CLARK, DR., *Finmere House, Oxfordshire.*—Astronomical clock, impelled by gravitation, requires no oil to the escapement.

[3234]

COATHUPE, CAPTAIN H. B., 1 *Abingdon Street, Kensington.*—Everlasting shilling "silent clocks;" painting-engraving; printing-embossing; printing-painting.

[3235]

COLE, JAMES FERGUSON, 5 *Queen Square, Bloomsbury.*—Chronometers, watches, tempered springs; new horological models and descriptive treatise.

[3236]

COLE, THOMAS, 6 *Castle Street, Holborn.* — Ornamental and portable clocks of original construction and design.

[3237]

CONDLIFF, JAMES, 4 *Fraser Street, Liverpool.*—A skeleton clock.

[3238]

COOKE, THOMAS, & SONS, *Buckingham Works, York.*—Church and turret clock, astronomical clocks, and time regulators.

[3239]

CRISP, W. B., 81 *St. John Street Road.*—Chronometers.

[3240]

DAVIES, C. W., *Notting-hill.*—Clock showing time and longitude at the most important places on the globe.

BROOKS, S. A., *Northampton Square, London, E.C.*—Watch jewels ; sets of jewel gauges for watchmakers and material dealers.

The exhibitor manufactures the RUBY BOTTOMED HOLES for thin cocks or plates, and is also the Inventor and sole manufacturer of the JEWEL-HOLE GAUGE, for determining the size of pivots or jewel holes. Specimens of these manufactures are shown in his case. He can supply merchants and dealers in watch-material with every description of clock, chronometer, and watch jewels, set or unset ; diamond-powder, bort, rubies, sapphires, chrysolites, garnet, &c.

The Export Watch-jewel Case (see engraving), with set jewels arranged and assorted, so that any size required may be instantly found, will be of great service to watchmakers or dealers in material residing in distant parts of the world. A broken jewel can be immediately replaced from it with the greatest accuracy, at a cost of little more than one-third the usual charge, and without the risk and loss of time attending the custom of sending to London the watch or part of watch requiring the jewel.

Persons who do not wish to keep a stock of watch jewels, can be supplied with the Jewel-hole Gauge, which will enable them, by sending the measure of the hole, to obtain the jewel of the exact size required, without the necessity of sending the balance or wheels to a jeweller, whereby risk of loss or damage is incurred.

The Jewel-hole Gauges are valuable for all purposes where accuracy is required, as they neither wear nor corrode. They are arranged as follows :—

Gauge.	Holes.	
1.	1 to 12	inclusive, will gauge the escapement pivots to any modern watch.
2.	13 to 24	inclusive, will gauge the small wheel pivots of three-quarter plate and small frame watches.
3.	25 to 36	inclusive, will gauge the small wheel pivots to large frame watches.
4.	37 to 48	inclusive, will gauge centre wheel, also chronometer third and fourth pivots.
5.	49 to 60	inclusive, will gauge chronometer seconds' pivots.
6.	61 to 72	inclusive, will gauge regulator and clock-work pivots, also lower fusee and hollow centre pinions to watches.
7.	73 to 84	inclusive, will gauge small three-quarter plate fusee upper pivot.
8.	85 to 96	inclusive, will gauge large ditto ditto.
9.	97 to 108	inclusive, will gauge frame fusee upper pivot.
10.	109 to 120	inclusive, will gauge large frame fusee upper pivot.

A set of pivots, numbered to correspond in gauge with each jewel-hole can be supplied, for measuring the size of the hole required, should the balance or wheel-pivot of the watch be broken.

F 2

[3241]

DAVIS, W., & SONS, 84 *King William Street, City, London.*—Chronometers, watches, clocks, and specimens of horology.

The exhibitors are manufacturers of clocks, watches, and chronometers; jewellers; dealers in diamonds and other gems, and in onyx, shell, and other cameos; and importers of Geneva watches, French clocks, bronzes, &c. They keep on hand a stock of church and turret clocks, of various sizes, and constructed on approved principles. The time is given by electricity at their city establishment, from the Royal Observatory, Greenwich.

Davis and Sons have a branch establishment at 57 New Street, Birmingham.

[3242]

DELOLME, H., 48 *Rathbone Place, Oxford Street.*—Regulator, chronometers, clocks, and watches.

[3243]

DENT & Co., 61 *Strand, and* 34 & 35 *Royal Exchange.* — Chronometers, regulators, watches, and every description of time-keepers.

[3244]

DENT, M. F., Inventor and Manufacturer, 33 & 34 *Cockspur Street, Charing Cross, London, S. W.*—Watches, clocks, and chronometers; new auxiliary compensation balance. (*See pages* 69 *to* 71.)

[3245]

DE SOLLA, J., & SON, 34 *Southampton Terrace, Waterloo Bridge.*—Original manufacturers of the royal liliputian alarm clocks.

[3246]

DETTMAN, THEODORE, *Minories.*—Astronomical clock, constant ball escapement, compensation regulator, &c.; electro-magnetic clock, half-minute time.

[3247]

EHRHARDT, WILLIAM, 26 *Augusta Street, Birmingham.*—Various kinds of watches, and instruments connected with the manufacture thereof.

[3248]

FAIRER, JOSEPH, 188 *St. George's Street, E.*—The "Village Clock," and other turret clocks, watches, &c.

DENT, M. F., Inventor and Manufacturer, 33 & 34 *Cockspur Street, Charing Cross, London, S. W.*—Watches, clocks, and chronometers; new auxiliary compensation balance.

No. 1.—M. F. Dent's *new* compensation balance with outside auxiliary bows for extremes of temperature.

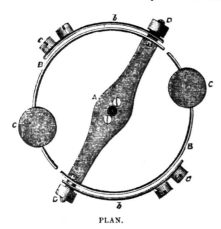

PLAN.

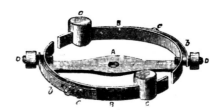

PERSPECTIVE VIEW.

A is the bar of the balance.

B B are the compensation bows, the steel within and the brass without the rim.

c c are the compensation brass weights.

These parts are the same in form as the ordinary balance, but the bows are made thinner and lighter in order that they may move through a larger space. On the studs for the timing-screws (D D) are fastened two outside auxiliary bows (*b b*), the metals being reversed, namely, brass within and steel without the rim.

These auxiliary bows are provided with a row of screw-holes, and carry one or more platina screws (*c c*), which increase or diminish the action according to the distance they are placed from the timing-screw (D).

At present the range of the ordinary compensation balance is limited, because if the brass weight (c) is placed near the extremity of the bow, the balance is, in technical terms, "over compensated;" but this is qualified by the auxiliary action, which, being reverse to that of the primary bows, adds to the error which the primary balance is intended to compensate. This enables the weight c to be placed further out on the primary bow, and by the corresponding adjustment of the platina screws on the auxiliary, a much wider range is obtained of controlling power. The general effect is that the compensation power is greatly increased in high temperatures.

This new balance is simple in construction; all its bows act perfectly free, and the correction for high and low temperature is entirely under control.

2. A marine chronometer fitted with Dent's new auxiliary compensation.

3. M. F. Dent's model watch, in gold hunting-cases, lever escapement, compensation balance, with helical pendulum spring, winding and setting at the knob, and having fusee, and swivel pendant to prevent robbery; constructed to go *two* days without winding, and having dial indicator showing the time when last wound. This watch has the "répétition a tact," whereby the time can be ascertained by an external hand; *the only kind of watch that could be used by one who is deaf and blind.*

4. Gold hunting-cased watch with independent centre seconds, lever escapement, compensation balance, Breguet pendulum spring, winding and setting hands without key.

5. Gold hunting-cased chronometer with *perpetual* calendar.

6. Gold minute repeater in hunting-cases, keyless.

7. Gold hunting-case keyless watch, with lever escapement, compensation balance, engraved case, and ornamental dial. A specimen for the Spanish market.

8. Gold observation watch; a valuable instrument for timing the transit of a star, the phase of an eclipse, or for any purpose where delicate accuracy is essential to determine the exact time of commencement, continuance, and end of any period of observation.

The effect is obtained by having the centre seconds' hand double, one part closely overlying the other, so as to give the appearance of a single hand in ordinary action.

By pressing a knob at the pendant on commencing an observation the under hand is instantly stopped; but the upper hand will continue in action until—as the moment of observation ceases—the knob is pressed a second time: both parts of the seconds hand are then stationary, and the exact interval of time observed is seen registered on the dial. The common action of the watch is not interfered with, it continues going, and on pressing the knob a third time the two parts of the seconds' hand immediately reunite and fly to the nearest point to correspond with the minute.

DENT, M. F.—*continued.*

9. A gold hunting-cased watch with duplex escapement and cylindrical pendulum spring.

10. A specimen of a gold hunting-cased watch, lever escapement, compensation balance, helical pendulum spring, winding without a key and having fusee.

11. A specimen of a plain gold hunting lever watch with extra fine cases.

12. A specimen of a gold open-faced chronometer watch.

13. A gold open-faced watch in imitation of Brequet's celebrated flat watches with eccentric dial and solid key.

14. Under a glass-shade—the movement of a chronometer watch taken to pieces; a specimen of high manipulation, and the most approved calibre.

15 and 16. A specimen of two ladies' gold watches, engraved cases.

17, 18, and 19. Three ladies' gold watches, lever escapements, compensation balances, keyless. The cases enamelled and set with diamonds, varied designs.

20. Gold open-faced watch, silver dial, keyless "*répétition à tact.*" The bottom cover blue, enamelled with monogram in diamonds.

21. A specimen of a silver hunting-cased lever watch with compensation balance.

22. A miniature regulator with mercurial pendulum and remontoir train.

23. Gold open-face chronometer watch with patent fusee winding.

> This chronometer watch is a facsimile of that made in 1859 by M. F. Dent, for Sir William Armstrong, the inventor of the Armstrong Gun, who certifies its actual variation at the end of a year to be only 45 seconds.

24, 25, 26, and 27. Four specimens of chronometer clocks, in gilt and German silver cases.

28. A chronometer clock, with patent balance for extreme temperatures, chiming the quarters upon eight bells, with perpetual calendar of the most perfect construction, indicating the days of the week and month, the phases of the moon, the equation and the bissextile, in a superbly finished case of gilt bronze and crystal glass.

29, 30. Two marine chronometers of the ordinary construction.

31, 32. Two time-pieces with duplex escapements compensated, gilt bronze cases, plain and engraved.

33. A boudoir time-piece, lever escapement, compensation balance; a gilt engraved case, silver dial.

34, 35. Two circular lever time-pieces with compensation balances, one in bronze and the other in a gilt bronze case; specially suitable as portable time-pieces.

36. A specimen of a library clock in bronze case, portable, lever escapement, compensation balance, chiming quarters.

37. A similar clock in ebony-case with improved gongs for fine tone.

The following are extracts from the reports of scientific persons as to the accuracy of Dent's horological instruments :—

Sir WILLIAM ARMSTRONG, inventor of the Armstrong Gun, says :—

"9 Hyde Park Street, W., 14*th November*, 1861.

" The chronometer watch you made for me in December 1859, has never been affected by travelling or riding ; its variation at the end of a year was only 45 seconds. It has proved in every respect a most satisfactory watch.

"W. G. ARMSTRONG.

"MR. M. F. DENT,
33 Cockspur Street, Charing Cross."

The ASTRONOMER ROYAL, Greenwich Observatory, reporting in 1829 on the celebrated public trial, by order of the Lords of the Admiralty, which lasted thirteen years, during which nearly 500 chronometers were tested, says :—

" Your chronometer, No. 114, is entitled to the first premium. Actual variation in the year 54 hundredths of a second.   This is superior to any other yet tried.

"J. POND, *Astronomer Royal.*

"MR. DENT."

The RUSSIAN IMPERIAL ASTRONOMER, M. STRUVE, of St. Petersburg, reporting upon 81 chronometers tested by the Russian chronometrical expedition, in 1843, says :—

"The Dent chronometers have held first rank in a brilliant manner. They contributed, beyond dispute, the most effectually to the exactitude of the results.

"M. STRUVE."

By command of the Emperor, the Russian gold medal of the highest order of merit was presented to Mr. Dent.

G. B. AIRY, Esq., Astronomer Royal (in testimony of the excellence of Dent's turret clocks), says :—

"Royal Observatory, Greenwich, 22*nd July*, 1845.

" I believe the clock which you have constructed for the Royal Exchange to be the best in the world as regards accuracy of going and of striking.

"G. B. AIRY.

"MR. DENT,
33 Cockspur Street, Charing Cross."

Dent, M. F.—*continued.*

38, 39. Specimen drawings of heraldic and other designs, richly executed in enamel and jewels upon the cases of watches, made to special order. The following are a few selections :—

[3249]

FORREST, JOHN, 29 *Myddelton Street, E.C.*—Every description of pocket watches, various escapements and springs—London work.

The following specimens of fine London work are exhibited :—

Pocket chronometer, spiral spring.
Duplex chronometer, Breguet spring.
Lever chronometer, ditto.
Duplex ¾ jewelled tongue, ditto.
Duplex frame, ditto, capped, ditto.
Two-pin lever, ditto, ruby roller, ditto.
Best one-pin. Lever, new balance.
Do. ¾ lever with fly cap.
Independent centre seconds, double train.
Ditto ditto single train.
American block work.

Samples of watches which can be supplied by the exhibitor at the prices quoted per dozen :—	£	s.	d.
¾-Plate gold dome hunters, compensated		..	
¾ Ditto consular, ditto		..	
¾-Plate gold hunters.	from 156	0	0
¾ Ditto consulars	do. 138	0	0
Gent's ditto frame hunters	do. 132	0	0
Ditto consulars	do. 126	0	0
Ladies' ¾-plate ditto	do. 132	0	0
Ladies' frame ditto	do. 96	0	0
Silver ¾-plate hunters, compensated		..	
Silver ¾-plate hunters	do. 76	0	0
Ditto consulars	do. 63	0	0
Silver frame hunters	do. 50	0	0
Ditto consulars	do. 43	0	0

[3250]

FRODSHAM, CHARLES, 84 *Strand, London.* — New caliphers of chronometers, watches, and astronomical clocks; new equation double compensation balances. (*See page* 73.)

[3251]

FRODSHAM & BAKER, 31 *Gracechurch Street, City.*—Chronometer, watch, and clock manufacturer to the Admiralty.

[3252]

GANEVAL & CALLARD, 27 *Alfred Street, Islington.*—Watch, pendulum, spring, and wire manufacturers.

[3253]

GREENWOOD, J., & SONS, 6 *St. John's Square, E.C.*—Quarter and bracket clocks; regulators, dials, and cases.

[3254]

GUIBLET & RAMBAL, 11 *Wilmington Square, Clerkenwell, London.*—Keyless fuzee watches for scientific purposes; pocket chronometers.

[3255]

GUILLAUME, EDWARD & CHARLES, 16 *Myddelton Square, E.C.*—Watches and repeaters.

[3256]

GUMPEL, CHARLES GODFREY, 2 *Gordon Cottages, Holland Road, Brixton.*—A system of electric clocks.

[3259]

HAWLEYS, 287 *High Holborn.*—Regulator—only requires winding once in twelve months.

[ ]

HEYES, THOMAS, Manufacturer, *Appleton, Widnes, near Warrington, Lancashire.*—Steel and brass wire for pinions, clicks, screws, &c. (*See* 3295—PRESCOTT COMMITTEE.)

Pinion wire in steel and brass, round steel and other wires, and pinion wire gauges.

[3260]

HIGHFIELD BROTHERS, 5 *King Edward Terrace, Liverpool Road, N.*—Marine and pocket chronometers, duplex and lever watches, and an improved regulator.

[3261]

HILL, CHARLES JOHN, late W. H. HILL & SONS, *Chapel Fields, Coventry.*—Watches and patent pearl dials.

FRODSHAM, CHARLES, 84 *Strand, London.*—New caliphers of chronometers, watches, and astronomical clocks; new equation double compensation balances.

[Obtained, in 1831, the Government Premium Prize of £170; in 1848, the Telford Medal; in 1851, at the Great Exhibition, the First Class Medal; in 1855, at the Paris Exhibition, the Gold Medal of Honour; in 1860, the Grand Gold Medal "Præmia Digno," from the Imperial Russian Government, for the superior performance of his Chronometers during the great Russian survey.]

The following specimens of high-class horological workmanship are exhibited :—

Pocket chronometers, chronometer repeaters, stop-split centre seconds, and other timing and stop-watches.

Specimens of his "new series" lever chronometer watches, drawn to an entire new calipher of unrivalled timekeeping properties.

A month marine chronometer.

Large eight-day and two-day marine chronometers.

New model eight-day and small two-day marine chronometers, drawn to new and defined proportions, with important and useful changes, all founded on reliable measurements, and the result of long, accurately noted experiments.

Astronomical and sidereal clocks, with important improvements, the result of long-continued and accurate experiments.

Specimens of portable regulators, carriage clocks with compensation balances and chronometer escapements.

Carriage clocks, with lever and chronometer escapements of the highest and finest adjustments.

Small chime clocks.

Instructive specimens of new chronometer and watch movements.

Double compound Micrometric Equation balance, invented and fecit by C. Frodsham.

Compound double inverted Differential balance, invented and fecit by C. Frodsham.

Compound triple Equation balance, invented and fecit by C. Frodsham.

An instrument to illustrate the motion of the compensation balance, showing the causes of the losing error in the extremes of temperature.

New double compensation balance of great accuracy.

New double compensation micrometric balance, extremely sensitive to sudden changes of temperature.

A model church and turret clock, constructed after designs proposed for the clock of the New Houses of Parliament, of astronomical accuracy.

C. Frodsham also exhibits an entirely new system of nomenclature for chronometer and watchmaking.

Tables to facilitate their construction.

New "Duo in Uno" balance springs for perfecting the adjustments of high-class watches and chronometers in their various positions.

New standard to facilitate universally the measurement of watches, with tables of comparisons and coincidences in French new and old measurements, and a work to exhibit CHARLES FRODSHAM's system of chronometer, watch and clock making.

He also exhibits the model of the chronometer-maker's ice-box and oven. C. F.'s new differential compensation balance, perfect for every degree of temperature, will not be ready for exhibition until August.

[3262]

HISLOP, WILLIAM, 108 *St. John Street Road, London.*—Standard or observatory clock, showing mean and sidereal time.

This clock is especially intended as a standard time-keeper. The arrangement for showing sidereal time by means of a supplementary dial may be applied to any clock, and may show mean time when the primary dial shows sidereal time. It prevents the necessity of re-ducing by calculation a sidereal observation to mean time, or vice versâ. The wheelwork may also be applied to show both times on a single dial. Price of clock com-plete, 60 guineas; in a plain case, from 35 guineas. Sidereal dial work, independent of fittings and adjust-ment to clock, 10*l.*

[3263]

HOLDSWORTH, SAMUEL, 220 *Upper Street, Islington, N.*—Chronometer and watch jewels: chronometer pallets and duplex rollers.

[3264]

HOLL, FREDERICK RICHARD, 284 *City Road.*—Patent non-winding chronometers and watches.

[3265]

HOLLIDAY, THOMAS, 304 (late 108) *Goswell Road, London.*—Gold, silver, and metal watch-case and dial maker.

[3266]

HOLLOWAY & CO., 128 *Minories, and New Square, London.*—Pendulum and lever clocks of the simplest construction.

[3267]

HOWARD, RAYMOND, 29 *King Square, Goswell Road.*—Sunk seconds dial maker and enamel maker.

[3268]

HOWELL, JAMES, & CO., 5, 7, 9 *Regent Street.*—Clocks, watches, &c. (*See page* 75.)

Fig. 1. English ormolu candelabra.—Gothic.
Fig. 2. Ditto   ditto clock, silver dial.— Gothic.
Fig. 3. Ormolu candelabra, jewelled enrichments.—Moresque.
Fig. 4. Elaborate pierced star timepiece.—English Gothic.
Fig. 5. Pierced ormolu timepiece.—Mediæval.

Fig. 6. Ormolu travelling 8-day timepiece.—Registered padlock.
Fig. 7. Ormolu clock, jewelled enrichments, silver dial—Moresque.
Fig. 8. Ormolu 8-day travelling timepiece.—Registered horseshoe.

[3270]

HUTTON, JOHN, 10 *Mark Lane, London.* — Marine chronometers, Hartnup pocket chro-nometer, and other sorts; improved cheap watches.

[3271]

JACKSON, W. H. & S., 66 *Red Lion Street, Clerkenwell.*—Chronometers, day of month, key-less, and other watches.

[*Obtained a Prize Medal in Class X.,* 1851.]

The following specimens of chronometers and watches, day of month, eight day, local and mean time, keyless, solid key, with several improved modifications of the lever escapement are exhibited :—

DAY OF MONTH WATCH.

A. Two-day marine chronometer.
B. Pocket chronometer.
C. Day of month, adjustable, with ruby solid impulse lever escapement.
D. Eight-day (fuzee), with J. F. Cole's re-silient pallet.
E. Watch (toothed barrel, solid key), with J. F. Cole's patent repellant lever escapement.
F. Watch showing local and mean time from one train. Hands set independently; lever es-capement, with horizontal ruby pin, adjust-able.
G. Various keyless and solid key watches.
H. Tool for indicating pallet angles and arc of lever escapement.

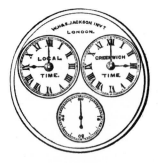

EXTERNAL ARRANGEMENT OF LO-CAL AND MEAN TIME WATCH.

Howell, James, & Co., 5, 7, 9 *Regent Street.*—Clocks, watches, &c.

Fig. 1.

Fig. 2.

Fig. 3.

Fig. 4.

Fig. 5.

Fig. 6.

Fig. 7.

Fig. 8.

[3272]

JOHNSON, EDWARD DANIEL, 9 *Wilmington Square, Clerkenwell, London.*—Chronometers, watches, pendulums, horological machinery, and various improvements and inventions.

MARINE CHRONOMETERS, eight-day and two-day.

HERMETIC BOX for Marine chronometer.

Magnetic Disperser for Marine chronometer. Rotating machinery in the case causing the chronometer to revolve on its own axis in 24 hours, thus dispersing the effects of local magnetism.

Surveying Chronometer. An ordinary small-sized two-day movement, fitted in a silver case as well as the ordinary gimbals, so as to make it portable in the pocket as well as suitable to the navigation of a ship. Removed from its gimbals by turning round the glass cover.

Pocket Chronometers, half plate and frame.

Duplex watches, half plate.

Lever watches, half plate and three-quarter.

Railway watches, full plate and three-quarter.

"Automaton seconds' watches. Keyless watches.

Combination of both these last.

"Universal seconds," a new watch, designed and patented especially to commemorate the Exhibition of 1862 horologically; consisting of a new caliper and train of wheels, effecting the union of "Automaton seconds" and permanent side seconds without complexity.

A new Escapement for Equatorial Telescopes, for circulating pendulums; consisting of a single crank motion, giving freedom to the motion of the pendulum, with the equable continuous rotary motion to the telescope required.

New and improved models of mercurial pendulums.

Model suspensions for pendulums.

New auxiliary compensator for wooden pendulums; can be applied to any pendulum in one minute, at a cost of 7s. 6d. It consists of a glass tube, divided into two chambers by being drawn out into an upper and a lower part, joined by a small tube; the lower, and part of the upper chamber containing mercury. This arrangement effects the transposition of small quantities of the mercury long distances, doing proportionately more work. Adjustable by a screw at the bottom.

Model of a public Timeball, discharged by electric current from Greenwich Observatory.

Groups of watch-movements, showing various constructions and qualities of workmanship.

Manufacturer of Chronometers and Watches, of which fair samples only are exhibited in Class 15. No article among those shown is made at unnatural expense on purpose to show, but each is a fair representation of his ordinary work, and his stock is manufactured of the same material and workmanship.

Inventor and Patentee of:—

The automaton-seconds watch.

The self-contained winder.

The magnetic disperser.

The hermetic box or chronometer safe.

The universal seconds watch.

And manufacturer of goods for all the foreign markets, on the models specially suited to each.

Patronized by the Admiralty.

[3273]

JONES, JOHN, 338 *Strand.*—Watches.

Case containing the following specimens of watches :—

1st Row.—Ladies' gold watches, with a new application of jewels in the notation of minutes on the dials, and decorated cases.

2nd Row.—Gold watches, with a new application of colour for the adornment of enamel dials appropriate for ladies' use.

3rd Row.—Specimens of the perfection of railway watches adjusted for position and temperature; also 2-day watches with correct adjustments.

4th Row.—Gold ¾-plate hunting levers, with specimens of the most perfectly proportioned escapements that the trade can produce, with Isochronal springs and compensated balances.

5th Row.—Gold hunting lever watches, with newly arranged spring caps, suitable for use in foreign climates.

6th Row.—Silver levers to compete with the foreign manufacturer in price while retaining the English superiority in quality, 3l. 3s. each.

[3275]

KLAFTENBERGER, CHARLES J., 157 *Regent Street.*—Minute repeaters, chronometers, &c.

[3276]

KULLBERG, V., 12 *Cloudesley Terrace, N.*—Chronometers, watches, and clocks.

[3277]

LANGE, CHRISTIAN, 9 *Salisbury Street, Strand, London.*—Watches and timepieces.

[3278]

LEONARD, G. W., 1 *Cloudesley Terrace, Liverpool Road.*—Compensation balances.

[3279]

LOSADA, JOSÉ R., 105 *Regent Street.*—Watches, marine chronometers, table clocks, turret clocks, and astronomical pendulums. (*See pages* 78 & 79.)

[3282]

MARRIOTT, BENJAMIN, 38 *Upper Street, Islington, London.*—Watches, gold chains, &c.

[3283]

MERCER, THOMAS, 45 *Spencer Street, Clerkenwell.*—Marine chronometers.

[3284]

MOORE, B. R. & J., 38 *Clerkenwell Close.*—Turret and other clocks.

[3285]

MORRIS, WILLIAM, *Blackheath, S.E.*—Electric regulator with centre seconds, and other companion clocks, all beating simultaneously.

[3286]

MUIRHEAD, JAMES, & SON, *Glasgow.*—House, turret, and railway clocks, &c.

[3287]

MURRAY, JAMES, 30 *Cornhill, London.*—Chronometers, watches, clocks, patented keyless watches, patented regulator, models, jewelry, &c.

[3288]

NEAL, JOHN, Watchmaker and Jeweller, 18 *Edgware Road, London, W.*—Jewelry; onyx clocks; duplex, lever, and chronometer watches—new construction.

[3289]

NICOLE & CAPT, 14 *Soho Square.*—Nicole's patent keyless watch and conteur.

[3290]

ORAM, GEORGE JOHN, 19 *Wilmington Square, Clerkenwell.*—Watches.

[3291]

PARKINSON & FRODSHAM, 4 *Change Alley, Cornhill, E.C.*—Chronometers, watches, regulators, astronomical clocks, &c.

[3292]

PLASKETT, WILLIAM, 12 *Alderney Road, Globe Road, Mile End, London, N.E.*—Marine chronometers with improved compensation.

These chronometers are manufactured with improved compensating auxiliary balances for correcting the difference of time occasioned by extreme temperature. They are also furnished with air-tight valves which perfectly exclude all damp from the works.

[3293]

POOLE, JOHN, 57 *Fenchurch Street, London.*—Marine and pocket chronometers and watches.

[3294]

PORTHOUSE & FRENCH, 16 *Northampton Square, Goswell Road.*—Specimens of marine chronometers and watches for home and foreign markets.

[3295]

PRESCOTT COMMITTEE FOR THE EXHIBITION OF TOOLS, HOROLOGICAL INSTRUMENTS, &C.:—

Preston, J.	Brown, Ann.	Molyneux, Wm.
Hewitt, S. & J.	Johnson, C. B.	Whitfield, J. J.
Wycherley, J.	Houghton, S.	Alcock, J.
Copple, J. & W.	Pendleton, P.	Jacques, J.
Scarisbruk, C.	Stockley, Jas.	Smith, J.
Hunt, J., & Co.	Taylor, Richard.	Naylor, Thos.
Ford, R.	Preston, Wm.	Heyes, Thos.
Welsby, J.	Saggerson, E.	

[3297]

QUAIFE, THOMAS, Clockmaker, *Hawkhurst, Kent.*—Chime clock, fifty changes, in marble and gold; and chronometer.

[3300]

ROTHERHAM & SONS, *Coventry.*—Gold and silver watches, and parts of a watch in every stage of manufacture.

[3302]

RUSSEL, THOMAS, & SON, *Liverpool.*—Watches, hard tempered nickel movements, patented; especially adapted to hot climates.

LOSADA, JOSÉ R., 105 *Regent Street.*—Watches, marine chronometers, table clocks, turret clocks, and astronomical pendulums.

DE S.S. M.M. C.C., REAL FAMILIA Y ARMADA MILITAR.

[Thrice decorated by her Catholic Majesty for merit in his art.]

1. Astronomical pendulum, escapement jewelled, in glass case.

2. Two astronomical pendulum movements complete, escapements jewelled, dials unfinished.

3. Musical chiming clock, to strike the quarters on eight bells, and the hours on a deep gong; plays one of four different overtures at each of the hours; in rosewood case, gilt engraved dial.

4. Same as No. 3, in oak case and silvered dial.

5. Chiming quarter clock, with centre seconds and duplex escapement, compensated and adjusted, carved mahogany case, with carved dolphins as supports, gilt engraved dial.

6. Skeleton centre seconds clock, under glass shade, with chronometer and escapement compensated and adjusted, with emblem of *Fidelity.*

7. Small table chronometer with brass engraved and gilt case, and gilt engraved dial.

8. Ting tong carriage clock, with lever escapement, brass gilt case, and gilt engraved dial.

9. Binnacle clock, with lantern and reflector, lever escapement compensated and adjusted, brass bronzed case.

10. Cabin dial, with lever escapement compensated and adjusted, in black mahogany case.

11. 8-day marine chronometer.

12. 2-day ditto.

13. Two marine chronometers in construction.

14. Two silver acompañantes with mahogany case.

15. Gold hunting grand clock watch, to strike the hours and quarters, and to repeat the hours and quarters every quarter of an hour, and hours, quarters, and minutes at pleasure, showing the days of the week and month. Jewelled in 40 holes.

16. Gold hunting clock watch to strike the hours and quarters, and to repeat the hours and quarters every quarter of an hour, and at pleasure. Jewelled in 24 holes.

17. Gold hunting minute repeater. Jewelled in 24 holes. Highly ornamented.

18 Gold hunting half-quarter repeater. Jewelled in 20 holes. Highly ornamented.

19. Gold hunting duplex watch, to show 6 different meridians. Jewelled in 8 holes.

20. Gold hunting pocket chronometer, 13 jewels. Highly ornamented.

21. Gold hunting pocket chronometer, 13 jewels. Plain.

22. Gold hunting duplex, independent centre seconds. Jewelled in 20 holes. Highly ornamented.

23. Gold open face, ditto, ditto. Plain.

24. Gold hunting duplex, centre seconds. Highly ornamented.

25. Gold open face duplex, centre seconds.

26. Gold hunting duplex watch. Highly ornamented.

27. Gold demi-hunting watch. Highly ornamented.

28. Gold hunting duplex watch. Plain.

29. Gold demi hunting lady's duplex keyless watch. Highly ornamented.

30. Gold hunting lever watch. Highly ornamented.

LOSADA, JOSÉ R.—*continued.*

31. Gold hunting lever watch. Plain.
32. Gold demi hunting lever watch.
33. Gold hunting lady's lever watch. Highly ornamented.
34. Gold hunting lady's lever watch. Plain.
35. Watches in construction.
36. Silver hunting duplex watch.

37. Silver hunting lever watch.
38. Three orders, conferred by her Catholic Majesty Isabella the Second for merit in his art, viz. :—
    a. Cross of Charles the Third.
    b. b. Orders of Comendador de Numero of Isabella the Catholic.

39. A very elegant brooch, being the device borne on the reverse of the Mexican doubloon, and representing the secretary bird destroying a serpent; the body of the bird is composed of a very large pearl; the head, neck, wings, tail, and feet of brilliant and rose diamonds, on a spray, also of diamonds and gold, with a large single pendant, the snake of gold beautifully enamelled; the whole set in gold.

Vease anuncio en los **Catálogos** é Iluminado.

[3303]

SAMUEL, A., & SON, 29 *Charterhouse Square, E.C.*—Various descriptions of English watches, manufactured by exhibitors.

[3304]

SANDERS, JOHN, 15 *West Bar, Sheffield.*—Regulator, timepiece, and keyless watches.

[3305]

SCHOOF, WILLIAM GEORGE, 9 *Ashby Street, Northampton Square.*—Regulator, with detached escapement and mercurial pendulum.

[3306]

SEWILL, JOSEPH, 61 *South Castle Street, Liverpool.*—Gold and silver watches; pocket and marine chronometers.

[3307]

SHEPHERD, CHARLES, 53 *Leadenhall Street, City.*—Galvano-magnetic clocks.

[3309]

SMITH, J., & SONS, *St. John's Square, Clerkenwell, London.*—Church, turret, and house clocks, &c.; illuminated and other dials. (*See page* 81.)

[3311]

STRAM, NUMA, *Ashby Street, Northampton Square.*—Reversible and self-winding watch.

[3312]

STRATH BROTHERS, 7 *Park Terrace, Camden Town.*—Models of the English and Geneva watches.

[3313]

TANNER & SON, *Lewes.*—Clock with perpetual register of day, week, and month—requires no correction.

[3316]

THOMSON & PROFAZE, 25 *New Bond Street, W.*—Watches, clocks, timepieces, "tell-tale," and jewelry.

English skeleton clock, supported by figures emblematic of day, night, twilight, and dawn, designed and manufactured by the exhibitors. English chronometer repeating clock. The specimen of engraving on brass case is unique. Chronometer timepiece in gilt case, ornamented with river gods, &c.

English timepieces of various kinds.

Tell-tale timepiece registering time within five seconds; could be adapted for astronomical and meteorological observations. English watches with the latest improvements, winding and setting hands by pendant, the engraving and enamelling on cases of the best and most elaborate description. Gold chains, &c.

Marine set, bracelet, brooch, necklet and earrings with dolphins and shells enamelled and set with rubies, emeralds, and diamonds.

Further particulars may be learned upon application.

SMITH, J., & SONS, *St. John's Square, Clerkenwell, London.*—Church, turret, and house clocks, &c.; illuminated and other dials.

1. Turret clock tower and summer-house, with eight-day turret striking clock, with four faces 3 ft. 6 in. diameter, intended for illuminating. The clock is constructed on the repeating principle; has maintaining power to keep it going during winding; inside dial plate to set the four pairs of outside hands by; and various other improvements. The clock tower is surrounded by seats and bronze rail, and surmounts the summer-house, which has wings that may be used for choice flowers, &c. The intention of the whole arrangement is to supersede the old custom of placing a turret clock on stables, by rendering this most useful article an ornament to the park, lawn, or ornamental garden.

2. Turret timepiece, suited for railway termini or public buildings, stables, &c.

3. Eight-day skeleton clock, strikes on cathedral tone gong, and the half-hour on bell. The decoration of this clock is of a very elaborate character.

5. Skeleton striking clock (design, Temple of Flora).

6. Ditto   ditto, plain design.

7. Eight-day chiming bracket clock, in carved oak case of Old English style, introducing dolphins and acorns; chimes the quarters on eight musical bells, and strikes the hours on a gong.

8. Striking bracket clock, carved oak case (new design).

9. Ditto   ditto   ditto, solid mahogany carved case.

10. Ditto   ditto   ditto.

11. Regulator or astronomical clock, mercurial compensated pendulum, suited for a gentleman's hall, ornamental carved Spanish mahogany case.

12. Detector clock, or watchman's clock, which, in addition to forming a bracket timepiece, detects and registers neglect of duty in watchmen or night wardens.

13. Skeleton eight-day striking clock, mosque pattern.

14. Model of the turret clock tower and summer-house, erected by Messrs. J. Smith and Sons in the Eastern Annex, Class IX.

15. Various models and samples of eight-day office shop dials. Clocks for various climates, all manufactured by the exhibitors.

16. Samples of materials and tools used in the manufacture of English clocks.

17. Eight-day turret or church clock, of the same construction and material as that supplied by the exhibitors to the order of the Government Department of Science and Art, and which may be seen in the Museum, South Kensington. The wheels and bosses for the pivots to act in are of gun metal, the mixture being the same as that used for the manufacture of ordnance-bearings, the pinions of wrought steel, cut and finished in an engine as well as the wheels; thus securing the greatest possible accuracy. The frames are of iron, and so constructed that any part can be removed for cleaning without disturbing the remaining parts. The escapement is on the principle of Graham's dead beat, and the steel pads are made to slide in turned grooves, so as to set the pitch with the greatest exactness; they may be removed, as they are secured by screws. The striking apparatus is on the repeating principle, which prevents the possibility of striking wrong hours—a fault so common in many clocks with locking plates. The maintaining power to keep the clock going during winding is by lever and bolt; there is a small inside dial to set the hands by. The pendulum has a heavy spherical ball, and the rod, which is of prepared pine, coated with varnish and afterwards French polished, is thus secured against the action of air or damp; the pendulum is set in beat by means of a traversing screw, and the crutch has also two large screws to regulate and reduce its friction.

18. Metal drum case dial, made expressly for India, China, and tropical climates. The face of this is twelve inches diameter, though all sizes are made on the same principle and construction. The front of the case solid brass, with thick plate-glass; the movement has jointed steel chain, and neither case nor clock can be injured by climate or insects.

19. Revolving machine, strong spring movement in mahogany box, with circular plate, for the exhibition of figures in shop windows; adapted for "hairdressers," models, &c., &c.

20. Small models of office dials in oak, walnut tree, and mahogany, carved in various styles, suited for public buildings, lecture-rooms, in Elizabethan, Gothic, Grecian, Mediæval, and modern styles of architecture.

21. Illuminated dial, for outside of public buildings; the numerals, minute stops, and mouldings are of copper, and glazed with opal glass. By the construction of this dial perfect distinctness and durability are secured, and the gas light equally diffused over the surface of the clock face.

22. Eight-day school dial in solid oak case.

23. Eight-day bedroom clock with alarum.

24. Eight-day striking kitchen or country clock in long case.

WHITE, EDWARD, 20 *Cockspur Street, Pall Mall, S.W.*—Chronometers, watches, clocks, and gold chains.

No. 1. A monthly astronomical clock, with mercurial compensation pendulum, and pallets jewelled with sapphires.

CHRONOMETERS.

2. An eight-day marine chronometer.

3. A two-day do. do.

4. A ditto, with auxiliary compensation.

5 An eight-day chronometer timepiece, in plain gilt metal case, with enamel dial and engine-turned gilt dial cover.

6. A smaller do., in ornamental gilt metal case with chased columns, enriched mouldings and chased lion on top. (Registered design.)

PORTABLE CLOCKS.

7. An eight-day lever clock with compensation balance (striking hours and half-hours, and repeating the last hour on bell-spring, with very fine cathedral tone), in German silver case.

8. A do. of different pattern.

9. A do. in bronze metal case.

10. A do. chiming the quarter on four bells (Cambridge chimes) and striking the hours on bell-spring, in very handsome gilt metal case, with chased columns and figure on top. (Registered design.)

GILT DRAWING-ROOM CLOCK, "THE TRIUMPH OF NEPTUNE."

11. A gilt drawing-room clock, "The triumph of Neptune," with base and columns of Algerine onyx, designed by E. W., manufactured and registered by his agent at Paris.

GOTHIC HALL CLOCK.

BRACKET HALL CLOCKS.

12. An eight-day clock, striking hours on bell-spring, and quarters on four bells, in richly carved oak case, with columns, roof, crockets, finials, crestings, and panels in polished brass. (Registered design.)

13. An eight-day 3 part quarter clock, chiming the quarters on 4 bell-springs, and striking hours on large ditto. Black wood case with chased gilt metal mouldings; the cornice supported by caryatid figures of the four seasons, and with eagle on top. (Registered design.)

14. A ditto chiming quarters on four bells (Cambridge chimes), and striking hour on large bell. Carved Gothic case of various woods. (Registered design.)

15. A ditto in carved oak Gothic case with crockets, crestings, finials, and side panels in polished brass. (Registered design.)

16. A case containing eighteen specimens of monograms, arms, crests, &c., in engraving, enamelling, and precious stones.

KEYLESS WATCHES.

17. A gold hunting pocket chronometer, with two dials—one to show English and the other Turkish time—the case richly engraved with oak leaves and acorns, and with very handsome gold Albert chain to correspond.

18. A gold hunting minute repeater, with dark-blue enamel dial to show the repeating work in the centre—the case richly engraved with vine leaves and grapes, and with very handsome gold Albert chain to correspond. (See opposite page.)

19. A gold hunting quarter repeater, with duplex escapement and compensation balance—the case ornamented with "lilies of the valley," the leaves being in green enamel and the flowers in diamonds, and with brooch and chain to correspond. (See opposite page.)

20. A gold hunting duplex watch, with compensation balance; the case set with diamonds on dark-blue enamel ground, and with brooch and chain to correspond.

21. A ditto, the case set with pearls and diamonds on Maroon enamel ground.

22. A gold hunting lever watch, with compensation balance and independent seconds.

23. A gold open face "blind man's" watch.

24. A gold hunting duplex watch, with compensation balance, repeating hours and quarters.

25 A ditto, repeating half-quarters.

26. A gold open face observation watch, with double eccentric stop seconds, to register the commencement and termination of an observation without stopping the watch. Eight other keyless watches of different patterns.

WATCHES WINDING WITH A KEY.

27. A gold hunting pocket chronometer.

28. Ditto, open face   ditto.

29. A gold hunting lever watch, with compensation balance and brequet pendulum spring. Plain case, with hour circle on cover.

30. A gold open face ditto.

31. A ditto ditto, with double roller escapement.

32. A ditto ditto, with gold balance.

Six ladies' gold watches, with engraved cases and dials of different patterns.

An assortment of gold Albert and neck chains, with lockets and other pendants.

WHITE, EDWARD—*continued.*

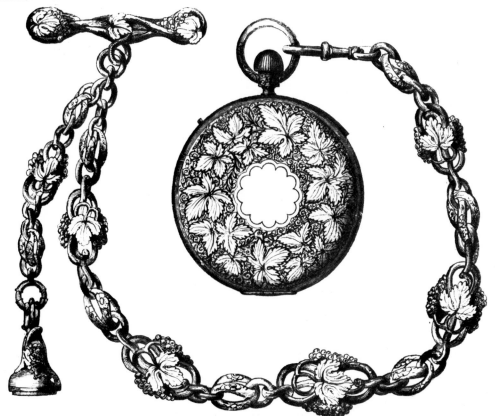

GOLD HUNTING MINUTE REPEATER.

GOLD HUNTING QUARTER REPEATER.

[3318]

VIVIER, O., 21 *Sekforde Street, Clerkenwell.*—Patent fusee keyless watches, with various movements.

[3319]

WALES & M'CULLOCH, 56 *Cheapside, and 32 Ludgate Street.*—Gold and silver watches.

The exhibitors will send post free, on application, an illustrated catalogue of their stock. They can supply handsome drawing-room clocks, in gilt cases, at 5*l.* 5*s.*, and in variegated marble, at 3*l.* 3*s.*

[3320]

WALKER, JOHN, 68 *Cornhill, and 48 Princes Street, Leicester Square.*—Watches and clocks.

[3321]

WALSH, A. P., 46 *Wilmington Square, Clerkenwell.*—Watches and chronometers.

[3322]

WATKINS, ALEXANDER, 67 *Strand, London.*—Model of the new patent direct action time-keeper; watches, and movements of the same.

[3324]

WEBSTER, RICHARD, 74 *Cornhill.*—Watches, chronometers, keyless watches, centre seconds, repeaters, touch watches, regulators, and railway clocks.

[3325]

WHITE, EDWARD, 20 *Cockspur Street, Pall Mall, S.W.*—Chronometers, watches, clocks, and gold chains. (*See pages 82 to 85.*)

[3326]

WHITTAKER, RICHARD, 7 *Great Sutton Street, Clerkenwell.*—Improved dome-capped lever watch, combining quality, cheapness, and flatness.

[3327]

WOOD, THOMAS JAMES, 12 *Long Lane, City.*—Black Forest clocks, with brass works, partly English manufacture.

		s.	*d.*
1. The International clock	.. .. price	5	6

Exhibited as the smallest cost at which a really durable and accurate clock has yet been produced.

		s.	*d.*
2. A small dial	.. .. „	7	6
3. The school and workshop dial..	.. „	12	0
4. Clock to strike the hours	.. .. „	12	0
5. Ditto, large size ..	.. .. .. „	16	0
6. Striking clock, with buhl frame	.. „	27	0
7. Ditto, large size ..	.. .. .. „	35	0

Nos. 6 and 7 are exhibited as specimens of ornamentation.

		s.	*d.*
8. An alarum clock ..	.. .. .. price	8	6
9. Ditto, large size ..	.. .. .. „	14	0
10. Double action alarum clock	.. .. „	18	0
11. Alarum clock, striking the hours	.. „	14	0
12. Ditto, large size ..	.. .. .. „	18	0

Gravity being both the maintaining and regulating power of these clocks, they possess an accuracy of performance unsurpassed by the most costly productions.

[3329]

YOUNG, JAMES, *Knaresborough.*—Improvements in the construction of lever watches to save time in repairing, &c.

[3330]

MCLENNAN, J., 6 *Park Place.*—Pocket chronometers.

[3331]

PETIT, S. A., 69 *Princes Street, Leicester Square.*—Regulators, watches, &c.

APPENDIX E

CLASS XV.

HOROLOGICAL INSTRUMENTS.

JURY.

Dr. Frick, *Zollverein* ; Professor of Physics, Freiburg.
Charles Frodsham, Secretary and Reporter, *London* ; Chronometer Maker.
Rt. Haswell, *London* ; Watch Tool Maker.
E. D. Johnson, *London* ; Chronometer Maker.
Laugier, Deputy Chairman, *France* ; Member of the Institute and of the Bureau of Longitudes.
Sylvain Mairet, *Switzerland* ; Watchmaker, Lôcle.
Rear-Admiral Manners, F.R.A.S., *London*.
Viscount de Villa Maior, Chairman, *Portugal* ; Director-General of the Agricultural Institute ;
  Professor of Chemistry at the Polytechnic of Lisbon ; and Member of the Academy of Science.
Lord Wrottesley, F.R.S., *London* ; late President of the Royal Society.

INTRODUCTORY REMARKS.

The difficulty which the Jurors had to contend with in their decision upon instruments, depending so much upon results without the means of testing them in their double quality of excellence of finish and accuracy of construction and adjustment, was very great ; yet I feel that the Jurors' awards, given with so much care and earnest desire to do justice to every exhibitor, have been almost without exception to the satisfaction and encouragement of the Exhibition, and fair to the public.

The Jurors entirely concurred in the excellent instructions given them by the Royal Commissioners ; and therefore did not confer their awards on the greatest ability or the highest branches only, but to exhibitors of every grade in the art. Men devoting themselves to jewelling, making of main-springs, drawing of steel wire for balance-springs, watch and chronometer movements, wheels and pinions, &c., all bring their quota to the advancement of the art, and are equally essential to the whole. This mode of giving awards we consider to be the true principle of giving encouragement to the whole manufacture.

The Medals were all similar. If we had been called upon to award a Medal to the most eminent exhibitor in horology, we could not have found him, for although the advancement and perfection of every art and manufacture depends much on the energy and direction of a few minds, yet the talent of execution is seldom combined with the genius of invention, and the inventive power seldom accompanies the perseverance and judgment to combine the various parts into one harmonious whole, and bring about a final result of excellence and good performance.

Whatever may be the immediate results of exhibitions, there cannot be a doubt that they are great schools of information which could not have been arrived at in any other form than by such a concentration ; and the amount of experience and information given on such occasions, is very much greater than is generally admitted to have resulted from the memorable exhibition of 1851 ; and this was a marked feature of the present horological exhibition. The total number of Medals awarded to the horological class in 1851 was about 34, whilst in 1862, 102.

The English exhibitors alone obtain 37.

COUNTRIES EXHIBITING.	Medals.	Honourable Mention.	Number of Exhibitors.
United Kingdom	37	44	97
Austria	3	2	10
Baden	8	8	26
Bavaria	—	—	1
Belgium	—	—	1
Brazil	—	1	1
Denmark	2	1	5
France	19	14	54
Hanse Towns	1	—	3
Italy	—	1	4
Mecklenburg	—	1	1
Netherlands	—	1	1
Norway	2	1	3
Portugal	1	—	
Prussia	1	4	6
Russia	—	1	1
Saxony	1	2	4
Spain	—	—	2
Sweden	2	2	5
Switzerland	24	33	72
Würtemberg	1	—	3

The whole of the English section was a remarkable instance of the good effect which had been produced by the fact that "the schoolmaster was evidently abroad." The general progress was great and marked ; and although great geniuses can seldom be surpassed, it is no mean acquisition to come very near them. Valuable inventions might be almost stumbled upon in the early history of mechanical progress, but now the discovery of new principles is rendered a thousand times more difficult—another example of the utility of scientific men and mechanicians being brought together. I think there is little doubt that there has been more time spent by great minds upon clocks and watches than upon any other science, and therefore they may be truly said to have been the nursery of engineering and mechanical skill.

There were but few new or important inventions in any of the horological sections, though there were many very clever adaptations of old principles to new processes; yet no competent judge ever for a moment supposed that this arose from a want of mechanical genius, but rather from the advanced knowledge of the art, and that the existing principles had not yet been fully developed and understood.

I think I shall best perform my duty as a reporter by endeavouring to elucidate these principles and clear up some of the difficulties which have beset our researches, and so leave to the intelligent manufacturer his whole time to devote to the improvement of his productions rather than the costly process of continued experiments founded upon uncertain and technical data. Such a plan I think will be preferable to the unsatisfactory and onerous task of paying panegyrics to each individual exhibitor, which would be as tedious as useless, seeing that the Jurors confirm their awards and leave their annotations against each exhibitor's name to speak instead.

CHRONOMETERS.

The marine chronometers were the first objects that occupied the attention of the Jurors. We expected much, and were not disappointed. No branch of mechanical science can possibly reflect greater credit upon this country. There was a remarkable fact apparent:—it seemed as if every mechanical contrivance employed had been reduced to its simplest form, cleared of almost all doubtful effects, and reduced to a solid utilitarian principle, ready to respond to the importance of its requirements, and almost declaring that it is equal to the trust so unreservedly reposed in it for the safety of any vessel that may venture to confide in its predictions for its longitude.

The great points of interest which attend this branch of chronometrical research, are four distinct and prominent inquiries:—

1. Perfection of compensation for errors of temperature. What are these errors, and how do they arise?
2. Perfect and permanent elasticity.
3. Acceleration of rate, its cause and period of duration.
4. The true momentum of the balance, or, in other words, the weight and diameter of the balance suited to a given velocity, and a given power of main-spring, determined by the cubic contents of the barrel.

Compensation Balance.

Error of Compensation, and its Cause.—Almost every chronometer-maker of repute has devoted much of his time to the correction of these perplexing errors with various success, and a number of very taking theories have been in existence, to which we have all, more or less, been disciples; "it is said that the balance, in heat, does not approach the centre fast enough, and that in cold, it comes out too fast; whereas the reverse should be the case," together with sundry other reasons which we propose to examine.

As this subject has occupied the most eminent chronometer-makers for 50 years without coming to any decision, a chronometer was exhibited with a plain uncompensated brass balance, which the Astronomer Royal had tried at Greenwich, and by which it was shown there was a uniform decrease of rate for equal increments of temperature measured by a mercurial thermometer, amounting to 6·11 seconds in 24 hours for each degree of Fahrenheit's scale. The table I subjoin. I believe no similar authentic table of the kind has been published, though the learned men of France came nearly to the same conclusion in the last century.

ROYAL OBSERVATORY, GREENWICH.

MEAN DAILY RATES OF EXPERIMENTAL CHRONOMETER CHARLES FRODSHAM WITH A SIMPLE BRASS BALANCE, *i. e.*, WITHOUT COMPENSATION. No. 3148.

1859.	Mean daily rate.	Difference.	Mean Temperature.	Difference.	Mean daily variation for one degree of Temperature.	NATURE OF TRIAL.
	Seconds.	Seconds.	Degrees.	Degrees.	Seconds.	
June 22 to June 25	+ 45·9	—	68·7	—	—	
„ 25 „ July 2	+ 21·6	24·3	71·4	2·7	—	} In chronometer room.
July 2 „ „ 6	+ 10·0	11·6	73·2	1·8	6·44	
„ 6 „ „ 9	- 142·5	152·5	99·3	26·1	5·83	
„ 9 „ „ 16	- 131·9	10·6	97·7	1·6	6·63	
„ 16 „ „ 23	- 45·2	86·7	83·8	13·9	6·22	
„ 23 „ „ 30	- 45·4	0·2	83·0	0·8	—	} Exposed to heat in the gas stove.
„ 30 „ Aug. 6	- 101·1	55·7	93·7	10·7	5·20	
Aug. 6 „ „ 13	- 121·0	19·9	95·4	1·7	—	
„ 13 „ „ 20	- 28·9	92·1	81·8	13·6	6·78	
„ 20 „ „ 27	+ 11·8	40·7	74·6	7·2	5·66	
„ 27 „ Sept. 3	+ 54·7	42·9	66·7	7·9	5·44	
Sept. 3 „ „ 10	+ 50·5	5·8	66·4	0·3	—	
„ 10 „ „ 17	+ 83·9	23·4	62·7	3·7	6·32	
„ 17 „ „ 24	+ 86·9	3·0	61·9	0·8	—	
„ 24 „ Oct. 1	+ 56·6	30·3	66·7	4·8	6·31	} In chronometer room.
Oct. 1 „ „ 8	+ 42·7	13·9	69·0	2·3	6·05	
„ 8 „ „ 15	+ 77·8	35·1	63·3	5·7	6·16	
„ 15 „ „ 22	+ 103·2	25·4	59·2	4·1	6·20	
„ 22 „ „ 29	+ 168·0	64·8	48·7	10·5	6·17	
„ 29 „ Nov. 5	+ 168·4	0·4	50·0	1·3	—	
Nov. 5 „ „ 12	+ 180·4	12·0	47·3	2·7	4·44	} Exposed to external air under shed outside north window.
„ 12 „ „ 19	+ 225·2	44·8	40·9·	6·4	7·63	
„ 19 „ „ 26	+ 206·8	18·4	43·8	2·9	6·35	
					103·83	
					$\dfrac{103·83}{17} = 6·11$	
July 6 „ July 9	- 142·5 } 367·7 {		99·3 } 58·4 {		*6·30	} Mean daily variation for one degree of temperature.
Nov. 12 „ Nov. 19	+ 225·3		40·9			

* This difference is caused by the chronometer having slightly accelerated on its rate.

The same chronometer, with compensation applied, gave the following results :—

Mean Temperature.	Mean Daily Rate. Seconds.
88°	0·0
55°	0·0
32°	2·4 losing

I think few persons are prepared for such variations of rate arising from changes of temperature as the following :—

Mean Temperature.	Daily rate.
July 6 . . 99°·3	142·5 losing.
Nov. 12 . . 40°·9	225·0 gaining.

What must have been the feelings of the first chronometer-makers, when they found such a fearful error to contend with ! To the navigator this should be a special warning that he will do well to ascertain that his chronometer has been carefully adjusted in temperature by skilful hands. For this purpose chronometer-makers keep an ice chamber all the year round as well as gas ovens.

The Astronomer Royal, in his report to the Admiralty relating to the performance of chronometers, stated that the principle cause of their errors was defective compensation, either too much or too little, which is often aggravated by bad oil. I shall show later in the report that the very best chronometers, after a period of from ten to twenty years' service, become nearly useless under wide changes of temperature, though showing very fair average rates under nearly uniform temperatures. This arises from no mechanical error, but from the balance spring's decay, losing its original cohesion, and hence having an impaired elasticity; this decay is still more quickened by the slightest particle of rust on the spring. The remedy is a new balance-spring when it will renew its original character (when once a good chronometer, always a good chronometer). This restoration will be attended with an expense of about twelve guineas, according to the state of the instrument. No labourer is more worthy of his fee than the English chronometer-maker.

Now this remarkable fact having been ascertained, as shown by the table, we can calculate the error arising from the elongation of the spring. The strength of springs being inversely as their length and the effect on time as the square roots of their lengths : the loss amounts to about 17 seconds per diem for 60 degrees of increased temperature. The decrease of rate by the expansion of the balance is also easily found by figures, it being inversely as the diameter, and in a plain brass balance amounts to about 63 seconds per diem for a change of temperature of 60 degrees of Fahr. But $17 + 63 = 80$ only, whilst the fact is established of a uniform rate of 6·11 seconds for each degree of Fahr. ; and since $6·11 \times 60 = 367$ seconds, it leaves 247 seconds of daily rate still to be accounted for, and this has been satisfactorily proved to arise from the spring's loss of elastic force by an increase of temperature.

This enormous error, fifteen times greater than that caused by the lengthening of the spring, is corrected in the Arnold Earnshaw compensation balance, composed of brass and steel laminæ, and so constructed as to vary the momentum of the balance in the ratio of the spring's elastic force throughout the range of temperature of about 60°, and with balances of the best proportions, chronometers may be adjusted to within four seconds of daily error for a change of temperature of 60° of Fahr. ; but if we adjust for the extremes we gain in the middle temperatures, thus :—

Thermometer 90°	daily rate	0·0 seconds.
60°	,,	+ 2·5 gaining.
30°	,,	0·0

If we adjust for the heat and middle we have the following :—

90°	daily rate	0·0
60°	,,	0·0
30°	,,	− 4·0 losing ;

and if we adjust for the middle and the low we have the following :—

30°	daily rate	0·0
60°	,,	0·0
90°	,,	− 4·0 losing.

The smallness of this error of four seconds against 367 I confess surprises me, and particularly that the rate should be so nearly uniform in all the intermediate changes of temperature; because in the combination of these two metals they have no natural antagonism, but are subject to the same law only in different ratios,* and if the motion were required to be greater than it is we should have a greatly increased error in the extremes ; whilst the reverse effect would arise if the main error were less, as in glass springs, in the employment of which Mr. Arnold informed me the main error was not above twenty seconds, and the intermediate errors not perceptible.

The total decrease of the diameter of the compensation balance to restore the chronometer to time for a daily loss of 367 seconds for 60° of temperature, by a direct motion, is but about $\frac{1}{1000}$ of its diameter, or about $\frac{2}{1000}$ at the compensation masses or weights; but it requires 80° of laminæ to effect this object, because this motion is not direct, but by leverage, and moves diagonally, and consequently with loss of motion in the ratio of the hypothenuse to the perpendicular : whilst therefore the direct decrease of the diameter of the balance of $\frac{1}{1000}$ affects a compensation 6 min. 7 sec., the compensation weights or masses being moved nine times that quantity on the circular compensation rim, would only correct the compensation to the amount of one second daily, supposing the weights to stand at 90° on the compensation laminæ. Thus the travelling forward in heat and backward in cold instead of towards the centre is one of the chief causes of the error in the extremes. The forward or diagonal motion I have proved to amount to nearly the entire motion towards the centre of the balance. Another most important discovery was also exhibited, which is, that the centre of motion is not from the root or portion of the laminæ adjoining the diametrical bar, but from a point in the rim that never varies its distance from the centre of the balance, no matter how great the variation of temperature, and this point becomes the pivot of motion in the elongation and contraction of the bar, and the curling inwards or opening outwards of the compound laminæ to effect the compensation. Another curious circumstance, tending to explain the loss of direct motion in compensation due to a given temperature, is that a given chord or arc of a circle must increase and diminish as the diameter, hence 90° will in heat become 91°, and by decrease of the diameter in cold 90° will become 89° : these are the true causes of the error, and show that to obtain perfect and uniform compensation the masses should move telescopically in the same ratio and uniform manner that the plain balance is known to expand and the balance spring to lengthen and lose its elastic force. A proper diagnosis of the actual motion of the balance had never been made before—if it had, by such talent as that by which we have been surrounded, the remedy would have been discovered, whereas most of the remedies suggested were the cause of the error.

Auxiliary Compensation.—A great variety of auxiliary compensations were exhibited, most of them being modifications of Messrs. Molyneux, Eiffe, Ulrick, Pennington, and Arnold, also some suggested in 1851. Among the variety of exhibitors who showed auxiliary compensations were Messrs. BARRAUD and LUND, 41 *Cornhill* (*United Kingdom*, 3223), who effected this by compensation in the weights : it was rather complicated, and difficult of explanation without a diagram ; but Mr. Lund, an excellent authority, told us that with some painstaking it answered the purpose. Messrs. DENT, 34 *Cockspur Street* (*United Kingdom*, 3244), exhibited a new compensation balance by using an inverted compensation balance along with

---

* Both brass and steel expand in heat and contract in cold, the ratio of the former to the latter being nearly as 3 to 2.

the usual compensation. I had tried this some years before, to ascertain whether any fault existed in the bending and unbending of the laminæ, but found no such effect; indeed. there were many compensation balances in the Exhibition made with entirely reversed compound laminæ.

Mr. J. F. COLE, 5 *Queen Square, Bloomsbury* (*United Kingdom*, 3235), exhibited a new mode of compensation by a spiral compensation of bis-metal acting upon a polished steel arm radial to the centre; but as we could not test it, and he had no results, we were unable to pronounce an opinion of its merits.

The following is Mr. Cole's account of his new compensation balance.

"An eight-days marine chronometer with a new compensation balance having four equidistant radial arms of steel proceeding from a central boss, and all in the same horizontal plane; two opposite arms have the principal weights tapped, and screwed upon them for mean time regulation, and also for final adjustment of heat and cold.

"The other pair of solid arms are turned true and finished as axes, each arm carrying a movable steel socket enclosed within a laminated helical compensator, with the root end of each laminæ fitted friction-tight on the solid arms close to the balance centre.

"To the outer free end of each compensation and socket is attached a pair of lighter arms moving transversely to the plane of the balance; these arms carry a pair of small spherical weights for compensation, which stand at the full diameter of the balance when they agree with the horizontal plane. From this position any axial motion of the weights arising from either heat or cold will induce a gaining effect, but supposing the root ends of the compensators purposely moved by a proper key, ninety degrees on their fittings, the weights will then stand vertically, and will have advanced in a direct line to the centre of the balance a quantity equal to half the radius of the balance.

"From this vertical position of the arms and weights, any motion arising from heat or cold will induce a contrary losing effect, showing those extreme positions as normal points, and therefore, if the compensators and weights when standing horizontally are influenced by heat, motion towards the centre of balance will go on to the angle of 45° at an increasing rate of gain, but beyond 45° of the moving arms, the gaining will be continuous at a gradually decreasing rate up to 90° again, the vertical position, at which point the rate of gain will be reduced to nothing.

"The angle 45° should represent the correction for 120° of temperature, while the normal point at the horizontal position represents zero (Fah.); between those points the mean temperature of 60° will be represented by 22½° of angular position of the arms and compensation weights, and, supposing this position really correct, the compensating effect will depend on the relative proportion between the general dead weight of the balance and the fractional compensation weights, determinable by a few short trials in heat and cold; these proportions, once fixed, will afterwards be known, and the final adjustment made exact by shifting the compensation weights a little, in or out, on the movable arms, and drawing the dead weights out or turning them in, for restoring mean time."

Mr. BLACKIE, 24 *Amwell Street, E.C.* (*United Kingdom*, 3227), showed a balance which was thinned or tapered at the end of the laminæ with long radial screws, in the same manner as was years ago described by Mr. Ulrick, and which was exceedingly captivating; but although I have often tried them I never saw any improvement. Mr. Blackie, however, assured us that he did get some improvement; but this was due, in our opinion, to his thinning the laminæ of the rim, and thus preventing it running forward and backward in temperature, instead of tending to the centre: several exhibitors showed similar applications; Mr. Hutton, 1 noticed, had used it for years. M. HOHWÜ, *Amsterdam* (*Netherlands*, 191a), showed the same principle also, first invented by Ulrick.

Mr. B. CRISP, 81 *St. John Street Road* (*United Kingdom*, 3239), who exhibited a number of well-proportioned

marine chronometers, had in many instances adopted the Hartnup gridiron compensation, so called from its bars being of bis-metal in that shape; but it would be impossible to describe it without diagrams. When this balance first appeared, years ago, it gave in many instances excellent results, but it afterwards failed to hold its place. There is nevertheless great ingenuity in it, and it is evidently the result of no mean study.

Messrs. PARKINSON and FRODSHAM, 4 *Change Alley, E.C.* (*United Kingdom*, 3291), exhibited a number of chronometers with various modifications of compound laminæ compensation, as well as some pocket chronometers and watches which bear the stamp of their well-known manufacture.

Messrs. FRODSHAM and BAKER, 31 *Gracechurch Street, E.C.* (*United Kingdom*, 3251), exhibited various excellent compensations after the principle of Eiffe and Molyneux.

Mr. KULLBERG, 12 *Cloudesley Terrace, N.* (*United Kingdom*, 3276), exhibited a number of highly finished chronometer watches, and a small regulator with a short mercurial pendulum, peculiar for its suspended pallets at the escapement; but our attention was more particularly drawn to his very original modification of the compensation balance, a description of which could not be given without very accurate drawings. It would have been an excellent plan if every exhibitor had had a photograph taken of his exhibition.

The balance that met with the Jurors' attention was one of the ordinary construction, with, however, two remarkable changes: the rim, instead of being of the usual width of about $\frac{12}{100}$ of an inch, is nearly double that quantity, and is fluted on the top instead of being square: the inner side is of the reverse shape, the object of which is to make a natural check in cold, as the rim would curve into a greater hollow groove, whilst in heat the reverse effect would take place and become more sensitive. Mr. Kullberg employed gun-metal and steel instead of brass and steel.

Mr. J. POOLE, 57 *Fenchurch Street, E.C.* (*United Kingdom*, 3293), used as auxiliary compensation a check-piece acting on the main compensation to compel it to act to a more limited degree in cold, and apparently with success. This application, though originating with Mr. Eiffe, was first applied successfully, more than twenty years ago, to a chronometer the property of the Government (1957). The principle at that time was not considered safe to trust in inexperienced hands, on account of its acting on the main balance. Mr. Poole also exhibited a number of excellent pocket chronometers and watches.

Mr. R. WEBSTER, 74 *Cornhill, E.C.* (*United Kingdom*, 3324), employed as auxiliary compensation a very neatly and safely applied modification of the plans published by the Admiralty of a minor check-piece, which has the advantage that it does not interfere materially with the main compensation.

M. TIEDE, *Berlin* (*Prussia*, 1442), showed us an application of a mere auxiliary compensation bar placed in the same plane as the arm of the balance, composed of compound metal, with timing screws or cylindrical weights at the end. The principle was that the bis-metal bar would curve and shorten in the two extremes of either heat or cold, and consequently would cause a slight gaining in the two extremes just equal to the known error of losing. This was a very taking position; but we had had so much experience that we ceased to be allured by a principle, however plausible, and preferred to form our judgment on actual trial, to which M. Tiede submitted with a courtesy and confidence that did him credit. The result of the test was an entire failure. This we well knew before from previous experiments. Mr. Arnold's compensation-bar balance was formed entirely with this view; but the results showed no improvement. However plausible, therefore, these plans may appear of shortening the bar in both extremes, they are not facts, for if they did shorten, as the authors wished them, the results would be in accordance with the facts, and are so; but the reality of the case is, that the amount of curvature is so minute that it has no shortening power. The curve, it must be recollected, is merely the result of a different rate of expansion of the two metals, and, consequently, while the tendency to curve is going on, the lengthening or shortening of the metals is also going on, thus destroying the very principle on which the assertion has been built. No other foreign exhibitor had gone much into this subject; and certainly it is best left alone unless practised with the greatest simplicity, because for all the ordinary purposes of navigation the simple compensation balance with good proportions of bis-metal is a very "wonderful compensator."

Every captain of a ship should study to ascertain the error of his chronometer in temperature, and not take for granted that chronometers are perfect, though their performance is often wonderful; for when one looks at the table I have published on the subject of temperature, it is placing rather too much faith in the chronometer-maker not to look out for one's self.

If I were going to sea I should take with me three chronometers, one with an equation balance, one with a micrometric balance, and the third with the ordinary Arnold and Earnshaw balance with the best proportions. I should carefully ascertain their errors, and then form a table of corrections, by which I should hope to be able to determine any longitude to a mile. Such tables have been used with great success; and the able astronomer of Liverpool, Mr. Hartnup, has recently devoted himself to the subject, and is drawing up tables for the purpose.

Having now reported upon the compensation balance, and the errors on which so much time as well as talent has been spent, I hope we have cleared up most of its difficulties, and now direct a path of new research in the right direction.

Acceleration of Rate.*

The next point of interest, and one which is a serious difficulty and drawback to the young chronometer-maker, is the acceleration of rate. This subject is so interesting that I shall endeavour to enlist the attention of the philosopher as well as that of the practical chronometer-maker and navigator.

Suppose a new chronometer has been completed with all requisite care and skill, examined and corrected over and over again until it has been cleared of all mechanical errors, its balance-spring applied, and what is technically termed timed and adjusted for isochronism and temperature, until it is pronounced by its author to be one of the best and most successful chronometers he has ever made; no sooner, however, is it put on the register to ascertain its daily rate of going, than up starts this error of acceleration on its daily rate, that is to say, supposing the chronometer to be gaining uniformly one second per day, before the month is out it will be gaining daily, say in an extreme case, five seconds, and this takes place, not by starts, but by a gradual daily increase, and so continues for a whole year, or perhaps two, only in a lesser proportion. It has already been supposed that the chronometer has been cleared of all mechanical errors, whence then the cause of the error?

Some very plausible arguments have been adduced: 1, that the works become more free, the surfaces more highly polished, and in better working gear; and that the chronometer should gain on its daily rate is only a natural consequence; 2, that the balance-spring acquires more elastic force by its vibratory action; 3, that the balance tends to contract itself.

Now, neither of these assertions can be borne out by experience.

1. A new balance-spring, applied to an old chronometer of ten or twenty years' service, with all the rubbing surfaces worn together, accelerates on its rate just as much

as when applied in a new chronometer—the escapement and pivots faultless in both cases.

2. As to its vibratory action, it has been ascertained that a chronometer accelerates on its rate, whether in motion or not in motion—that is to say, that if a new balance-spring, hardened by fire and water, and tempered to a blue colour, say about 600° of Fah., be laid by in a drawer, gaining one second per day, and left unwound for a month, then the chronometer, being one such as was first supposed, it will be found to have accelerated upon its daily rate of going as much as if it had been kept wound and going, viz., five seconds per day per month.

3. The third reason is settled by the first remark, viz., the balance being ten or twenty years old, must have settled to itself; but the most conflicting circumstance is, that a balance-spring only hardened by compression, that is, by being drawn through mills, will, under each of the above circumstances, lose on its rate to a much more serious rate of loss, according to the nature of the steel and the degree of hardness produced.

If the vibratory action of the balance-spring produced a gaining property, the chronometer ought never to cease its gaining tendency, which is an acquisition of power; but this is not the case, because, after two years, a chronometer with a well-made balance-spring takes up a permanent rate, and will then last for fifteen or twenty years, according to its original quality; but after that period it begins to wane, and will no longer bear sudden changes of temperature without a serious disturbance of its daily rate, and shows symptoms of decay, and a tendency to lose on its rate; and, what is very remarkable, it cannot be re-adjusted for temperature with anything approaching the accuracy with which it was adjusted when the spring was new. The cause of this decay, though it is difficult to pronounce any very decided opinion upon, is, however, to be expected; for we must bear in mind, that in some instances the elastic force of a balance-spring is doubled by the process of hardening: the same spring, in its soft state, will only carry its balance, 360°, whereas the same spring when hardened and tempered will have increased its elastic force so much, that it will now carry the same balance to time, all other things being alike, over an extra 90° of arc, and even more.

Now, in order to do this, one of three things must take place: either the mainspring must be increased in the ratio of the square of 4 to square of 5, or the weight must be diminished in the same ratio; but as we maintain these points intact, it follows that the balance-spring, by the process of hardening and subsequent tempering, has increased its force as 1 to $1\frac{1}{2}$; ought we then to be surprised that this artificial force should in time fail, and require renewal? For the want of this knowledge, men are at a loss to account for the bad performance of a chronometer, once an excellent one, and propose to clean it, instead of at once condemning the balance-spring, and by the application of a new one, restore to the chronometer its original character.

Some have supposed the mainspring to have some influence; but that is too ridiculous a point to argue. The well-practised chronometer-maker has rather a contempt for the mainspring; he feels that with a good one, or with an indifferent one, or a very bad one, if all his other adjustments and proportions are good, he has little to fear, comparatively, from the bad one, or to rely upon in the good one.

We have stated that a balance-spring hardened only by drawing the wire by strong compression through mills, has a tendency to lose on its rate of going, and that a balance-spring hardened by fire and cold water, and subsequently tempered at a given heat, has a tendency to gain on its rate of going. The reasons for these different effects I consider to be, that in the case of hardening a spring by compression, the molecules are unnaturally pressed and serried together, and that by the action of the spring in the watch, the molecules re-arrange themselves after their own order, and thus cause that losing tendency we observe in practice. The reverse case, or that of gaining on the rate, I consider to arise from the violence done to the molecular particles of the steel by the process of making the spring

---

* I may here venture to give a hint to nautical men, that they should be cautious how they condemn a chronometer for a moderate acceleration on its daily rate during the first few voyages, as, if not in extreme, it is a fair symptom of its ultimate value; but I should look with great suspicion on one that shows a losing tendency.

red-hot, and then plunging it suddenly into cold water, say at 55°, in which case it is called flint-hard, and cannot be filed; it has also but very imperfect elasticity. It is then tempered to a pale straw-colour, at 450°, at which point its elasticity is marvellous: whilst in its hard state it can scarcely be handled without the risk of breaking, whereas it may now be handled with almost any amount of rough usage, without the fear of injury. A balance-spring, however, is never passed at this high temper; a deep sapphire blue is the colour of the temper at which the best chronometer springs are left: the proper heat of the fire, and the temper, are points of experience that practice and time alone can give. The cause of the acceleration is closely allied to the process of hardening by fire, during which the molecular particles are separated to a violent degree, though they are again partially restored in the tempering, and afterwards, by continuous motion in vibration, they gradually re-arrange themselves more closely, or according to their natural proximity, thus gaining strength, and thus producing that acceleration of daily rate. The attraction of the particles or atoms of steel in a spring sometimes take a form of repulsion; this causes them to lose their elastic force, and lose altogether their integrity, and so break. It may seem strange to talk of the atoms of steel floating to their natural places; but such is the case, cohesion being a relative, and not an absolute state, but depending upon the degree of temperature to which the steel is subjected. To destroy the cohesion of steel, it must be subjected to a violent and long-continued heat, and to procure the cohesion of mercury, it must be subjected to a very considerable degree of cold, when it becomes solid, and may be submitted to the blows of a hammer. Molten steel, having lost its cohesion by the separation of its particles by heat, becomes fluid; but when cooled, its power of cohesion is such, that the smallest bar will bear tons weight.

I have now only to state the proportions upon which the best English chronometers are constructed, and finish with an authentic account of their performance when made under the direction of a master mind. The English chronometers are in general constructed to go two days, or fifty-four hours, and to be wound daily. The extra day is a provision, in case the winding be forgotten. A considerable number are constructed to go eight days, and are to be wound every seventh day, one day's grace being allowed. There is also an indication on the dial-plate which points out how long the chronometer has been going since last wound, and how many hours it has still to run before it entirely runs down.

There are now in use two different callipers of the two-days marine chronometer, which have undergone various modifications, but they may both be said to be highly satisfactory in their proportions. There are also two models of the eight-day chronometer, one called the double-frame, which when well made is a splendid instrument; the other is a smaller calliper after the two-days model, and when in good proportions, is also a very satisfactory chronometer. I have introduced an entirely new set of marine chronometer callipers, and have given the proportions of every part in English measures in inches. I also introduced an entirely new set of watch callipers, which will be made the subject of a separate chapter. I think it advisable to record the exact state of some of the proportions of the English marine chronometers which have so signally served the purposes of navigation and nautical science, and which have been so universally approved by men of all nations with whom I have conversed, though it will not be necessary for me to state any details of the minor or subordinate parts, but to point out the relations between the motive force and the momentum of the balance or work it is called upon to perform.

All English marine chronometers are constructed with a fusee, not merely for its quality of equalizing the force of the mainspring, but also for the value of its auxiliary spring, which, being only intended in the first instance to keep the chronometer going whilst being wound up, was originally effected by a wheel and pinion gearing into the fusee; it was then but a going-fusee, and no more; but the introduction of a going spring constantly in tension by the force of the mainspring, became a kind of regulator or corrector of any defective action of the mainspring. It was many years before the fusee was adopted in chronometers abroad, nor is it wholly so now.

The escapement now employed as the very best has been long definitively settled to be the Arnold Earnshaw escapement, commonly called the "chronometer detached escapement;" the balance-spring is the helix, formed of hardened and tempered steel, glass and gold having been abandoned. The balance also is the Arnold Earnshaw compound laminæ compensation balance, the weight, diameter, and proportions of which will be given against their respective sizes.

The best train for marine chronometers experience has proved to be the half-second, which makes 240 beats per minute.

I have made the discovery of a law depending upon the cubic dimensions of the barrel, divided by the number of hours required by the fusee to make one revolution, to determine the weight and diameter of that balance which shall make any given number of vibrations per hour of the desired extent. This law was founded upon experiment, but its accuracy has been since verified by a collection of thousands of facts.

Extract from the Table of Momentum.

PARTICULARS OF THE ENGLISH DOUBLE FRAME EIGHT DAYS OR 192 HOURS MARINE CHRONOMETER, WITH SIXTEEN-TURN FUSEES.

BARREL.				CHRONOMETER TRAINS.						
Height in inches.	Diameter in inches.	Diameter squared.	D² × Height. Cubic 10ths of an inch.	Force on fusee at 1 inch rad. in Troy ounces.	Hourly expenditure at centre pinion in dwts. at 1 inch rad.	Vibrations 14,000 per hour, or 240 per minute. Weight B.*		Vibrations 18,000 per hour, or 300 per minute. Screw B.†		
						Diam.	Weight in grs.	Diam.	Weight in grs.	
125	185	342	4278	58·	96·75	1·10	106	1·10	56	
130	185	342	4449	60·5	101·	1·10	111	1·10	58	
125	185	353	4418	60·	**100·**	1·10	110	1·10	58	
120	190	361	4332	59·3	99·3	1·10	109	1·10	57	
130	190	361	4693	64·40	107·3	1·10	119	1·10	62	

* Weight B, signifies Weight Balance diameters taken across the compound rim.
† Screw B, signifies Screw Balance diameters taken at the extremity of the screws.

PARTICULARS OF THE ENGLISH TWO DAYS 54 OR 56 HOURS MARINE CHRONOMETER WITH NINE-TURN FUSEES.

BARREL.				CHRONOMETER TRAINS.						
Height in inches.	Diameter in inches.	Diameter squared.	D² × Height cubic 10ths of an inch.	Force on fusee at 1 inch rad. in Troy ounces.	Hourly expenditure at centre pinion in dwts. at 1 inch rad.	Vibrations 14,000 per hour, or 240 per minute. Weight B.*		Vibrations 18,000 per hour, or 300 per minute. Screw B.†		
						Diam.	Weight in grs.	Diam.	Weight in grs.	
55	130	169	930	28·6	82·0	1·10	90	100	56	
								Weight B.		
60	137½	189	1130	35·	100·	1·10	110	100	68	
72	150	225	1620	49·8	143·	1·18	136	105	83	
75	155	240	1800	55·4	159·	1·20	147	110	85	

* Weight B, signifies Weight Balance diameters taken across the compound rim.
† Screw B, signifies Screw Balance diameters taken at the extremity of the screws.

Note.—From the preceding tables it is seen that the 8 days chronometer and the medium size two days chronometers have the same exact amount of force at the centre or hour pinion, and consequently the same diameter and weight of balance, and the same strength of balance springs.

ASTRONOMICAL CLOCKS, THEIR ESCAPEMENTS AND PENDULUMS.

I approach this part of the Report with considerable diffidence, well knowing how many able minds have occupied themselves in this research, and furnished horology with so large a number of remarkable inventions, that it would require almost a lifetime to report what has been done. I shall therefore confine myself to the facts of the case, and the necessities of this important branch of the art. We have shown that in the chronometer, the remontoir escapement has been entirely discarded, and only in one instance of note was it employed in the present Exhibition. It had been introduced as the philosopher's stone that was to turn all mechanical errors, all want of judgment and talent, into good order and undeviating time-keepers; but although a very large amount of talent and perseverance have been devoted to these escapements, they have never done any good for chronometrical science; because there has been too much reliance upon escapements by their authors, and too little attention to the well-known laws of time-keeping. Nevertheless, although these remontoirs and gravity escapements have been discarded, and proved to be a fallacy in chronometers and watches, they may still find a home in clocks, and under certain conditions render good service, particularly in large turret clocks.

The number of clocks in the Exhibition entitled to the rank of being called astronomical or regulators were few, but those that were shown were very good. Messrs. BENNETT, BLACKIE, DENT, WALKER, DELOLME, WEBSTER, WHITE, and LOSADA all showed excellent regulators. Each had employed the Graham or dead-beat escapement with excellent results; but we were not furnished with particulars of construction. DR. CLARK, *Finmere House, Oxfordshire* (*United Kingdom*, 3233), a very able amateur, exhibited a regulator with a remontoir or gravity escapement, of the success of which he was very sanguine; but as we were not furnished with any results of its performance, nor could it be tested, no positive opinion of its merits can be reported. I append a full description of its construction.

There were several other gravity escapements, but they were not new; though a very clever gravity escapement was exhibited by Mr. GUMPEL, 2 *Gordon Cottages, Brixton* (*United Kingdom*, 3256), its application was, however, more adapted to electric clocks. The work here was exceedingly well executed.

Mr. G. HAWKSLEY of *Bromley-by-Bow* exhibited a gravity escapement which he called a detached gravity escapement, suited for large turret clocks: it was very ingenious, exceedingly well executed though complicated, but with more experience Mr. Hawksley will no doubt bring it to perfection.

Gravity Escapement by Dr. Clark, for an Astronomical Clock with Seconds Pendulum.

This escapement is of the remontoir class, the motive power being employed to raise alternately a pair of small secondary weights, each of which being held in suspension during the respective intervals of vibration, are in succession disengaged and made to act upon the pendulum, as a definite gravitating impulse force, whereby the arcs of vibration are rendered constant to one extent, less only the small difference from impediment at the lockings, arising from variable force through the train of wheel work by change of condition in the oil, &c.

In the above general principle, Dr. Clark's escapement accords with various other English and foreign examples of remontoir gravity escapements in the present Exhibition and elsewhere, all being modifications of the original by Mudge and Cumming for clocks, and by Harrison, Mudge, and others for portable time-keepers; in such the locking resistance has hitherto been the chief defect against uniformity of vibratory motion, together with liability to tripping in the action, a fault so objectionable as to render the performance too uncertain to be relied on without the complex addition of a fly to check the momentum of the train.

In the escapement by Dr. Clark, the fly is dispensed with, as by his original plan of locking by a reversed action of the detents, tripping is rendered impossible to occur under any circumstances; though without the fly there is a visible reaction of the seconds hand, the action of the escapement is perfectly sure, and reaction of the hand being no detriment to time keeping, is disregarded by Dr. Clark; but if a decided action of the hand be preferred, he adapts a simple spring check as a remedy.

The construction is as follows: On the usual pinion arbor which carries the seconds' hand, is fixed a common toothed wheel, driving an extra pinion in the ratio of ten revolutions per minute, the arbor of which pinion projects through the back plate of the clock frame, carrying the escapement wheel outside; this wheel is formed as a star of six repose teeth, the full diameter being three inches; these teeth are bent alternately sideways, three to the right and three to the left of the true plane of the wheel surface, the teeth representing two distinct wheels of three teeth each, while only three pins at equal distances from each other are fixed near the star wheel centre in a true circle of three-eighths of an inch diameter, the pins projecting outwardly from the wheel surface as lifting pins. Dr. Clark places the locking edges of his two detents exactly in the vertical line below the star-wheel centre, while the centre of the wheel is in the same vertical line of the pendulum rod. The repose teeth act alternately on the locking edges of two movable detents pivoted into the back plate, each pivot hole being planted on a horizontal line tangental to the lower circumference of the star, the distance of each detent pivot hole being three-eighths of an inch right and left from the vertical line, that measure will therefore be the length of the detent arms, one of which is straight and locks the star tooth by abutment, while the other arm is bent as a rectangle at the acting end for receiving the next tooth on the inner face of the detent as a hook locking, and both these arms range in the horizontal line.

On the axis of each detent is fixed a second arm, bent at a suitable curvature, and ascending as an arm of impulse two inches above the detent pivots on each side of the pendulum rod, the centre of suspension of the pendulum being five inches above the horizontal line of the detents: at the upper ends of the bent arms a gold pin half an inch long is in each as the pins of impulse on the pendulum rod; these pins are adjustable by bending the impulse arms which are fixed on their axes, or by moving a pair of set screws which bind the two locking arms to the same axis. The centre of the star is in the vertical line of the pendulum rod, and as the diameter is three inches, the centre will be one and a half inches above the horizontal line of the detent pivots; these points thus arranged agree with the rule given by Dr. Clark as the best proportions, viz.: The place of the pin of impulse two-fifths of the distance upwards, between the detent centres and the centre of the pendulum suspension, and it must be further observed that the two pins of impulse should have a range of action on the pendulum rod coincident with their lines of centre and the centre of motion of the pendulum; friction at the points of impulse will then be so small as to be no detriment to the time keeping.

The bent arms of impulse have a solid continuation downward, each being carried under and beyond the opposite detent axis, so far only as to allow room on each of those branches for attaching small spherical weights; these are the gravity weights for propelling the pendulum.

The peculiarity of inverting the escapement may be objected to as not giving impulse concentric with the pendulum's point of suspension; but its freedom from tripping may perhaps excuse this apparent defect. This escapement bears so close a resemblance to Denison's gravity escapement, that had the Doctor's appeared first, Mr. Denison's would certainly have been considered a copy: we do not, however, for one moment infer that Dr. Clark's was not equally as original to him as Denison's was to himself. There comes a time when such escapements are again in fashion, and many minds perfectly independent of each other are pursuing each his plan in his own way, and come probably to the same result, and if they prove to be alike, it occurs no doubt that they have been disciples of the same great masters, have read the same books, or have derived their previous knowledge from the same sources; for gravity escapements are more than a century old. The application of a fly was, I believe, first used by Harrison; but whether he was the first or not matters little: a fly to check the rapidity of a wheel in motion is the clockmaker's common remedy, and exists in every clock. In fact, we have such a boundless store of horological inventions on this subject by the early masters, that any man of mechanical genius and ability will find endless resources of every kind for escapemental combinations.

Dead-Beat Escapements.

The interest which is felt by a chronometer-maker in the accomplishment of a perfect astronomical clock, induced me to prepare three high specimens to prove the value of the dead-beat over all others for regulators, and I seemed to be almost unanimously seconded in this opinion. The dead-beat escapement is, however, one that requires the greatest care and the utmost mathematical accuracy in all its principles and details in order to insure the accomplishment of that perfection of which I know it to be susceptible.

When we talk of detached escapements, or any escapement applied to a pendulum, it is necessary to bear in mind that there is always one-third at the least of the pendulum's vibration during which the arc of escapement is intimately mixed up with the vibration either in locking,

unlocking, or in giving impulse; therefore, whatever inherent faults any escapement may possess are constantly mixed up in the result; the words "detached escapement" can hardly be applied when the entire arc of vibration is only 2°; or in other words, what part of the vibration is left without the influence of the escapement? at most 1°. In chronometers the arc of vibration is from ten to fifteen times greater than the arc of escapement.

The dead-beat escapement has been accused of interfering with the natural isochronism of the pendulum by its extreme friction on the circular rests, crutch, and difficulty of unlocking, &c. &c., all of which we shall show is only so when improperly made, and quite at variance with the truth when constructed according to the rules subsequently herein laid down.

Mr. Bloxam considered the friction of the dead-beat escapement to be very great, and the cause of all its errors. The Astronomer Royal, in his able paper upon this escapement, when saying there is no friction, no doubt means there is no injurious friction "when the arc of escapement is equal on both sides;" now this position convinces me that the Astronomer Royal is master of the question which my three models were intended to illustrate, namely, these important facts:—

That when the dead-beat escapement has been mathematically constructed, and is strictly correct in all its bearings, its vibrations are found to be isochronous for arcs of different extent from 0·75 of a degree to 2·50 degrees;—that injurious friction does not then exist;—that the run up on the lockings has no influence, nor is there any friction at the crutch; — that oil is not absolutely necessary except at the pivots; and that there is no unlocking resistance nor any inclination to repel or attract the wheel at its lockings.

The general mode of making this escapement is very defective and indefinite, and entirely destroys the naturally isochronous vibrations of the pendulum.

The following is the usual rate of the pendulum's performance in the different arcs of vibration with an escapement as generally constructed after empirical rules:—

Arc of vibration 3° rate per diem 9·0 seconds.

2½°	,,	,,	6·0 ,,
2°	,,	,,	3·5 ,,
1½°	,,	,,	1·5 ,,
1°	,,	,,	0·0 ,,

Thus for a change of vibration of 1°, we have a daily error of 3·5; but what would any chronometer-maker say if he found his chronometer vary its daily rate 3½ seconds for 1 degree of arc? When the mere difference of vibration in the hanging and lying positions of his chronometer is 90°, giving an error of 315 seconds, would he attribute it to the balance-spring? or, would he not rather conclude that the instrument must be grossly defective, and seek the cause? And such is the cause (mechanical errors) as stated above. And we find men saying they cannot repeat the experiments of the late W. J. Frodsham, F.R.S., who wrote upon this subject, and attributed a certain length, breadth, and strength of suspending spring, as best suited to the isochronous vibrations of the pendulum.* But no change of suspending spring will alter inherent mechanical errors destructive of the laws of motion. With clocks made in the usual manner, whether you apply a long or short spring, strong or weak, broad or narrow, you will not remove one fraction of the error; so the sooner the fallacy of relying upon the suspending spring to cure mechanical errors is exploded the better.

That the suspending spring plays a most important part must be admitted, since when suspended by a spring, a pendulum is kept in motion by a few grains only, whereas if supported on ordinary pivots, 200 lb. would not drive it 2' beyond its arc of escapement, so great would be the friction at the point of suspension. It is much to be regretted that Mr. Vulliamy, who wrote a very able pamphlet on the dead-beat escapement, did not connect it with pendulum experiments, and equally so that Mr. Frodsham, F.R.S., did not connect his pendulum experiments with

---

* See his Paper in the Transactions of the Royal Society.

the escapement; for, as I have previously shown, they cannot be separated, no matter the character of the escapement employed, whether gravity, remontoir, detached, or dead-beat.

The condition on which alone the vibrations of the pendulum will be isochronous are the following :—

1. That the pendulum be at time with and without the clock, in which state it is isochronous "suspended by a spring."

2. That the crutch and pallets shall each travel at the same precise angular velocity as the pendulum, which can only happen when the arc each is to describe is in direct proportion to its distance from the centre of motion, that is, from the pallet axis.

3. That the angular force communicated by the crutch to the pendulum shall be equal on both sides of the quiescent point ; or in other words, that the lead of each pallet shall be of the same precise amount.

4. That one or any other number of degrees marked by the crutch or pallets shall correspond with the same degree or degrees shown by the lead of the pendulum, as marked by the index on the degree plate.

5. That the various vibrations of the pendulum be driven by a motive weight in strict accordance with the theoretical law ; that is, if a 5 lb. weight cause the pendulum to double its arc of escapement of 1°, and consequently drive it 2°, all the intermediate arcs of vibration shall in practice accord with the theory of increasing or diminishing their arcs in the ratio of the square roots of the motive weight.

To accomplish the foregoing conditions, there is but one fixed point or line of distance between the axis of the escape wheel and that of the pallet, and that depends upon the number of teeth embraced, and only one point in which the pallet axis can be placed from which the several lines of the escapement can be correctly traced and properly constructed with equal angles, and equal rectangular lockings on both sides, so that each part travels with the same degree of angular velocity, which are the three essential points of the escapement.

Much difference of opinion has been expressed upon the construction of the pallets, as to whether the lockings or circular rests should be at equal distances from the pallet axis with arms and impulse planes of unequal length ; or, at unequal distances from the pallet axis with arms and impulse planes of equal length. In the latter case the locking on one side is 3° above, and on the other 3° below the rectangle, whereas, in the former, the tooth on both sides reposes at right angles to the line of pressure ; but the length of the impulse planes is unequal. When an escapement is correctly made upon either plan, the results are very similar, though I decidedly prefer the pure right angled locking, although the arm of one pallet is longer than the other by the thickness of the pallet. The angle at the tooth will, however, be the same.

It is possible to obtain equal angles by a false centre of motion or pallet axis; but then the arcs of repose will not be equal ; this, however, is not of so much consequence as that of having destroyed the conditions Nos. 2, 3, 4 ; for even at correct centres, if the angles are not drawn off correctly by the protractor and precisely equal to each other, the isochronous vibrations of the pendulum will be destroyed, and unequal arcs will no longer be performed in equal times ; and I consider that the quiescent point is not the centre of the vibration, except when the driving forces are equal on both sides of the natural quiescent point of the pendulum at rest.

Now this is the very pith of the subject, and which few would be inclined to look for with any hope of finding in it the solution of this important question, the isochronism of the pendulum.

One would naturally suppose that unequal arcs on the two sides of the vertical lines would not seriously affect the rate of the clock, but would be equal and contrary, and consequently a balance of errors, and so they probably are for the same fixed vibration, but not for any other ; because different angles are driven with different velocities, the short angle has a quicker rate of motion than the long. Five pounds motive weight will multiply three times the pendulum's vibration over an arc of escapement of 0°·75 ; but the same pendulum, with an arc of escapement of 1° would require 11·20 lbs. to treble its vibration ; whence I proved that the times of the vibration varied in the same ratio as the sum of the squares of the difference of the angles of each pallet, compared with the spaces passed over ; nor is this a very difficult question to solve mathematically, nor difficult of practical proof.

The conclusion here arrived at, being dependent upon much analogous reasoning on the motions of the balance and pendulum, with regard to time, would require more detail than can be admitted in the report.

When any facts can be tabulated, I think it to be a good plan to do so, as they serve as a diagram, and the whole subject may then be viewed and studied as a drawing.

Now touching the effects of friction on the circular rests : I found no effect produced when using the same clock and pendulum with pallets embracing 6, 8, 10, or even 11 teeth, in which case the lever's lineal friction was in the ratios of 6, 10, 15, and 20 respectively, the latter having three times the rubbing surface. Some of the French exhibitors were escaping over five teeth, with 40′ arc of escapement, in order, they said, to avoid the friction ; but there is a limit in this respect, for as you diminish the number of teeth embraced, you increase all the criticalities of the escapement, and its construction requires the utmost care, since it is more affected in proportion by the shake of the holes and the shake of the crutch, &c.

I consider eight teeth to be a good number to be embraced by the pallets, and an arc of escapement from 0·75 to 1 degree from zero ; but these short arms are very silent, and are also proportionately more difficult to make. I usually make my regulators to embrace ten teeth, as a loud beat is desirable in an observatory. A loud beat may be obtained by a great drop, a fault in every escapement ; but particularly in the dead beat, wherein the drop should be as fine as possible and the amount of locking repose on the circular rest only just safe, with the locking corners nicely rounded off. Much stress has been laid upon the advantage of regulators being made to go with very small motive force in order to avoid friction ; this, to some extent, is a popular error : doubtless a clock that will do the same work with half the weight, all other things alike, is a great proof of its mechanical accuracy ; but what I particularly desire to impress is, that it is not advisable to use so small a driving weight that it is barely more than sufficient to be in equilibrium with the point of the escape wheel tooth. A motive weight of five pounds (including the pulley) is a good rule for the best English regulators ; but for a small library regulator, with the *same pendulum as above*, and a fine light train not much heavier than that of a marine chronometer, and with a barrel of only an inch diameter and a fall of three feet in eight days, the pendulum is often driven by a motive weight of from three to four pounds, a little extra power is then no cause of either friction or wear. Wear and uncertain friction arise from bad materials, but principally from the defective forms of wheel and pinion teeth, and imperfectly constructed escapements, which cause bad gearing : but the friction, in the clockmaker's sense of the term, is here entirely very small. These small clocks generally escape over only five or six teeth, with an angle of escapement of 40′ and an arc of vibration of 1° 30′, depending upon its accuracy of construction. Well, in this case, to increase the motive force would be a benefit instead of a defect, as is generally supposed.

In pallet arms of this small radius the increased vibration of the pendulum and the consequent run up on the lockings, so much dreaded as a source of disturbing the isochronism of the pendulum, is so small as scarcely to be visible by the addition of nearly twice the motive weight.

There is something very pleasing in the proportions when escaping over five teeth, as the radii of the pallet arms are just half the radius of the wheel ; these are the proportions we employ in the chronometer escapement. When the pallets embrace eight teeth, we see by Table II., in the following page, that the radii of the pallet arms and wheel are equal ; and when embracing ten teeth the pallet arms are 1½ times that of the wheel. These are points worthy of close attention, but experience can alone determine their value.

We regretted that no specimen of Hardy's gravity

escapement was exhibited ; it is one of those gravity escapements that, from the nature of its construction, does not trip. There are also peculiarities about this escapement that merit careful investigation, and particularly as the train of wheel work in Hardy's regulators is among the best in England, and the shape of the wheels and pinions makes the most perfect gearing I ever witnessed.

The following is a table of the principal parts of the Graham or dead-beat escapement for astronomical clocks, suited for an escape wheel of one inch radius and thirty teeth, for each of the several numbers of teeth that may be embraced from two teeth or one space, to thirteen teeth or twelve spaces; from which table those for any other radius may be obtained by simple multiplication :—

TABLE I.—*On the Vulliamy principle, with pallet arms of equal length and circular rests, or lockings at unequal distances.*

Teeth embraced.	Spaces.	Angle at the wheel formed by the radii through the middle of the pallet.	Angle at the pallet axis corresponding to the same chord as the angle at the wheel.	Chord of the two angles at the wheel and pallet axes.	Distance of the pallet axis from that of the wheel.	Radius of the outer rest, or circular locking.	Radius of the inner circular rest, or locking.
		Deg.*	Deg.*	Inches.	Inches.	Inches.	Inches.
2	1	18	162	·3124	1·0111	·2105	·1058
3	2	30	150	·5169	1·0339	·3199	·2152
4	3	42	138	·7157	1·0697	·4357	·3310
5	4	54	126	·9067	1·1208	·5612	·4565
6	5	66	114	1·0878	1·1907	·7008	·5962
7	6	78	102	1·2569	1·2850	·8610	·7563
8	7	90	90	1·4123	1·4123	1·0510	·9463
9	8	102	78	1·5522	1·5868	1·2856	1·1809
10	9	114	66	1·6750	1·8336	1·5911	1·4844
11	10	126	54	1·7796	2·1997	2·0226	1·9076
12	11	138	42	1·8646	2·7866	2·6538	2·5492
13	12	150	30	1·9292	3·8584	3·7793	3·6746

TABLE II.—*On the principle of circular rests or lockings at equal distances from the pallet axis, and unequal pallet arms.*

Angle at the wheel axis.	Angle at the pallet axis.	Chord of the angle at the wheel and its corresponding angle at the pallet axis.	Distance of the pallet axis from that of the wheel.	Radius of the circular rests or lockings at equal distances from the pallet axis.	Radius of the short pallet arm.	Radius of the long pallet arm.
Deg.*	Deg.*	Chord inches.	Secant inches.	Tangent inches.	Inches.	Inches.
18	162	·3129	1·0125	·1584	·0537	·2630
30	150	·5176	1·0353	·2679	·1633	·3726
42	138	·7167	1·0711	·3838	·2792	·4885
54	126	·9080	1·1223	·5095	·4048	·6142
66	114	1·0893	1·1924	·6494	·5447	·7541
78	102	1·2586	1·2868	·8098	·7051	·9144
90	90	1·4142	1·4142	1·0000	·8953	1·1047
102	78	1·5543	1·5890	1·2349	1·1302	1·3396
114	66	1·6773	1·8361	1·5399	1·4352	1·6445
126	54	1·7820	2·2027	1·9626	1·8579	2·0073
138	42	1·8672	2·7904	2·6051	2·5004	2·7098
150	30	1·9318	3·8637	3·7320	3·6274	3·8367

The calculations in the above tables are based upon two slightly different plans, which may be thus defined :—

In No. I. the centre of the pallet axis, a point of the utmost importance to the correct gearing of the escapement, is found in the point of meeting of the two chords representing the thickness of the pallets prolonged to their intersection ; or it may be otherwise described as the corrected tangent of the upper and lower rest.

In No. II. the centre of the pallet axis is found in the intersection of two tangents drawn from the points where the said radii of the wheel teeth meet the circle circumscribing them, a construction which makes the circular rests or lockings at equal distance from the pallet axis, and requires the pallet arms to be of unequal length.

In either case, when the centre of the pallet axis is found as here directed, and all the several measures given in the tables have been properly carried out, the escapement will be found to possess properties and advantages which are not to be obtained by any other method.

1. The action of the tooth upon the inclined faces of the pallets will be uniformly the same for each pallet.

2. If the line connecting the wheel and pallet axes be bisected, and upon the point so found a circle be described with a radius equal to half this distance, the circumference will pass through the centres of the two axes and also through the locking points as each tooth and pallet in action becomes alternately engaged; thus proving that the locking points are angles in a semicircle, and consequently *right angles*, and also that the two semi-angles at the wheel and pallet axes will be equal to a right angle, and therefore complements to each other.

3. The arc described by the pendulum and that described by the escapement will be perfectly equal, the result of which will be that the same amount of force being constantly transmitted through the escapement to the pendulum, it will be driven through various arcs in equal times, and the pallet, crutch, and pendulum, instead of interfering with each other's motion, will travel together step by step, with the precise angular velocity due to their respective distances from their centre of motion. And because the angles at the lockings are right angles, and consequently perpendicular to the action of the main force, there will be neither draw nor repulse.

It now only remains to explain the manner in which the table has been calculated, and to give an example of its use for obtaining the measures of any other escapement, by merely multiplying the numbers taken from the table by the radius or semidiameter of the escape wheel you design to employ.

Rules for the Calculation of a Graham or Dead-beat Escapement.

All the lines of the Graham escapement are trigonometrical, and the numbers in the table are the natural numbers of the sum of three logarithms, as in the following example :—

Required the measures of an escapement for a 30-tooth

---

* The number of degrees in these angles in correct escapements is always divisible by 12 with a remainder of 6, which is the pallet space.

It is impossible to examine these tables without the attention being specially called to the numbers peculiar to the plan of escaping over eight teeth, upon the true rest principle, in which the following facts appear :—

1. That the angles at the wheel and pallet axes are each 90°.

2. That the radius of the circular locking is equal to the radius of the wheel.

3. That the chord of the opening of the wheel, and the distance of the pallet axis from that of the wheel are each equal, and equal to the square root of the sum of the squares of the radius of the wheel and the radius of the pallet arm at its locking.

This number, therefore, embraces all the points in Euclid's 47th problem—renders the escapement most easy to delineate and make a working sketch; and were a diagram admitted here, it would probably win for itself the title of the geometrician's number, and so fix it in the mind as to promote its universal adoption.

wheel of 1·135 inches radius, the pallets of which are to embrace ten teeth or nine spaces.

9 spaces × 12° = 108°, and 108° + 6° = 114°, the angle at the wheel formed by the two radii through the middle of the pallet; that is, 57° on each side of the vertical line representing the pendulum at rest.

1. For the chord of the angle at the centre of the wheel, add together the logarithm of the diameter of the escape-wheel   2·27 in. = 0·3560259
Log. sine of ½ the angle at the wheel 57° = 9·9235914
  „ cos. of ½ the thickness of pallet   3° = 9·9994044
Natural number = chord of 114°} to rad. 1·135 = 1·90117 inches } sum = 0·2794217

2. For the distance of the centres of the wheel and pallet axes, add together the log. of the radius . . . . . 1·135 in. = 0·0549959
Log. secant . . . . . 57° = 0·2638912
  „ cosine . . . . . 3° = 9·9994444
Nat. numb. distance of the centres} = 2·08109 inches } log. = 0·3182915

3. For the corrected tangent of the semi-opening of the wheel formed by the radii through the pallets, add together log. radius . . . . . 1·135 in. = 0·0659959
Log. tangent . . . . . 57° = 0·1874827
  „ cosine . . . . . 3° = 9·9994044
Natural number = corrected tangent of} 57° = 1·74535 inches . . . .} = 0·2418829
Radius 1·135 log. . . . . . = 0·0549959
Log. sine 3° . . . . = 8·7188002
Nat. sin. 3° to rad. 1·135 = ·05940 (this number is to be added to and subtracted from the corrected tangent in order to obtain the outer and inner rests) . .} = 8·7732005

Corrected tan. 57° = } = { 1·80475 = outer rest.
1·74535 ± 0·5940 }   { 1·68595 = inner rest.

Example of the use of the table by simple multiplication.

In the table against 10 teeth are
Chord . . 1·6750 × 1·135 = 1·9011)
Distance . 1·8836 × 1·135 = 2·0811 } as before.
Outer rest . 3·5911 × 1·135 = 1·8011)
Inner rest . 1·4844 × 1·135 = 1·6847)

In Table II., or that for true rests at equal distances from the pallet axis with pallet arms of unequal length, the numbers in the table are merely the natural numbers belonging to the sines, tangents, &c., of the several lines they represent, without any correction, thus :—

The chord of the angular opening of the pallets } = { 2 sine of half the angle at the wheel formed by the radii through the pallets.
The distance between the axes . . . . . } = { The secant of the said semi-angle.
The radius of circular rest } = { The tangent of the said angle.
The length of the short arm . . . . } = { The said tangent — ·0103 (= 2 sine 3° to rad. 1).
The length of the long arm . . . . } = { The said tangent + ·0103 (= 2 sine 3° to rad. 1).

These tables may be consistently styled universal, since there is scarcely a question that can be asked relative to the measures of an escapement that they are incapable of answering.

Example.—Let it be required, for instance, to find the measures of an escapement, the pallets of which shall embrace nine teeth, or eight spaces, the centres of the wheel and pallet-axes being fixed at two inches distance, and the circular rests at equal distances and unequal arms?

First of all, for the radius of the escape-wheel, which depends upon the line that happens to be given, thus :—

$$\text{The rad. of the wheel} = \frac{\text{given chord}}{1·5543} = \frac{\text{given distance}}{1·589}$$
$$= \frac{\text{Rad. cir. rest}}{1·2349} = \frac{\text{short arm}}{1·1302} = \frac{\text{long arm}}{1·3396}.$$

In the present instance
$$\text{Rad.} = \frac{\text{distance 2 inches}}{1·589} = 1·26 \text{ inches, then}$$

The chord . = 1·5543 × 1·26 = 1·958) These calcula-
Distance . . = 1·589 × 1·26 = 2·002 } tions sufficiently
Rad. cir. rest = 1·2349 × 1·26 = 1·559 } prove the uni-
Rad. short arm = 1·1302 × 1·26 = 1·424 } versality of the
Rad. long arm = 1·3396 × 1·26 = 1·688) tables.

I have now to show the defective results arising from the usual mode of making this escapement, and then what may be done by following the rules laid down in the table of the dead-beat escapement, which will of course always depend upon each person's individual notion of the accuracy of construction as applied to the details of carrying out this escapement.

EXAMPLE by the Trade plan against the true principle.			Constructed after Table No. I.; arc of escapement just under one degree.				Constructed after Table No. II.	
No. 1.			No. 2.				No. 3.	
Vibrations.	Sec. of Daily Rate.	Sec. of Daily Rate.	Motive Weight.	Vibrations.	Daily Rate.	True Daily Rate.	Vibrations.	True Daily Rate.
			lbs. oz.	Degrees.	Sec.	Sec.	Degrees.	Sec.
2·40)		(−1·6	6 7	2·30	−1·7	−2·70	3·0	−0·7
2·40 }	−7·0	{ −1·6	6 7	2·15	−1·5	−2·60	2·0	−0·6
2·40)		(−1·6	6 7	2·28	−0·8	−2·70	2·0	−0·5
2·19)		(−1·4	5 1½	1·95	−0·8	−2·00	1·75	−0·4
2·19 }	−5·5	{ −1·3	5 1½	1·98	−0·5	−2·00	1·50	−0·4
2·19)		(−1·4	5 0½	1·70	−0·6	−1·80	1·25	−0·9*
1·80)		(−1·3	3 12	1·70	−0·4	−2·00	1·10	−0·7
1·80 }	−3·5	{ −1·3	3 12	1·45	−0·5	−1·70	—	—
1·80)		(−1·25	2 12	1·45	−0·7	−1·60	—	—
1·25)		(−1·2	2 4	1·30	−0·1	−1·60	—	—
1·25 }	−0·0	{ −1·2	1 12	1·05	−0·4	−1·60	—	—
1·25)		(−1·1	—	—	—	—	—	—

The same pendulum and springs have been used throughout the experiments.

* During my recent experiments I have continually found the rate slow at about 1°·20, without being yet able to account for it satisfactorily. My experience leads me to declare in favour of such a result of isochronism as Nos 1 and 2.

I must also endeavour to remove various myths of trade traditions : such as that the isochronism of the pendulum suspension-spring will counteract all mechanical errors of construction, and that the pallets should be the one convex and the other concave ; and some have said that they should be both concave, but with different degrees of concavity, instead of positive plane surfaces ; while others have suggested as a remedy for non-isochronism, to destroy the truth of the rest by a partial recoil. You might as well expect good gearing from bad-sized wheels and pinions, or that the machine should not wear nor stop, as to rely upon such shallow principles. Another favourite discussion on this escapement is that of the unequal friction of the tooth of the wheel upon the pallets ; a circumstance which probably suggested the idea of Cumming, Berthoud, and others, of making the pallets as before referred to ; but the best answer that I can give to these trade prejudices, is, to recommend persons to construct the escapement according to the rules I have laid down, and they will see how soon these fallacies will vanish.

Let me again repeat, that the vibrations of the pendulum are isochronous for an arc of 3°, if it be not destroyed by the application of an imperfect escapement. It will no doubt be remarked that an able writer has condemned the view I have taken of this escapement in Table II. ; but if there is any law or advantage in correct gearing, Table II. is the right one. This is particularly shown in the pin-pallet escapement : Table II. is a decided refinement of the question ; but the examples I have given of their separate trials under different vibrations and different motive weights, are certainly very similar.

The first example is that by an intelligent workman, who made it, much against his will, as he had hitherto followed the rules of trade tradition. I shall never forget his delight when he saw the result, and his subsequent veneration for true mechanical law *versus* mere empirical rules.

The ancient as well as the modern mode of attaching the pallets of the escapement to the pendulum without a crutch, though not shown in the Exhibition of 1862, may be worthy of a few remarks. It was always so practised by Whitehurst of Derby, in his large turret clocks, in which case he employed the pin-wheel escapement, and he assured me it answered well. I made many experiments upon the Graham escapement so applied, but with unsatisfactory results. The pin-wheel is doubtless better adapted for this mode of application. The double-pendulum clock by Breguet, to which I shall refer presently, has pin-wheel escapements so applied to the pendulum, and answers perfectly ; but it must be recollected that this clock is a masterpiece throughout.

If diagrams had been admissible, I should have given proper rules for the construction of the lever-escapement for watches, the principal points of the escapement being the same as those of the Graham dead-beat, which indeed is its origin ; and the same rules for the distance of the pallet-axis from that of the wheel must be strictly followed, with this difference, that in the clock the rests of the pallets are perfectly circular, whereas in the lever they unfortunately require a small amount of draw. I however subjoin a table of the lever escapement, the study of which cannot fail to be interesting to the intelligent workman. (See page 13.)

As the name of Graham has been so often mentioned in this report, it may be interesting to say that he was the immediate successor of the celebrated Tompion, was born in 1765, served the office of Master of the Company of Clockmakers of the City of London in 1721-22, was elected a Fellow of the Royal Society 1728, and died 1751. His remains were interred in the aisle of Westminster Abbey, by the side of Tompion.

Pendulums.

The compensation-pendulum now most generally employed for the best regulators, is the mercurial ; and the glass jar has in most cases given way to a steel jar, the rod dipping into the mercury, so that the whole is almost simultaneously affected by changes of temperature, which cannot, however, be so with a glass jar, which is a bad conductor. This pendulum is now very generally used by the foreign manufacturers in preference to their gridiron

pendulum, which hitherto had been always preferred abroad, and which they in France executed with great skill. The mercurial compensation pendulum was until lately almost unknown in France ; the strict requirements, however, of science have compelled its adoption both on account of its simplicity, greater accuracy, and facility of adjustment. The following are the particulars and dimensions of the best mercurial pendulums, with steel jars, now in use :—

Particulars of Mercurial Compensation Pendulums with Steel Jars, for Astronomical Clocks.

		In.	'	"
Round steel rod . . .	{ Diameter	0	3	0
	Weight	15 oz.		
Jar	{ Diameter	2	4	0
	Inside.	2	0	0
	Length.	8	7	5
	Weight.	3 lb. 14 oz.		
Screw threads to the inch	. . . .	30		
Divisions engraved	60			

Value of a division equals about half a second daily.

			lb.	oz.
Mercury	Weight	11	2½	
Pendulum	„	4	13½	
Total	16	0		

Suspension spring . .	{ Length, from ·30 to ·80	Inches.
	Breadth „ ·040 to ·060	
	Thickness „ ·004 to ·007	

Turret Clocks, their Pendulums and Escapements.

The progress of improvement in English turret clocks since 1851 was very marked.

Messrs. T. Cooke and Sons, *York* (*United Kingdom*, 3238), exhibited several very highly-finished models. They introduced the Harrison going-fusee work, which, whilst it keeps the clock going during the process of winding, acted also as what is technically called a jack-wheel, by which very heavy weights are wound up with great ease. Messrs. Cooke employed the several escapements in use— the Graham dead-beat and Denison's gravity ; but there was an extraordinary departure from the rules of making the gravity escapement, particularly in combining it with an extra remontoir train ; from which it was evident that they intended these for showing their powers of workmanship and combination. The wooden-rod pendulum was employed with a cylindrical iron weight of from 80 to 180 lbs., according to the size, as well as the usual zinc compensation pendulum (the original invention of the late Mr. Arnold) ; and we remarked also that Messrs. Cooke used a seconds and seconds and a quarter pendulums only, alleging as a reason, that they seldom found room for a greater length, which we all know is too often the case. Architects generally forget that a clock is a very large piece of machinery, requiring room and fall for the weights. One hundred feet for a very large clock, and from thirty to forty for a small one, would be a great boon, both to buyers and makers. I heard it repeatedly said that these clocks were unnecessary highly finished and consequently expensive. These remarks are also very often made even on smaller works, that polish is unnecessary ; and so it is ; but good workmen do not pride themselves so much upon polish as on truth and squareness. Now the worst of attempting to manufacture clocks, watches, and chronometers in a plain way is soon to fall into a slovenly method, and thus discourage good workmen. If the pride of high-finished work is destroyed, you never can retain first-rate hands. A good workman will soon tell you he has a soul above bottle-jacks, and find employment elsewhere. We had got low enough in the scale of turret-clock making, with almost one solitary exception, until 1851 ; and it is very easy to return down to the lower level. Turret clocks may be made well and cheap at the same time : it only requires three or four good models ; because it is the large repetition of the same models that enables the manufacturer to work cheaply and economically. For example, the English marine chronometer can now be bought for a

THE PRINCIPAL PARTS OF THE LEVER ESCAPEMENT.

The basis of these measures is—Radius of the wheel taken at one-tenth of an inch; and all the other parts are brought into connection therewith by calculation, according to the several numbers of the teeth into which the wheel is divided, and the number of these teeth to be embraced by the pallets.

Teeth in the wheel.	Teeth embraced.	Angular space between the teeth.	Half-thickness of the pallets in degrees.	Semi-angle at the centre of the wheel.	Corresponding angle at the pallet axis.	Chord of the angular opening of the pallets = 2 sin. of the said semi-angle.	Distance of the pallet axis from that of the wheel.	Radius of the outer rest.	Radius of the inner rest.	Chord of the angular opening of the pallets, or 2 sin. of the semi-angled wheel.	Distance of the centres of the wheel and pallet axes.	Radius of the circular rest or lockings.	Radius of the short arm.	Radius of the long arm.
		o '	o '	o '	o '	Tenths of an inch and decimals.				Chords 2 sin. of ½ the arc.	Secant.	Tangent.		
12	2	30 0	7 30	22 30	67 30	·7588	1·0731	·5412	·2801	·7653	1·0824	·4142	·1531	·6752
	3	,,	,,	37 30	52 30	1·2071	1·2496	·8913	·6302	1·2175	1·2604	·7673	·5062	1·0284
14	2	25 43	6 25·7	19 17	70 43	·6563	1·0525	·4596	·2357	·6604	1·0594	·3498	·1223	·5774
	3	,,	,,	32 8·5	57 51·2	1·0573	1·7360	·7363	·5124	1·0640	1·1809	·6281	·4005	·8550
15	2	24 0	6 0	18 0	72 0	·6145	1·0457	·4276	·2186	·6180	1·0514	·3249	·1159	·5340
	3	,,	,,	30 0	60 0	·9947	1·1484	·6787	·4696	1·0000	1·1547	·5773	·3683	·7864
16	2	22 30	5 37·5	16 52·5	73 7·5	·5776	1·0400	·4000	·2039	·5806	1·0450	·3033	·1073	·4993
	3	,,	,,	28 7·5	61 52·5	·9382	1·1284	·6300	·4340	·9428	1·1340	·5345	·3384	·7305
17	2	21 10·5	5 17·6	15 53	74 7	·5450	1·0353	·3754	·1912	·5473	1·0397	·2845	·0969	·4721
	3	,,	,,	26 28·2	63 31·8	·8876	1·1123	·5879	·4036	·8914	1·1171	·4978	·3103	·6855
18	2	20 0	5 0	15 0	75 0	·5156	1·0313	·3541	·1798	·5176	1·0353	·2680	·0936	·4422
	3	,,	,,	25 0	65 0	·8420	1·0991	·5517	·3774	·8452	1·1033	·4663	·2920	·6406
19	2	18 57	4 44·2	14 12·6	75 47·4	·4893	1·0280	·3330	·1698	·4909	1·0315	·2532	·0870	·4194
	3	,,	,,	23 41	66 19	·7988	1·0882	·5196	·3546	·8033	1·0920	·4386	·2724	·6048
	4	,,	,,	33 9·5	56 50·5	1·0900	1·1904	·7342	·5680	1·0939	1·1945	·6537	·4875	·8200
20	2	18 0	4 30·0	13 30	76 30	·4654	1·0252	·3178	·1609	·4669	1·0284	·2401	·0832	·3969
	3	,,	,,	22 30	67 30	·7630	1·0790	·4914	·3345	·7653	1·0824	·4142	·2573	·5711
	4	,,	,,	31 30	58 30	1·0418	1·1692	·6893	·5324	1·0449	1·1728	·6128	·4658	·7697
	5	,,	,,	40 30	49 30	1·2948	1·3114	·9985	·6996	1·2989	1·3151	·8541	·6971	1·0110
22	2	16 22	4 5·4	12 16·3	77 43·7	·4239	1·0021	·2885	·1461	·4251	1·0234	·2175	·0727	·3622
	3	,,	,,	20 27·3	69 32·7	·6772	1·0646	·4433	·3008	·6989	1·0674	·3730	·2282	·5177
	4	,,	,,	28 38·2	61 22·8	·9560	1·1348	·6170	·4723	·9594	1·1397	·5467	·4020	·6914
	5	,,	,,	36 49	53 11	1·1954	1·2459	·8190	·6742	1·1985	1·2491	·7485	·6038	·8933
	6	,,	,,	45 0	45 0	1·4106	1·4106	1·0698	·9251	1·4142	1·4142	1·0000	·8552	1·1447
	7	,,	,,	53 11	36 49	1·5970	1·6645	1·4049	1·2602	1·6011	1·6687	1·3359	1·1912	1·4806
24	2	15 0	3 45	11 15	78 45	·3893	1·0174	·2639	·1331	·3902	1·0196	·1989	·0681	·3297
	3	,,	,,	18 45	71 15	·6415	1·0538	·4041	·2733	·6429	1·0560	·3394	·2086	·4702
	4	,,	,,	26 15	63 45	·8827	1·1126	·5575	·4267	·8846	1·1150	·4931	·3623	·6233
	5	,,	,,	33 45	56 15	1·1087	1·2011	·7321	·6013	1·1111	1·1207	·6681	·5373	·7990
	6	,,	,,	41 15	48 45	1·3158	1·3272	1·0059	·7443	1·3187	1·3300	·8770	·7461	·9077
	7	,,	,,	48 45	41 15	1·5004	1·5134	1·2032	1·0724	1·5037	1·5166	1·1403	1·0595	1·2711
	8	,,	,,	56 15	33 45	1·6945	1·7961	1·5588	1·4280	1·6630	1·8000	1·4966	1·3668	1·6274
30	2	12 0	3 0	9 0	81 0	·3124	1·0111	·2105	·1058	·3128	1·0124	·1584	·0537	·2630
	3	,,	,,	15 0	75 0	·5169	1·0338	·3200	·2153	·5176	1·0353	·2680	·1633	·3726
	4	,,	,,	21 0	69 0	·7157	1·0697	·4356	·3310	·7167	1·0711	·3838	·2792	·4885
36	6	10 0	2 30	27 30	62 30	·9226	1·1263	·5717	·4844	·9235	1·1234	·5205	·4133	·6728
	7	,,	,,	32 30	57 30	1·0735	1·1845	·6801	·5928	1·5373	1·1857	·6371	·5298	·7443
	8	,,	,,	37 30	52 30	1·2164	1·2190	·8102	·7229	1·2175	1·2175	·7673	·6600	·8745
	9	,,	,,	42 30	47 30	1·3499	1·3550	·9591	·8718	1·3512	1·3563	·9163	·8291	1·0035
	10	,,	,,	47 30	42 30	1·4731	1·4781	1·1339	1·0466	1·4745	1·4802	1·0913	·9840	1·1985
	11	,,	,,	52 30	37 30	1·5925	1·6411	1·3456	1·2584	1·5867	1·6427	1·3032	1·1960	1·4104
	12	,,	,,	57 30	32 30	1·6852	1·8594	1·6118	1·5245	1·6868	1·8611	1·5696	1·4624	1·6769

fourth of the price it fetched years ago, with the double advantage of improved construction. Mr. DENT, 61 *Strand* (*United Kingdom*, 3243), exhibited several good turret clocks, and exclusively employed the Denison gravity escapement and compensation pendulum. The wheels and pinions were principally of cast iron, which appeared very clean and good.

Messrs. MOORE of *Clerkenwell* (*United Kingdom*, 3284) exhibited a large turret clock of a very useful character. It was well made, and moderate in cost. A two-seconds wood rod pendulum was used, and considering that the errors in temperature for a steel rod is only twenty seconds for a change of temperature of 60°, the error of a wooden rod, with a cylindrical bob loosely fitted to the rod, ought to be very small. But when you come to deal with large masses, the changes of temperature affect the result in a different way from what they do in smaller works.

Messrs. FAIRER (3284), Mr. LOSADA (3279), Messrs. SMITH and SONS (3309), Mr. BENNETT (3225), and Mr. BENSON (3226), all in the English department, were also exhibitors of turret clocks; the three latter each used gravity escapements of different construction; but it was impossible to pronounce a decided opinion upon their merits without a trial.

House Clocks.—Of these there was a great variety, but they call for no special observation beyond the fact that they will probably last two centuries. The foreigners remarked that they were rather heavy and sombre; but if we did not excel in this department, we had the gratification of hearing it allowed that in portable and carriage clocks, both in taste, workmanship, and economy, we could not be surpassed, and, I think I may add, equalled.

Mr. THOMAS COLE'S exhibition (*United Kingdom*, 3236) was exclusively devoted to this department, and nothing could exceed the beauty of design and good taste of the varied models and general excellence of workmanship. The foreign visitors seem all of them to have accorded him the palm, and were anxious buyers of his beautiful works.

The chronometer-makers were a little more solid in their style of case; but for accuracy of construction, as well as economy, they were unequalled out of the English section. I saw very few small portable chime clocks; but most of the best English portable clocks had chronometer escapements, and chimed the quarters besides striking the hours.

ENGLISH POCKET CHRONOMETERS AND POCKET WATCHES.

No section of horology showed greater advance since 1851 than the pocket chronometers and watches. The most striking feature was an improved proportion of all the works; but the two most essential points of improvement were the increased weights and diameters of the balances, a rule which was introduced in 1851, but apparently at that time little noticed. Rules have since been written for their proper momentum; but perhaps the most essential improvement was in the balance-spring and in the improved shape of the wheels and pinions, which had become so bad before 1851 that they were a disgrace to the art of watchmaking. With the assistance of Mr. J. F. Cole and others a number of balance-springs were made, which were in every respect as near perfection as possible. They were all made by Mr. Cole and exhibited by me, being the result of our mutual study; yet they were hardly appreciated at that period. I believe many thought they were not hardened in fire and water and subsequently tempered, and were then too beautiful to be good for use; with some, however, it had a different effect, and they were loud in their praises; but yet they did not get a medal of reward. A few years, however, has proclaimed their worth. I should now not think a watch worth having that was made without one.

I will here make a few remarks upon escapements. I have already said that all kinds of remontoir escapements had failed to render any service to watch or chronometer making. On the present occasion the escapements principally in use were the chronometer or detached escapement, the duplex, and the lever: the two former, however excellent in themselves, are not well adapted for these railroad days, because they will not bear rough usage. The lever, on the other hand, is particularly suited for all the ordinary usages of life, and when all the other parts of the watch are of the same quality as the pocket chronometer a most reliable time-keeper is obtained. Moreover only skilled hands can make the chronometer and duplex escapement; whereas very inferior workmen can make a lever escapement that will perform to a limited degree. This is an advantage in some respects and a disadvantage in others, as it follows that much inferior work is manufactured; yet, again, there is no escapement in which there is more room for genius and talent to display itself.

Messrs. F. B. ADAMS and SONS, 21 *St. John's Square, Clerkenwell* (*United Kingdom*, 3218), showed a large number of well-made watches with chronometer balances, which were remarkable for good proportions and excellent balance-springs. They also showed a watch-case which at pleasure could be used either as a hunting-watch or with a glass,—a most useful watch for a traveller.

Messrs. BARRAUD and LUND, 41 *Cornhill, E.C.* (*United Kingdom*, 3223), exhibited a choice selection of pocket

chronometers and pocket watches of the best description, also one of nearly the smallest watches ever made.

Mr. J. F. COLE, *Queen Square, Bloomsbury* (*United Kingdom*, 3235), exhibited an assortment of the best hardened and tempered balance-springs in the Exhibition, for which alone he deserved a Medal, also

1. An eight-day marine chronometer, with adaptation of a new principle to the detached escapement, which renders the chronometer, whether for marine or pocket use, free from the common liability to acceleration of rate by repetition of the impulse action under influence of external motion.

2. A gold pocket chronometer with non-repetition escapement, based on the duplex principle, having the same properties of reliable time-keeping while subjected to external agitation (as in riding), these effects being successfully tested before the Jury.

This watch was shown at the Exhibition of 1851 and at Paris in 1855; its merits, like most other inventions, were not at first appreciated, and it may be yet another ten years before many are made; but, nevertheless, it is very clever, and renders a pocket chronometer and a duplex watch as safe and reliable time-keepers in rough motion as they are in a quiet state. Mr. Cole has this escapement now under some modification, and hopes to make it perfect. I do not think it requires much change, though I am quite aware that objections are made to it, as it destroys the entire detachment; but my experience has shown me that it does no harm whatever. I must not, however, be supposed to recommend it for marine chronometers.

Mr. Cole also exhibited—

3. Model of a pendulum for mercurial compensation with transverse suspension spring, and means of adjustment for isochronism.

4. Model of a gravity compensation pendulum, suspended on a pair of cycloidal springs kept always at one tension under varying temperatures, expansion of the rod being neutralized by an inverted counter-weight.

Mr. MCLENNAN (*United Kingdom*, 3330), besides exhibiting the smallest pocket chronometer with a fusee in the Exhibition, had a number of very high specimens of the best proportioned pocket chronometers, to all of which he had had applied the "duo in uno" balance spring, producing with a balance in perfect equilibrium almost a uniform rate in every position, a fact often pretended to exist, but never to be met with except in pocket watches of the very best construction and proportions, and then only with a ruinous waste of time, whereas in the above case it is a natural result of the uniform action of the spring; it is, however, a very difficult spring to make, and, I am afraid, sorely tries the eyes and the patience.

Mr. H. DELOLME, *Rathbone Place* (*United Kingdom*, 3242), Messrs. DENT and Co., 61 *Strand* (*United Kingdom*, 3243), and Mr. M. F. DENT, *Cockspur Street* (*United Kingdom*, 3244), also exhibited a number of excellent watches and clocks: the two latter exhibitors also showed some very choice designs of ornamented watches with diamonds.

Messrs. GUIBLET and RAMBAL, *Clerkenwell* (*United Kingdom*, 3254), exhibited a case of keyless fusee watches and repeaters which were very well executed.

Messrs. E. and C. GUILLAUME, *Myddelton Square* (*United Kingdom*, 3255), exhibited several highly finished repeating watches with chronometer balances and highly ornamented cases.

Mr. HISLOP, 108 *St. John Street Road* (*United Kingdom*, 3262), exhibited an excellent regulator, showing both sidereal and mean time by means of two dials. It is said that they will accord to within one second of error in four years. This is effected by means of four wheels of the respective numbers of 247, 331, 43, and 32. We were not furnished with the numbers employed to effect this object. The numbers here given are taken from the 'Philosophical Magazine' for Feb. 1850. There are now in existence several pocket chronometers by Arnold, made about forty years ago, when this kind of almanac information was fashionable, as applied to watches and clocks. A page of the 'Nautical Almanac' of the present day will however furnish at a glance all such information with the utmost accuracy. What is very remarkable is, that there were not fewer than six or seven clocks of this kind in the foreign department, where not one of the makers could certainly know what the others were doing, for they each bore the stamp of originality.

Mr. HUTTON, 10 *Mark Lane, E.C.* (*United Kingdom,* 3270), exhibited a number of good chronometers and watches, also several modifications in compensation balances, of which I have previously spoken.

Messrs. JACKSON, *Red Lion Street* (*United Kingdom,* 3271), exhibited an improved day of the month watch, and a new escapement, which he termed "repellent;" also some keyless watches.

Mr. J. JONES, 338 *Strand,* exhibited a number of handsome watches made under his own supervision.

Mr. KLAFTENBERGER (3275), Mr. J. MURRAY (3287), Messrs. PORTHOUSE and FRENCH (3294), Messrs. ROTHERHAM and SONS, *Coventry* (3300), all severally added to the interest of the English portion of the Exhibition.

Messrs. NICOLE and CAPT, *Soho Square* (*United Kingdom,* 3289), exhibited a number of keyless watches; but the most interesting specimen of their manufacture was a registering centre-seconds watch, which was quite unique, and answered the purpose admirably.

Mr. E. JOHNSON (Juror), *Wilmington Square, Clerkenwell* (*United Kingdom,* 3272), exhibited a variety of scientific manufactures. He also introduced a new registering centre-seconds watch; another remarkable fact of how often different persons are pursuing the same idea. These various chronometers, watches, and clocks were worthy specimens of the high repute gained by him, which rendered him so fit a person to be chosen by his brother exhibitors to act as a Juror.

Mr. WALSH (3321), Mr. WEBSTER (3324), Mr. WHITE (3325), all exhibited very superior work. The taste shown by Mr. White in the ornamentation of his watches and designs for clocks was quite unique. His astronomical clocks I have already referred to. Mr. Walsh also exhibited an original plan of pendant winding applied to the fusee, which seems the most simple and reliable of these very pleasing but objectionable contrivances.

To complete the English horological section I must not omit one of the most interesting cases in the Exhibition—that of the Lancashire movement-makers, watch-makers, and file-cutters' display of their several productions. All the world knows the value of a Lancashire file, but few are aware that all the best chronometer and watch-wheels and pinions are made in the Lancashire villages. Upwards of five Medals were awarded to the trades associated in this case of watch materials for construction.

The Teeth of Wheels and Pinions.—There was also a great improvement in the form of the teeth of wheels and pinions: one would scarcely have believed it possible that machinery could have been contrived to cut the minute teeth of the wheels and pinions of watch-work to the recognized mathematical form; indeed, the importance of the proper shape of the teeth, both in small and large works, is very great.

At the request of several exhibitors I published a table of measurement of the sizes of watches for international comparison, which I subjoin. (See page 16.)

FRENCH WATCHES AND CLOCKS.

Our intelligent neighbours did not come out in force. The ineligible position, and the small space allotted to them, was enough to discourage them. When I reflect upon the splendid exhibition they made in Paris in 1855, it was not to be wondered that so many remained away. Watch-making has been hitherto but a small manufacturing interest in France; but it is now fast reviving—the principal manufacture is clocks of all kinds, which have been their special forte; and some of the highest specimens, both of genius and workmanship, are made at Paris, equal to and perhaps superior to any produced in the world. Very large sums of money are paid for clocks on the Continent that are seldom given here.

M. BRÉGUET, *Paris* (1413), of so justly celebrated repute, exhibited productions both of the old and new house, one perhaps the finest specimen of a watch exhibited. It has occupied the house nearly fifty years, and was greatly admired by the Jurors, and indeed by a large number of scientific men. It was valued at 32,000 francs, and combined a perpetual calendar, repeater, and several other contrivances, which at first sight looked confusion worse confounded; but on a careful examination, it was all order and design. It required some study to know all about it; the oftener I saw it, the more I found to admire in its wonderful combinations.

I cannot pretend to enumerate all the inventions of the Bréguets. Among the many are a peculiarly constructed repeater; the self-winding watch; the blind man's watch; the sympathetic watch, which, placed upon a clock, re-sets itself to time if it be in error. Every variety of perpetual calendar clock and watch; the remarkable revolving escapement which he called the "tourbillon" that carried the balance round once in a minute, the object being to correct any errors that may exist in the equipoise of the balance. This escapement is, without exception, one of the most ingenious horological inventions that I know; and although no longer in use, except among amateurs, almost every exhibitor of repute in the Swiss department had revived it and exhibited excellent copies. Reid says that this escapement was the invention of the first Arnold: and it is difficult to say what that great genius Arnold did not invent, so fertile was his mechanical talent; but I have in my possession those facts that set the question beyond a doubt, and that it was the invention of the first Bréguet, viz.—"That the first tourbillon that Bréguet made was by his son, presented to the late Mr. Arnold in the year 1808." M. Bréguet was also the author of the celebrated double pendulum astronomical clock; and although he did not attain the object he sought to effect, it is nevertheless one of the most perfect pieces of work in existence. I have known this clock not to vary five seconds in six months. Its compound pendulum is also unique, being composed of a number of rods in three sections of about twelve inches long, instead of as in the usual rods of the pendulum's entire length : the three sections are connected together by a kind of hinge or joint. The cost must have been very great, but the result is a complete success. The escapements are dead-beat pin-wheel, with the pallets attached to the pendulums, and the train about the same size and weight as an eight-day marine chronometer; both clocks go with one weight.

M. LEROY, *Paris* (1623), exhibited an excellent specimen of a marine chronometer, having adopted the English model and discarded the wheel barrel : his compensation balances were also of good proportions, both as to the laminæ and also with regard to the diameter and weight.

M. VISSIÈRE, *Havre* (1622), showed an excellent specimen of a marine chronometer, also an astronomical clock, which bore the mark of great care and skill; its size and general proportions were admirable, and I observed that he had employed the Graham escapement after the Vulliamy system; but embraced as few as five teeth, with an arc of escapement of about 40'. The motion of the escape wheel at the point of repose was nearly *nil.* I am inclined to think it will be a good clock; but as I have previously remarked, all the nice points of the escapement will be more critical and exposed to derangement from the shake of the holes and the crutch. I have, however, no doubt that M. Leroy is quite aware of the extra personal care that such a system requires.

M. A. L. BROCOT, *Paris* (1588), exhibited a number of very choice specimens of ornamental clocks with sundry valuable improvements. He is also the reviver of a new dead-beat escapement, called the pin-pallet escapement, as distinct from the pin-wheel dead-beat : it is in fact the reverse of this useful escapement, for instead of a number of pins standing at right angles and acting upon a pair of pallets, two pins are placed perpendicular to the plane of the pallets, and the escape wheel is cut into teeth, after the shape of the usual Graham escape wheel, in which form it is really a Graham escapement. To make it perfectly dead, the teeth require to be slightly undercut, but so little that they are almost radial to the centre, for I found that when they are made strictly to the rule in table No. II. the dead effect was more perfect, and the gearing more natural. The pins are half cylinders, the diameter being equal to one space between the teeth. This escape-

TABLE OF THE CORRESPONDING SIZES OF ENGLISH WATCHES,

Taken by actual measurement across the PILLAR-PLATE, and given in English inches and decimals against each of the FOUR technical sizes now in use: viz.—

1. Charles Frodsham's new Movement increases by tenths and half-tenths.
2. The Lancashire Movement, by thirtieths of an English inch.
3. That by French Lines, each equal to ·0888 inches, or about $\frac{89}{1000}$ths of an Eng. inch.
4. That by Millimètres, each equal to ·03937 inches, or about $\frac{4}{100}$ths of an Eng. inch.

C. Frodsham's New Movement.

Technical size.	Inches.
10	= 1·00
10½	= 1·05
11	= 1·10
11½	= 1·15
12	= 1·20
12½	= 1·25
13	= 1·30
13½	= 1·35
14	= 1·40
14½	= 1·45
15	= 1·50
15½	= 1·55
16	= 1·60
16½	= 1·65
17	= 1·70
17½	= 1·75
18	= 1·80
18½	= 1·85
19	= 1·90
19½	= 1·95
20	= 2·00
20½	= 2·05
21	= 2·10
21½	= 2·15
22	= 2·20
22½	= 2·25
23	= 2·30
23½	= 2·35
24	= 2·40
24½	= 2·45
25	= 2·50

Lancashire Sizes.

3 sizes = $\frac{1}{10}$ of an inch.
1 size = ·0333

Technical Numbers.	Inches and Decimals.	
0 = 1	5/30	or 1·166
1 = 1	6/30	,, 1·200
2 = 1	7/30	,, 1·233
3 = 1	8/30	,, 1·266
4 = 1	9/30	,, 1·300
5 = 1	10/30	,, 1·333
6 = 1	11/30	,, 1·366
7 = 1	12/30	,, 1·400
8 = 1	13/30	,, 1·433
9 = 1	14/30	,, 1·466
10 = 1	15/30	,, 1·500
11 = 1	16/30	,, 1·533
12 = 1	17/30	,, 1·566
13 = 1	18/30	,, 1·600
14 = 1	19/30	,, 1·633
15 = 1	20/30	,, 1·666
16 = 1	21/30	,, 1·700
17 = 1	22/30	,, 1·733
18 = 1	23/30	,, 1·766
19 = 1	24/30	,, 1·800
20 = 1	25/30	,, 1·833
21 = 1	26/30	,, 1·866
22 = 1	27/30	,, 1·900
23 = 1	28/30	,, 1·933
24 = 1	29/30	,, 1·966
25 = 2	0/30	,, 2·000
26 = 2	1/30	,, 2·033
27 = 2	2/30	,, 2·066
28 = 2	3/30	,, 2·100
29 = 2	4/30	,, 2·133
30 = 2	5/30	,, 2·166
31 = 2	6/30	,, 2·200
32 = 2	7/30	,, 2·233
33 = 2	8/30	,, 2·266
34 = 2	9/30	,, 2·300
35 = 2	10/30	,, 2·333
36 = 2	11/30	,, 2/366
37 = 2	12/30	,, 2·400
38 = 2	13/30	,, 2·433
39 = 2	14/30	,, 2·466
40 = 2	15/30	,, 2·500

Value of French Lines in Eng. Inches.

F. Lines.	E. Inches.
10	= 0·888
11	= 0·977
12	= 1·066
13	= 1·154
13½	equal 1·200
14	= 1·243
15	= 1·332
16	= 1·421
17	= 1·510
18	= 1·598
19	= 1·687
20	= 1·776
21	= 1·865
22	= 1·954
23	= 2·042
24	= 2·136
25	= 2·220
26	= 2·309
27	= 2·398
28	= 2·486

Value of Millimètres in Eng. Inches.

Mill.	Inches
1 Mill.	= 0·03937
10 ,,	= 0·39371
25·4 ,,	= 1·000
26 ,,	= 1·024
27 ,,	= 1·063
28 ,,	= 1·102
29 ,,	= 1·142
30 ,,	= 1·181
31 ,,	= 1·220
32 ,,	= 1·260
33 ,,	= 1·299
34 ,,	= 1·339
35 ,,	= 1·378
36 ,,	= 1·417
37 ,,	= 1·457
38 ,,	= 1·496
39 ,,	= 1·535
40 ,,	= 1·575
41 ,,	= 1·614
42 ,,	= 1·654
43 ,,	= 1·693
44 ,,	= 1·732
45 ,,	= 1·772
46 ,,	= 1·811
47 ,,	= 1·850
48 ,,	= 1·890
49 ,,	= 1·929
50 ,,	= 1·969
51 ,,	= 2·008
52 ,,	= 2·047
53 ,,	= 2·087
54 ,,	= 2·126
55 ,,	= 2·165
56 ,,	= 2·205
57 ,,	= 2·244
58 ,,	= 2·283
59 ,,	= 2·323
60 ,,	= 2·362
61 ,,	= 2·402
62 ,,	= 2·441
63 ,,	= 2·480
64 ,,	= 2·520
65 ,,	= 2·559
66 ,,	= 2·598
67 ,,	= 2·638
68 ,,	= 2·677
69 ,,	= 2·717
70 ,,	= 2·756
71 ,,	= 2·795
72 ,,	= 2·835

Note.—Also illustrated by a small work with diagrams, entitled 'A Few Facts Connected with the Elements of Watch and Clockmaking.'

---

ment may be constructed with the smallest amount of drop, and is equally valuable for a highly finished clock as it is for an economical one, or for clocks of small price. It is also a good escapement for small turret-clocks, as it can be so easily repaired: the recoil and half dead escapement should now be discarded, and this escapement substituted.

The Jurors of 1851 awarded a Medal to M. Brocot for this escapement, and the Jurors of 1862, without reference to that fact, awarded to Mr. Brocot a Medal for his general manufacture and inventive genius. M. Brocot is also the author of several useful tables for the calculation of complicated trains; and an instrument for determining the length of pendulums required to make any given number of vibrations per hour.

M. REDIER, *Paris* (1589), exhibited a number of very clever centre seconds pieces for recording observations, also a number of regulators of excellent finish.

M. CHARPENTIER, *Paris* (1590), made a brilliant display of watches and clocks, all of which were of excellent construction and execution, as well of great taste; also three astronomical clocks, beating artificial seconds; that is, the pendulums were not of the usual one-second length, but he had accomplished the object by means of a kind of metronome added to the upper part of the pendulum beyond the point of suspension. This method did not recommend itself to the judgment of the Jurors, as it was considered destructive of the pendulum's general laws, and there being many very simple methods of effecting the same thing without such a derangement.

M. GONTARD, *Besançon* (1592), was awarded a Medal for his able effort to revive watch-making in France.

M. JACOT, *Paris* (1624), exhibited a number of excellently manufactured carriage clocks, in which were displayed great skill and ability, as well as economy.

M. COÜET, *Paris* (1626, exhibited a regulator with a new "*force constante*" escapement, of his own invention, of great merit; the proportions and design, as well as the execution and shape of the teeth of the wheels and pinions, were of the first order. The compensation-pendulum was perhaps the best executed piece of work in the French section.

M. PIERRET, *Paris* (1629), exhibited a number of very cleverly made clocks, and also some of the best watches that are made in France. The Jurors did not award a Medal to Mr. Pierret: they regretted that they had already exceeded their number. There were also some points of construction and economical production that the Jurors were anxious should be reconsidered.

M. SCHARF, *Paris* (1631), exhibited several excellent pieces of clock and chronometer work; also an astronomical clock of excellent construction and workmanship. Much care was bestowed upon the escapement, which was dead-beat, as well as upon the teeth of the wheels and pinions. The pallets embraced six teeth, which seems to have become the fashion in France of making this escapement. I have already commented upon the advantages and disadvantages of this number of teeth.

M. PHILLIPS, an eminent engineer of France, who had recently published a work entitled, '*Mémoire sur le Spiral Réglant des Chronometres et des Montres*,' exhibited the book, together with a set of models illustrative of the action of the spiral spring.

Phillips, on Isochronism.

Now, as no work had been written on this subject since that by George Attwood, F.R.S., in the 'Philosophical Transactions' for 1794, except the paper I read in 1848, before the Institute of Civil Engineers, "On the Isochronism of the Balance-spring, in connection with the higher order of adjustment of Watches and Chronometers," this work was received by all exhibitors with universal favour, and particularly so as it was never thought possible that so abstruse a subject could be illustrated by models, which, however, was most efficiently done; and what has added much to the value and interest of this exhibition was the fact that our able colleague M. Laugier attended every morning, and delivered a lecture on M. Phillips' beautiful models, demonstrating mathematically all the various laws of force that the different curves of the balance-spring have in producing or destroying the isochronous vibrations of the balance. It was shown that the friction on the pivots, when the balance-spring curves were theoretically correct, was so minute, that they appeared to act only as guides; for on removing the support of the upper end of the balance-axis, it continued to vibrate in the same plane without wobbling; when, however, the curves were not theoretical, the balance wobbled so much that it could scarcely be retained in its place, the motion became very unsatisfactory, and the balance-spring's free action seemed to have been seriously interfered with. The Jurors unanimously awarded a Medal to M. Phillips, and expressed a hope that he would present the models to the section, which no doubt he has done. I can assure M. Phillips that a series of such models would be received with due honour by any of the learned societies in London. The law of isochronism is always a great stumbling-block to every young watch and chronometer maker, who is following the higher branches of the art. *Errors of mechanism must not be confounded with errors of isochronism.* Every watch or chronometer must be cleared of all mechanical errors before any such adjustment as that for isochronism or temperature is attempted.

"Isochronism is an inherent property of the balance-spring, depending entirely upon the ratio of the spring's tension following the proportion of the arcs of inflection; a balance-spring, therefore, of any force whatever, having the progression required by the law of isochronism, will preserve this property whether it be long or short, strong or weak, and whether applied to a balance making few, many, or any number of vibrations. In other words, the conditions required by isochronism, are, that the force of a spring should increase in the direct ratio of the arc over which it is bent: that is, if fifty grains cause a spring to be bent over an arc of 30° from its station, when at rest, one hundred grains will inflect it over 60°, and so on; and since the force of an isochronal spring follows the same law as that of falling bodies, the spaces, that is the arcs, will be to each other as the squares of the times occupied in traversing them."

SWISS WATCHES.

In reporting upon this section of Class XV., we may be permitted to make a few observations upon the remarkable branch of industry settled in and among these mountainous regions. It is difficult to trace its first birth; but it is supposed to have come from France, and to have had very small beginnings. Even fifty years ago it had not grown to any great extent, and factories were few in number; a large number of the watchmakers being agriculturists or small farmers, who, in the winter season, devoted their time to watchmaking.

The repeating motion, which had its origin in England, as almost all practical principles in the art have had, was made in some of their remote valleys, and when such complicated mechanism as the repeater is considered, there must have been a large amount of latent mechanical ingenuity; for they had at that time but difficult access either to France or England. In 1851 it had grown to an enormous industry; some of their houses making as many as half a million watches, and a large number of houses turning out their ten and twenty thousand per annum. These watches of course are not either of high class or high price. Most of the works are still made in these localities; but those with the beautiful finish of the cases, both in enamel and with diamond setting, are principally done in the classical city of Geneva.

Before describing the various articles of this section of the Exhibition, I must do justice to M. FREDERIC COURVOISER, who, having lost his watches, did not appear till some time afterwards; from which circumstance his name does not appear in the Official Catalogue. A part of them were recovered, and he then received Honourable Mention.

M. SYLVAIN MAIRET, *Lôcle* (211), having very justly received from his countrymen the honour of being the "Swiss Juror," was therefore not a candidate for an award; he was nevertheless an exhibitor, and had formerly spent many years in this country. I am desirous of doing justice to one of his many inventions, which his love of science prevented him from patenting. I refer to watches having two barrels as independent centre seconds, which M. Mairet wound up at the pendant from the same knob, giving to one a right-hand motion, and to the other a left-hand one. We noticed a highly finished chronometer repeater, with perpetual calendar and thermometer, a work of great merit, and in which those high marks of finish were to be seen so characteristic of his manipulation and design. The callipers, or working plans of all M. Mairet's watches, were of very superior arrangement, giving ample room and freedom for all parts of the works. The whole of the watches had compensation balances, with hardened and tempered springs, and were adjusted with great care. Several of the lever-escapements were made with the entire angle of impulse on the wheel, the jewel-pallets being only fine edges: this, though one of the best methods, is beyond the reach of any but men of the first talent. The price of these watches varied from 240*l.* down to 35*l.*, and they were considered very cheap. I should think it will take some years to make another such watch as the grand chronometer-repeater to which I have referred.

Unfortunately, first-rate workmen are not more plentiful in Switzerland than elsewhere; and although quantity may be produced, watches of the highest quality are still of slow process.

M. L. AUDEMARS, *Le Brassus* (172), is one of the first manufacturers in *La Vallée*. He exhibited a number of highly finished pocket chronometer-repeaters, and one with the most intricate calculations of astronomical data. This watch was valued at 300*l.*, but it is doubtful if it could be repeated at that cost.

The pocket watches and repeaters of M. NARDIN, *Lôcle* (221), were also of very high quality. We observed that most of them wind by the pendant, and have a tourbillon escapement, which must have added to the cost nearly 15*l.* or 20*l.*, according to the talent of the workman employed. The reproduction of this escapement, which was first brought out by Bréguet in 1808, and whose use science had rendered no longer necessary, appeared to us a rather remarkable and unaccountable fact. This constitutes one of the great differences between the best watchmakers in Switzerland and those in England. The former display their talent in works of difficult combination; and it adds much to their credit to have selected that beautiful specimen of horological ingenuity; for, I am sure, that whilst watchmaking lasts, this escapement will find a place in the cabinet of the connoisseur. In England, however, we are called upon to display our abilities in the positive results of good time-keeping; to make chronometers for all the maritime nations of the globe; and to have our talents estimated by the test of within what fraction of a second our chronometers shall maintain their daily rates during long voyages, although exposed to every variety of temperature and motion.

But I should not be doing justice did I not repeat that I believe there are several of the Swiss who cultivate the art of horology "*con amore*," and devote themselves to its improvement with as much zeal as the French and English claim to do; but as they are principally watchmakers, there is not that scope that there is in the clock and chronometer.

Most of the exhibitors who obtained Medals displayed the tourbillon escapement.

Messrs. H. GRANDJEAN and Co., *Lôcle* (188), exhibited two marine box-chronometers, which, considering the infancy of this manufacture in Switzerland, showed great ability. They had maintained their rates from Neufchâtel to England so well that they agreed as nearly as possible to the longitude of Greenwich.

I have heard it said that on the Continent, artists work at artisans' wages. I could never find it so; but I think that such a remark may justly be applied to the English chronometer-makers, who sell their finest possible chronometers at from 40*l.* to 50*l.* each.

M. G. H. JEANRENAUD, *Fleurier* (200), residing at a village renowned for able men in all departments of the art, was awarded a Medal for his jewel-holes, their excellent quality, and finish.

ASSOCIATION OUVRIÈRE, *Lôcle* (171).—This case consisted of various watches finished, and unfinished, from an ordinary watch of 5f. to chronometer repeaters of 2000f. Here again we were met by the tourbillon escapement, and we could almost imagine that they were the production of one hand; but such was not the case, as they differed considerably in excellence, workmanship, and judgment.

In this department of the Exhibition was also shown a number of tools for various uses in the art; but the display was not great, new, nor equal to what we expected—perhaps in all things connected with machinery we expect too much from other nations.

We awarded a Medal to Messrs. MÜLLER (219), in this department. They had introduced measurement gauges; their general use is very desirable; indeed, now indispensable.

For the rest of this department we must refer the reader to the annotations of the Jurors; for the task of the Reporter was extremely difficult, as the exhibitors were seldom present, and never long enough to explain to us their special points of interest.

SMALLER EXHIBITS.

Denmark.—We had the pleasure to award Medals to M. A. FUNCH, *Copenhagen* (134), and to M. CARL RANCH, *Copenhagen* (137), for a marine chronometer, and an astronomical clock.

Norway.—M. C. CHRISTOPERSEN, *Christiania* (90), received a Medal for an excellent specimen of an astronomical clock; M. J. IVERSON, *Bergen* (91), for his marine chronometer; the work appeared well executed.

Hanse Towns.—To M. BRÖCKING, *Hamburg* (38), was awarded a Medal for regulator with compensation pendulum with steel jar, showing mean and sidereal time on two dials; the price asked for this clock was 100*l.*

Sweden.—To M. G. W. LINDEROTH (348), a Medal was adjudged for a marine chronometer with a going barrel and remontoir escapement, which, though rather complicated, was a masterpiece of workmanship and design. I have no doubt, however, that when M. Linderoth reads my comments upon the advantages of the fusee over the going barrel, he will adopt the former; for the production of his escapement must have been most laborious; yet he fixed the price of it at the modest sum of 55*l.* The Jurors regretted not to have the pleasure of seeing personally this able exhibitor, to explain more in detail the special objects he sought.

The Zollverein.—In this department we must refer the reader to the Jurors' annotations, and the able report made by our colleague Dr. Frick, Professor of Physics, Freiburg, who has given an immense deal of his time to these departments, and was always ready to assist, bring forward, and explain the many various articles exhibited therein, for which he was the special Commissioner and Juror. To Dr. Frick I was greatly indebted on many occasions for his assistance. He had made himself completely master of every department, and particularly of the difficult subject of the supplementary compensation-balance. He also suggested a new mode of compensation, which it would be impossible to describe here without a diagram.

CONCLUSION.

In presenting our report of the horological section of the marvellous Exhibition of 1862, we, the Jurors, in the faithful execution of our trust, confirm our awards, and only beg it may be borne in mind that it was impossible to award with perfectly accurate judgment without the dismantling of every piece presented to us. Yet even under these circumstances, the care and attention of the Jurors were so great, that we feel assured that justice has been done both to the exhibitors and to the public. We have also sought not to compare one manufacturer with another; but have endeavoured to extract as much knowledge as possible, to elucidate principles, clear up contending points of difficulty, strip away all technical mysteries, and have endeavoured to direct a new path of progress, and to make the Exhibition of 1862 the last boundary of horological science from which to start again to accomplish in continuation all that can be required of us by civil, nautical, and astronomical science.

CHARLES FRODSHAM, REPORTER.

MEDAL.

United Kingdom.

3218 ADAMS and SONS.—Mechanical excellence in productions.

3223 BARRAUD and LUND.—Mechanical excellence in productions.

3225 BENNETT, J.—Great display of watches and clocks of various sorts.

3227 BLACKIE, G.—Invention and mechanical excellence in chronometers.

3229 BROOKS, S. A.—Excellence of watch jewelling in all stages.

3235 COLE, J. F.—Inventive genius and mechanical excellence.

3236 COLE, TH.—Excellence of taste and design.

3238 COOKE, T., and SONS.—Construction and finish of turret clock, gravity and other escapements.

3239 CRISP, W. B.—Excellence of finish in marine chronometers.

3242 DELOLME, H.—Excellence in clocks and chronometers, and for new astronomical escapements.

3243 DENT and Co.—Great display of chronometers, turret clocks, and watches.

3244 DENT, M. F., and Co.—Great display of chronometers, watches, and turret clocks.

2352 GANEVAL and CALLARD.—Excellence of pendulum, and for wire and balance springs.

3254 GUIBLET and RAMBAL.—Ingenuity and excellence of work.

3255 GUILLAUME, E. and C.—Mechanical excellence, and ingenuity in repeaters.

3295 HEWETT, S. and J., *Prescott Committee.* — For general excellence in first parts of chronometers and watches, e. g., movements, wheels, hands, &c.

3270 HUTTON, J.—Originality of construction.

3271 JACKSON, W. H. and S.—Invention and excellence.

3275 KLAFTENBERGER, C. J.—Excellence and variety.

3276 KULLBERG, V.—General excellence.

3279 LOSADA, J. R.—General display of chronometers, astronomical, and turret clocks.

3330 McLENNAN, J.—For great skill and mechanical excellence in pocket chronometers.

3295 MOLYNEUX, W., *Prescott Committee.*—For general excellence in first parts of chronometers and watches, e. g., movements, wheels, hands, &c.

3284 MOORE, B. and J.—Good workmanship and cheapness in turret clocks.

3289 NICOLE and CAPT.—Invention in centre seconds and keyless watches.

3291 PARKINSON and FRODSHAM.—Mechanical excellence in chronometers, watches, and clocks.

3295 PENDLETON, P., *Prescott Committee.*—For general excellence in first parts of chronometers and watches, e. g., movements, wheels, hands, &c.

3293 POOLE, J. — Excellence in chronometers and watches.

3300 ROTHERHAM and SONS —Excellence and cheapness.

3295 SAGGERSON, E., *Prescott Committee.*—For general excellence in first parts of chronometers and watches, e. g., movements, wheels, hands, &c.

3306 SEWILL, J.—Excellence in watches.

3309 SMITH and SONS.—Excellence and cheapness in turret and house clocks.

3320 WALKER, J.—Watches, railway watches, and clocks.

3321 WALSH, A. P.—Mechanical excellence in chronometers, and watches.

3324 WEBSTER, R.—Mechanical excellence in watches.

3325 WHITE, E.—Great display and taste in watches.

3295 WYCHERLEY, J., *Prescott Committee.*—For general excellence in first parts of chronometers and watches, e. g., movements, wheels, hands, &c.

Austria.

684 KRALIK, S.—Excellence in astronomical clocks.

687 MARENZELLER, I.—Good small turret clocks.

691 SCHÖNBERGER, W.—Variety in pendulum clocks, and good workmanship.

Baden.

79 BOB, L.—Excellency of workmanship in regulators.

80 BOB, V.—Excellency of workmanship in regulators.

84 HERZER, VON, and STOCKER.—General good workmanship in regulators.

77 JOINT STOCK CLOCK COMPANY OF LENZKIRCH.—For parts of clocks and finished clocks.

86 KÄMMERER, S.—General good workmanship in spring clocks.

88 MARTENS, J. H., and Co.—Excellent watches and pocket chronometers.

93b SHULTHEISS, BROTHERS.—Invention of iron ornamental dials for clocks and watches.

91 THOMANN, P.—Good clock springs of every size.

Denmark.

134 FUNCH, A.—Mechanical excellence in clocks and chronometers.

137 RANCH, CARL.—Excellence in marine chronometers.

France.

1603 BOUTEY and SON.—Ingenuity in watches, general good workmanship and economy, with the desire to encourage the manufacture of watches in France.

1413 BRÉGUET, L. C. F.—Mechanical excellence in watches.

1588 BROCOT, L. A.—Invention, and good manufacture of clocks.

1590 CHARPENTIER, P. A.—Excellence and dispay in chronometers, and watches.

1626 COÜET, C. L.—New escapement to regulator.

1600 CRESSIER, E.—Ingenuity in watches, general good workmanship and economy, with the desire to encourage the manufacture of watches in France.

1581 DESFONTAINE, LEROY, and SON.—Display of watches and chronometers.

1585 DETOUCHE, C. L.—Great display in clocks and regulators.

1621 GINDRAUX, A., and SON.—Goodness in works for chronometers and regulators.

1592 GONTARD.—Ingenuity in watches, general good workmanship, and economy, with the desire to encourage the manufacture of watches in France.

1624 JACOT, H. L.—Invention and variety in travelling clocks.

1623 LEROY, T. — Mechanical excellence in chronometers.

1586 MONTANDON, BROTHERS. — Manufacture of good mainsprings.

—— PHILLIPS.—Work on the theory of isochronism illustrated by models.

1589 REDIER, A.—Invention in clocks.

1582 ROBERT, H.—Ingenious experiments in chronometers.

1599 SAVOYE, BROTHERS, and Co.—Ingenuity in watches, general good workmanship and economy, with the desire to encourage the manufacture of watches in France.

1631 SCHARF, B.—Mechanical excellence in chronometers and clock movements.

1622 VISSIÈRE, S.—Mechanical excellence in chronometers.

Hamburg.

38 BRÖCKING, W. — Skill and invention in the construction of a double astronomical clock.

Norway.

90 CHRISTOPHERSON.—Mechanical skill in the construction of an astronomical clock.

91 IVERSEN, J.—Excellence in the construction of a marine chronometer.

Portugal.

834 INDUSTRIAL INSTITUTE OF LISBON.—Excellence in an electric clock.

Prussia.

1442 TIEDE, FR.—Excellence in chronometers.

Saxony.

2339 LANGE, A., and Co.—For good workmanship in watches, and as an encouragement for the introduction of clock and watch making in Saxony.

Sweden.

348 LINDEROTH, G. W.—Mechanical excellence in marine chronometers, astronomical clock.

350 MOLLBERG, L. R.—For compensation balances and mechanical excellence in watches.

Switzerland.

171 ASSOCIATION OUVRIÈRE.—Variety and good execution.

172 AUDEMARS, L.—Mechanical excellence in watches.

173 BAUME and LEZARD.—Variety and good execution.

176 BOREL and COURVOISIER.—Variety and good execution.

177 BOURGEAUX and DELAMURE.—Excellence of productions.

181 COURVOISIER, A.—Variety and good execution.

188 GRANDJEAN. and Co.—Variety and good quality of products.

190 GROSCLAUDE and Co.—Mechanical excellence in marine and pocket chronometers.

192 HENRI, J.—Superiority in manufacture of watch dial-plates. Delicacy and beauty of execution.

200 JEANRENAUD, G. H.—Excellence in watch jewelling.

202 JOHANN, A.—Good execution and variety.

206 LANG and PADOUX.—Good execution and variety.

207 LECOULTRE, U.—Excellent pinions for watches and chronometers. Beauty and execution.

214 MATTHEY-DORET.—Excellence of products.

215 MONTANDON, C. A.—Variety and good execution.

217 MOULINIÉ and LEGRANDROY.—Variety and elegance of products.

219 MÜLLER, BROTHERS.—Variety and good quality of products.

220 MULLERTZ, J.—Good quality of products.

221 NARDIN, U.—Excellence and variety of products.

224 PERRET, J.—Beautiful execution.

227 PIGUET, BROTHERS.—Beauty and variety of production.

233 ROBERT-NICOUD, C. A.—Quality and economy.

234 ROSSEL and SON.—Variety and quality of production.

236 SANDOZ, BROTHERS.—Mechanical excellence in watches.

Würtemberg.

2742 WÜRTEMBERG CLOCK FACTORY.—Large variety of Dutch clocks.

HONOURABLE MENTION.

United Kingdom.

3221 AUBERT and LINTON.—Display of watches.

3226 BENSON, J. W.—Display of watches and clocks.

3228 BROCK, J.—Goodness of marine chronometers.

3230 CAMERER, KUSS, and Co.—Superior workmanship and design.

3232 CHEVALIER, B.—Workmanship in watch cases.

3233 CLARK, DR.—Ingenuity and novelty of an improved gravity escapement.

3241 DAVIS and SONS. — Good watches and chronometers.

3246 DETTMANN, T.—Good astronomical clock

3248 FAIRER, J.—Cheapness in turret clocks.

3251 FRODSHAM and BAKER.—General excellence.

3256 GUMPEL, C. G.—Ingenuity and adaptation.

—— HAWKSBURY, J.—For a new gravity escapement. Inventive skill.

3261 HILL, C. J.—General display.

3262 HISLOP, W.—Originality of application.

3263 HOLDSWORTH, S.—For the excellence of manufacture of chronometer pallets and rollers, and of chronometer, clock, and watch jewels.

3264 HOLL, F. R.—Originality in winding.

3265 HOLLIDAY, T.—Variety of watch cases.

3267 HOWARD, R.—Excellence of enamelled dials.

3268 HOWELL, JAMES, and Co.—Display of engraved clock cases.

6634 HUNT and ROSKELL.—Variety and good workmanship.

3273 JONES, J.—Cheapness of productions.

3277 LANGE, C.—Originality of construction.

3278 LEONARD, G. W.—Good compensation balance.

3282 MARRIOTT, B.—Fair workmanship and ingenuity.

3283 MERCER, T.—Very good workmanship in marine chronometers.

3285 MORRIS, W.—Ingenuity, adaptation, and economy.

3286 MUIRHEAD and SON.—General display.

3287 MURRAY, J.—General good workmanship.

3288 NEAL, J.—Variety.

3290 ORAM, G. J.—General good workmanship.

3331 PETIT, S. A.—Skill and invention. Clock escapements.

3292 PLASKETT and SON.—Skilful workmanship in marine chronometers and watches.

3294 PORTHOUSE and FRENCH.—General good workmanship.

3295 PRESCOTT COMMITTEE :—

ALCOCK, J.
BROWN, ANN.
FORD, R.
HEYES, TH.
HOUGHTON, S.
HUNT and Co.
JACQUES, J.
JOHNSON, C. B.
NAYLOR, TH.   } For general good work-
PRESTON, J.   { manship and ingenuity.
PRESTON, W.
SCARISBRICK, C.
SMITH, J.
STOCKLEY, JAS.
TAYLOR, R.
WELSBY, J.
WHITFIELD, J. J.

3297 QUAIFE, T.—Ingenuity in the construction of a chime clock.

3302 RUSSELL, T., and SON.—General good workmanship.

3303 SAMUEL and SON.—Economy and display.

3304 SANDERS, J.—Astronomical timepiece with gridiron pendulum. Scientific skill in the construction.

3305 SCHOOF, W. G.—Regulator with detached escapement and mercurial pendulum. Skill and ingenuity.

3307 SHEPHERD, C.—Galvano-magnetic clocks. Ingenuity and adaptation.

3311 STRAM, N.—Gold case making. Skill and good workmanship.

3316 THOMSON and PROFAZE.—Variety and good workmanship.

3318 VIVIER, O.—Keyless watches. Skill and economy.

3319 WALES and McCULLOCH.—Display of gold and silver watches.

Austria.

682 EFFENBERGER, F.—Good workmanship and display in clocks.

689 MÖSSLINGER, F. — Enamelled clock and watch dials.

Baden.

78a BEHA, J. A.—Good clocks.

82 FURTWÄNGLER, L.—Black Forest clocks.

85 KALTENBACH, L.—Regulators and Black Forest clocks.

88a MAURER, R.—Regulators.

89 METZGER, J.—Carved clock cases and frames.

91a TRITSCHLER, S.—Spring clocks.

92 WEHRLE, C.—Clockworks.

93 WEHRLE, E.—Trumpet clock.

Brazil.

140 GONDOLO and Co.—Ingenuity in the construction of a keyless watch.

Denmark.

135 JURGENSENS, URBAN, and SONS.—Fair workmanship in second-class watches and chronometers.

France.

1584 ANQUETIN, M.—Cheapness and economy in timepieces.

1612 BERTHET.—For general economy and fair workmanship in watches.

1628 DROCOURT, P.—Economy and fair workmanship in travelling timepieces.

1587 FAROOT, H. A. E.—For general economy and fair workmanship in watches and clocks.

1605 FAVRE-HEINRICK.—For general economy and fair workmanship in watches.

1593 FERNIER, L.—For general economy and fair workmanship in watches.

1625 FLÉCHET, P.—Invention in sun-dials.

1607 GROZ, BROTHERS.—For general economy and fair workmanship in watches.

1610 LAMBERT, H. — For general economy and fair workmanship in watches.

1620 LÉGER, P. J.—For general economy and fair workmanship in watches.

1595 MONTANDON. — For general economy and fair workmanship in watches.

1627 PATAY, P.—Economy and fair workmanship in travelling timepieces.

1606 PERROT, E.—For general economy and fair workmanship in watches.

1629 PIERRET, V. — Good sound workmanship in watches and clocks.

Italy.

1256 DECANINI, C.—Escapement for clocks.

Mecklenburg.

40 DREYER.—Pendulum clocks.

Netherlands.

191a HOHWÜ, A.—Good marine chronometers.

Norway.

92 PAULSEN, M.—Astronomical clock.

Prussia.

1437 BECKER, G.—Pendulum clocks.
1438 EPPNER and Co.—Chronometers and watches.
1439 FELSING, C.—Regulator.
1443 WEISS, C.—Eight-day turret clock.

Russia.

351 SON, H.—Clock with revolving pendulum.

Saxony.

2337 ASSMANN, J.—Good watches.
2338 GROSSMANN, M. — Watches and watchmakers' tools.

Sweden.

346 CEDERGREN, J. T.—Transparent clock, enamelled works.
347 LINDEROTH, Mrs. B.—Watch wheels and movements.

Switzerland.

171a AUBERT, BROTHERS.—Good quality of products.

174 BAUMEL and SON.—Watchmaking tools. Good quality of products.

178 BREITLING, L.—Good watches.

180 CORNIOLEY and SON.—Mainsprings.

182 COURVOISIER, BROTHERS. — Pocket chronometers and watches.

183 DARIER, HUGHES, and Co.—Horological appliances and watch keys.

184 DEVAIN, J.—Jewels for watchmakers.

186 EHNHUUS, H.—Watchmaking tools.

187 GOLAY-LERESCHE. — Variety of production.

189 GRANGER, J. M.—Enamelled dial plates.

191 GUYE, U.—Files and machine to round the teeth of wheels.

201 INGOLD, P. F.—Files to rectify the teeth of watch wheels. Invention and excellence.

195 JACCOTTET, P. E.—Economy and relative quality.

198 JEANJAQUET, C.—Watch mainsprings.

199 JEARENAUD, AMI, Sen.—Invention.

203 JUNOD, EUG., and Co.—Good watches and chronometers.

204 JUNOD, L. E.—Jewels for watchmaking.

231 LECOULTRE, A.—Good watches.

209 LERESCHE-GOLAY.—Watchmaking tools.

210 LESQUEREUX, L.—Watch mainsprings.

212 MARCHAND, P. A.—Gold repeater.

213 MATTHEY, A. O. — Polishing apparatus, fancy clock, and electric clock.

218 MÜLLER, A.—Electro-chronograph printing seconds and hundredth parts of seconds. Speciality of production.

222 PERREGAUX, H.—Marine chronometers.

223 PERRET, A.—Gold repeaters and other watches.

225 PETITPIERRE, D. L.—Watchmaking tools.

241 PROST, C.—Pocket chronometer.

228 RAUSS, A.—Dial plates.

229 RAYMOND and ROUMIEUX.— Mainsprings for chronometers.

230 REYMANN, F., SON.—Mainsprings for watches.

237 SORDET, H., and SON.—For a very small watch, and for a chronometer. Speciality of production.

238 VAUTIER, S., and SON.—Watchmakers' tools.

240 YONNER, C. A. —Stones for superior watches, screw plates.

JURORS OF CLASS XV. WHO ARE ALSO EXHIBITORS.*

3250 FRODSHAM, CHARLES, *United Kingdom.*
3272 JOHNSON, E. D., *United Kingdom.*
211 MAIRET, SYLVAIN, *Switzerland.*

---

* If Exhibitors accept the office of Jurors, or Associate Jurors or Experts, they cease to be competitors for prizes in the class to which they are appointed, and these cannot be awarded either to them individually, or to the firms in which they may be partners.—*Decisions regarding Juries, Section 5.*

NOTES